D0297288

Frameworks For Dating Fossil Man

Kenneth P. Oakley

Frameworks For Dating Fossil Man

WEIDENFELD AND NICOLSON

20 New Bond Street London W1

© 1964 by Kenneth P. Oakley
Second edition 1966

To my Father T. P. Oakley

MADE AND PRINTED IN GREAT BRITAIN BY
COX & WYMAN LTD., LONDON, READING AND FAKENHAM

Contents

Preface

THIS BOOK HAD its inception in 1958, the Darwin Centenary year, when Sir Gavin de Beer urged me to undertake such a work. Most of the script here used had been written by early 1961, when on account of ill health it was shelved. My intention was eventually to increase its scope considerably, perhaps quadrupling its length, before embarking on publication. However, early in 1963, Dr Errol White, Keeper of the Department of Palaeontology, persuaded me that I would be better serving the interests of all those concerned with dating fossil men if I revised the existing script in readiness for immediate publication.

On his recommendation the first part of the script, an historical review of attempts to date the earliest remains of man, was published in a number of the *Bulletin of the British Museum (Nat. Hist.), Palaeontology Series*. In the opinion of my professorial colleagues the remainder of the script, dealing with the bases of stratigraphical and cultural dating of early man, sufficed to form a book, without extensive further work being required. Messrs Weidenfeld & Nicolson agreed with this view and undertook publication.

Acknowledgements

As REGARDS THE details of this book the author owes much to those who supplied information or gave him their advice, notably Dr Karl Adam, the late Dr Alberto Blanc, Dr Bernard Campbell, Dr L. Cardini, Professor Desmond Clark, Mrs Sonia Cole, Professor G. W. Dimbleby, Professor H. Godwin, Professor R. F. Flint, Dr D. A. Hooijer, Professor Clark Howell, Dr Maxine Kleindienst, Dr G. H. R. von Koenigswald, Dr Björn Kurtén, Mrs Mary Leakey, Dr Charles McBurney, Mr Gale Sieveking, Dr Ralph Solecki, Dr J. C. Vogel and Dr John Waechter. The author hastens to add here that he alone accepts responsibility for any errors of fact and faulty synthesis that this book contains.

In the final stages of preparing the script for publication the author owed much to Mrs Sonia Cole and Mr Richard Carrington for practical advice; to Mrs Elizabeth Gardiner for her help in checking references and in preparing the stratigraphical bibliography; to Mrs Robin Kenward for help with the archaeological bibliography; to Dr Andrée Rosenfeld for her painstaking assistance in preparing the radiocarbon-dating charts; to Mr David Sisman and his able staff in the Art Department of the Reader's Digest for the final artwork and type-setting of these charts; and to Miss Theya Molleson for her unstinting and capable help in preparing the whole script for publication and finally in compiling the sixteen tables at the end of the book which apply stratigraphical, cultural and chronometric dating to the 300 or so more important specimens of fossil man now known.

The original manuscript of this book was typed by Mrs Marjorie Nixon of Amersham, and as this was a long continued onerous task my gratitude to her is considerable. I am also grateful to Lady Helen Greenfield who retyped those sections of the original script which required revision in 1963, to Miss Jane Beckett who prepared the index, and to Mrs Valerie Vowles for help in revising the text in readiness for the first reprinting.

I am greatly indebted to Mrs Maureen Conway and Miss Rosemary Powers for their care in preparing a number of the maps, charts and drawings. My gratitude is also due to to Miss Christine Court and Miss Mabel Miller for drawings which they contributed.

Lastly I wish to express my thanks to Dr E. I. White for permitting some of the work connected with this book to take place in his Department.

Thanks for permission to reproduce figures are due to various authors and institutions to whom acknowledgement is made in the legends. Fig. 21 and all later figures so indicated (B.M.N.H.) are reproduced by courtesy of the Trustees of the British Museum (Natural History).

Introduction

THE CHRONOLOGICAL PLACING of fossils, whether they be
early men or lower organisms, is fundamentally important for
understanding their evolutionary relationships. Several distinct
kinds of dating are involved. *Relative dating* places an event
with reference to some other event in a time-sequence. A fossil
or a deposit can be regarded as representing an 'event': the
interval of time when it was alive or being formed. In the
relative dating of fossils reference is generally made to irregu-
larly spaced, arbitrarily chosen events, which are geological,
palaeontological or archaeological. For example in Europe the
spread of the three mammalian genera *Elephas, Equus* and *Bos*
has been chosen to mark the beginning of *Pleistocene* time; the
ending of glacial conditions to mark the beginning of Recent,
Post-Glacial or *Holocene* time, and the change from hunting to
farming economy to mark the beginning of the *Neolithic* 'period'.
In the sense that none of the events occurred everywhere
simultaneously, the dating of a specimen by these criteria as
Basal Pleistocene, Early Post-Glacial or Early Neolithic does
not necessarily imply exact contemporaneity with specimens
similarly dated in other parts of the world.

All dating is in a sense relative, but when it relates an event
to a regular astronomical event-series, particularly the passage
of years or solar time, it is commonly called *absolute dating*.
Thus, to date a skull as Early Neolithic is to place it in a
sequence of archaeologically determined events; to date it as
6000 BC is to date it absolutely. Unfortunately the use of the
term absolute dating as synonymous with dating in years has
blunted the meaning of the word absolute, for it makes no
distinction between referring an event to a span of years and

referring it to a particular instant in time. Some authors (Ewer, 1956) have preferred to use the term absolute age with reference to contemporaneity between one deposit or species and another. For instance, if two deposits in widely separated regions were proved to be contemporaneous without being dated in years they could be said to be of the same absolute age. On the other hand, two deposits both dated as being 'between 20,000 and 25,000 years old' (so-called absolute dating) might not be contemporaneous. In such cases relative dating may be more informative.

To know the correct time sequence of the fossil remains of man and his ancestors is basic to interpreting their significance; but it is equally important from the point of view of understanding evolutionary process to obtain a measure of how much time separates one form from another. We are therefore concerned with two main classes of dating:

Relative Dating　　the stratigraphical or archaeological age of a specimen or formation.

Chronometric Dating (hitherto called Absolute Dating): the age of a specimen or formation measured in years.

In practice there are several kinds of relative dating, each depending on a different range of evidence. When a human skull, for example, is dug up in some ancient deposit, those interested in the discovery usually inquire at once: 'is it reliably dated?' The first question to be settled is whether the specimen is contemporaneous with the deposit in which it was found, or whether it has been instrusively buried, or whether (as sometimes happens) it has been derived from some older formation and redeposited. This primary dating, the age-relation of a specimen to its containing deposit and to the associated finds, has been termed for convenience *R. 1 or first-order relative dating*.* If the specimen is a bone (or tooth) determination of its chemical composition in comparison with that of other bones of known stratigraphical age in the same deposit is a valuable means of establishing whether it is contemporaneous, intrusive or derived, for the chemical com-

---

* The author developed this dating terminology at the Wenner–Gren symposium in New York 1952 (Oakley, 1953).

position of buried bone changes in course of time. The analytical methods of dating bones (Oakley, 1953, 1963, 1963a), including fluorine analysis, nitrogen analysis and radiometric assay, are mainly used for R.1 dating which is particularly important in connection with any doubtfully fossil human bones, because of man's long established habit of burying the dead.

It was this R.1 dating which was in doubt in all the discoveries of remains of *Homo sapiens* whose antiquity was controversial, as for instance in the cases of Moulin-Quignon, Calaveras, Galley Hill and Oldoway, which may be worthwhile summarizing briefly at this point.* The *Moulin-Quignon* jaw, found a century ago in the Somme terrace gravels, which contain Chellean hand-axes, was eventually shown by the 'gelatine' (= nitrogen) test to be not older than Neolithic, probably a fraudulent intrusion – really a predecessor of Piltdown.

The *Calaveras* skull, allegedly unearthed from a Pliocene bone-bed, was shown by means of an early application of the fluorine test to be relatively modern – probably planted in the mine-shaft by a cowboy as a joke.

The *Galley Hill* skeleton was found in 1888 in the Swanscombe terrace gravels containing Acheulian hand-axes. For some time it was regarded by Keith and others as an indication that *Homo sapiens* already existed in 'modern form' by Middle Pleistocene times. In 1948 Oakley and Montagu showed that comparison of its fluorine content with that of the fossil mammalia of the Swanscombe gravels indicated that it was an intrusive burial probably Post-Pleistocene and this was confirmed by radiocarbon dating of portions of the skeleton itself (Barker and Mackey, 1961, p. 41).

The *'Oldoway* human skeleton', discovered in 1913 by Professor H. Reck in what later became known as Olduvai Bed II, was for many years regarded by him as contemporaneous with the very ancient Bed II fauna. Later investigation (Boswell, 1932; Leakey *et al.*, 1933) showed that the skeleton was a burial, and mineral analysis of its matrix proved that the interment dated from a time after Beds III, IV and part

* All these controversial fossil *Homo sapiens* are discussed in detail by Oakley, 1964, and the revised dating of these and other remains is summarized in Table XVI at the end of this book.

of V had been eroded from the site, in fact from Epi-Palaeolithic times, the beginning of the Mesolithic Age.

However, in many discoveries of early human or pre-human remains there has been no reason to doubt their contemporaneity with the deposit in which they were found; for example the Swanscombe skull and the Olduvai fossil hominids found by the Leakeys. But in almost all cases the *stratigraphical* (including palaeontological) age or *archaeological* correlation has constituted a problem for discussion. The stage in the *local sequence* to which the deposit containing the fossil (or contemporaneous fauna or culture) is referable is called the *R.2 dating* of the specimen. The inferred position of that stage in terms of world, or at least *wider-scale* stratigraphy or culture sequence, may be called *R.3 dating*. The distinction between R.2 and R.3 dating may seem rather arbitrary, but the former is based on *fact* (*eg* item 2 below, associated industry: local Aurignacian), the latter on *inference* (*eg* item 2 below, stratigraphical stage: Mid–Würm in alpine sequence). There are of course some cases where R.2 dating and R.3 dating are synonymous. The eight examples of fossil man shown on the facing page serve to illustrate the distinction between the various orders of relative dating.

When a fossil bone or tooth (or indeed any fossil) is found in isolation unaccompanied by other organic remains serving to establish the R.2 or R.3 age, it can be sometimes dated by its form or morphology. This method of relative dating (which elsewhere I have termed *R.4 or morphological dating*) is reliable in some groups of fossils where the time-spans of the genera and species are relatively short and well known, but in other groups, particularly rare groups, it is very unreliable. It does not allow for unsuspected survivals. For example, before the discovery of a living coelacanth in 1938, any new fossil member of this group in rock of unknown age would have been dated morphologically as 'unquestionably Cretaceous or earlier' whereas in fact, as we now know, it might be Tertiary or even Quaternary. Morphological dating of fossil Primates (the group which includes man) has also proved unreliable, but it will no doubt become less so with the increase of our knowledge of the group. Few human palaeontologists would seriously question the correctness of inferring that the Neanderthal and

Names of Finds	R.1 age related to deposit	R.2 stage in local archaeological or stratigraphical sequence	R.3 position of stage in wider stratigraphy or archaeology
1. 'Oldoway' skeleton (*Homo sapiens sapiens*)	In Olduvai Bed II *i*	Post basal Bed V (= Upper Capsian)	Early Mesolithic Kenya
2. Cro-Magnon skeletons (*H. sapiens sapiens*)	*a c*	Aurignacian	Mid Würm
3. Spy skeletons (*H. neanderthalensis*)	*c*	Cold 'Mousterian'	Early Würm
4. Weimar–Ehringsdorf skeletons (*H. neanderthalensis*)	*c*	Warm 'Mousterian'	Riss–Würm (Eemian)
5. Swanscombe skull (*Homo cf steinheimensis*)	*c*	Middle Gravel Acheulian	Mindel–Riss (Hoxnian)
6. Choukoutien Loc. I skulls (*Pithecanthropus pekinensis*)	*c*	Choukoutienian	Mindel II
7. Heidelberg jaw *Euranthropus* (*Homo heidelbergensis*)	*c*	Mauer Sands	Günz–Mindel
8. *Zinjanthropus* (*Paranthropus boisei*)	*c*	Olduvai Bed I (Oldowan 'floor')	Upper Villafranchian

* Four R.1 categories are represented:
c - contemporaneous with deposit.
a c - approximately contemporaneous, *eg* Upper Palaeolithic interment in an Upper Palaeolithic deposit.
i - intrusive burial of appreciatively later date than the deposit.

Gibraltar skulls were of Upper Pleistocene age in view of their detailed similarity to the well-dated skulls of Spy, Le Moustier and elsewhere in Europe.

Morphological evidence is usually taken into consideration with other evidence bearing on the antiquity of fossil human remains of doubtful antiquity. Thus if a human skull is found in any early Pleistocene deposit and fails to pass any of the analytical tests for antiquity, the fact of its being indistinguishable from *Homo sapiens* would be regarded by most anthropologists as in keeping with the results of the tests; whereas if a skull found in similar circumstances were morphologically 'archaic', negative evidence of antiquity would be less convincing.

Establishing the R.2 and probable R.3 ages of human remains depends on the application of the usual methods of stratigraphical geology and archaeology: that is to say observing the stratification of the site where the remains have been found, noting any associated fauna, plant remains and artifacts, and comparing these with the contents of underlying and overlying deposits; and eventually comparing the sequence with that at other sites farther afield. The modern excavator pays particular attention to collecting shells and charcoal from the deposits under investigation, because these are likely not only to provide evidence of the climate prevailing when a deposit was being formed, but if found in sufficient quantities these materials can be chronometrically dated within limits by the radiocarbon method. The excavator also usually preserves samples of the deposits for mineral analysis (see above, p. 3) and pollen-grain analysis,* techniques which provide valuable evidence for relative dating of human remains at some sites.

In many parts of the world the sequence of land faunas through Tertiary and Quaternary times has been worked out in some detail, so that if a large assemblage of contemporaneous mammalian remains is found in association with a fossil human skeleton, or part of a skeleton, its stratigraphical age (R.2 or R.3 dating) is fairly easily determined within certain limits. Assemblages of molluscan shells sometimes provide valuable

---

* Pollen-grain analysis of matrices of the medullary cavities of one of the limb-bones of Tilbury Man showed in 1963 that this historic burial was not older than the Early Bronze Age; previously it had been regarded as possibly Mesolithic.

indications of the age of lake beds, river beds and aeolian or other terrestrial deposits. Land and freshwater molluscs are fairly sensitive climatic indicators, and therefore may show whether a deposit is periglacial, interglacial, interstadial or Post-Glacial, while many of the species have restricted time-ranges (either locally or universally).

In discussing the relative dating of fossil human remains in any detail, it is necessary to be familiar with current terms and methods of classifying and correlating Quaternary deposits. These matters form the subject of Part I of this book.

The *Absolute* or Chronometric dating of early human remains or other fossil bones provides the ultimate framework of hominid evolution, but it is important to recognize at the outset the differences between the various orders of absolute dating, which may be classified as follows:

A.1 dating: direct determination of the age of the specimen itself from internal evidence; for example by measuring the carbon-14 radioactivity of a sample of bone, as was done in the case of the Galley Hill skeleton, and in the case of the human skeleton found in one of the Dalkey Island shell-beds (Mesolithic), Northern Ireland (Barker and Mackey, 1961, p. 43).

A.2 dating: direct determination of the age of the source deposit; for example potassium/argon (K/A) measurements of volcanic minerals in the beds which contained the Olduvai hominids (Leakey, Evernden and Curtis, 1961).

A.3 dating: the age of a specimen in years inferred by correlation of the source bed with a deposit whose actual age has been determined. Thus the original *Pithecanthropus I* remains from river gravel at Trinil, Java, can be dated as c 500,000 years old on the basis of the K/A age of leucite in volcanic rock found elsewhere in Java but containing Trinil fauna (von Koenigswald, 1962).

A.4 dating: the age in years inferred from some theoretical consideration; for example, dates obtained by expressing the local geological sequence in terms of climatic fluctuations, and matching these with the curve of past insolation as calculated by Milankovitch (the 'Absolute Chronology' of Zeuner). Thus, the Keilor skull in Australia was at one time dated as 150,000 years old on the basis of the Milankovitch age of the Main

Monastirian beach with which the Keilor river-deposit was carrelated (Zeuner, 1944). Later A.3 dating, based on radiocarbon measurements, indicate that it is in fact only about 15,000 years old.

A more promising form of A.4 dating recently introduced is the matching of climatic fluctuations in the Pleistocene sequences on land with marine palaeotemperature changes recorded in ocean bed cores, and dating key layers of sediment in these cores by analysis of their content of uranium daughter elements.

It will be obvious that the validity of the A.2, A.3 or A.4 dating of a fossil is conditional on the contemporaneity of the specimen with the containing deposit (ie the R.1 dating) being assured. Recent studies have emphasized that attempts at chronometric dating (excluding the A.1 type) are really a waste of time unless the R.1 dating has been established beyond doubt.

The framework of relative chronology for Pleistocene deposits in Europe, Asia and Africa has become more dependable in recent years as a result of key points being dated chronometrically (cf Charts B–D). Already by 1957 (Gross, 1958) more than 120 samples of Upper Pleistocene deposits in Europe had been dated by the Carbon-14 method (limited to the last 70,000 years). Since 1958 the potassium/argon method of chronometric dating has been applied to numerous Lower and Middle Pleistocene volcanic deposits in Africa, Asia, Europe and America (Evernden and Curtis, in press). Thus in future, so long as their relative ages (R.1, R.2 and R.3) are well established, the majority of fossil human remains will be quite reliably dated in years by the A.3 procedure, and in many cases even more closely by the A.2 procedure.

In spite of several attempts to subdivide the Pleistocene on a palaeontological basis, the glaciations have been regarded by most geologists as providing the ultimate basis of subdivision. As researches extended farther afield, particularly beyond the glaciated areas into subtropical and tropical realms the need for other means of classifying and correlating deposits of this period became more apparent. The recognition that pluvials took the place of glacials in many of these regions has not altogether helped correlation because of uncertainty as to the extent to which these climatic phases are synchronous.

The sequence of flora has served well enough for correlations within Europe, but in the deposits of Asia and Africa the botanical evidence discovered so far reflects climatic conditions usually without providing any direct means of relative dating. Fossil mammalia have supplied some important clues for the inter-continental correlation of deposits, but the magnitude of the time-lags involved in animal migrations on that scale is still largely unknown, and there are several cases on record of mammalian genera restricted to the Lower Pleistocene in one continent but surviving throughout the Middle Pleistocene in another.

Fortunately there is a further class of evidence available for determining the relative ages of Quaternary deposits which has some advantage over the palaeontological: namely *archaeological evidence*. The method of dating based on the spread of early human cultures is really an extension of palaeontological dating, for early industries (assemblages of artifacts) may be regarded as fossilized patterns of behaviour which changed ('evolved') at varying rates and which were acquired and transmitted by tradition. There are a number of reasons for inferring that the time-lag in the spread of palaeolithic traditions was small in relation to the measurable subdivisions of Pleistocene chronology.

At the present time, in almost all parts of the world, cultures of many kinds and varying levels of complexity occur within short distances of one another, but before the Neolithic Revolution this was not so. The cultures of the early hunters and food-gatherers evolved slowly and their traditions spread widely long before there was any marked change. Where a palaeolithic culture can be defined and identified on the basis of sufficiently large assemblages of artifacts, it is legitimate to regard its 'industries' as approximately contemporaneous throughout their area of distribution. Until recently this view was based wholly on theory, but radiocarbon dating of early archaeological horizons in Africa at least supports the conclusion that in pre-Neolithic times cultural evolution was proceeding contemporaneously over very large areas. To that extent palaeolithic industries may be used as means of approximate synchronic dating of Pleistocene deposits.

One of the advantages of archaeological dating of deposits as

compared with the palaeontological is that a high percentage
of the known early industries are in quartzite, flint or other
almost indestructible stone, whereas in many regions plant and
animal remains have only been preserved under exceptional
conditions. In Africa, for example, the number of exposures of
Pleistocene deposits in which palaeolithic artifacts can be found
vastly outnumbers those containing fossils.

Where fossil human remains occur, associated artifacts are of
course invaluable as dating evidence. The Rhodesian Skull
found in the Broken Hill Bone Cave could 'not even be placed
in one of the three major divisions of the Pleistocene' (Zeuner,
1946, p. 296) until its archaeological associations had been
fully investigated (Clark, 1950).

As the cultures which provide the archaeological frameworks
used in dating fossil men – in the sense of Pleistocene and Early
Holocene hominids – are almost exclusively those of the
Palaeolithic and Mesolithic stages of Old World Prehistory,
these are the ones surveyed in detail in Part II of this book.

Part One

Stratigraphical Dating

Chapter 1

Relative Chronology of Quaternary Deposits

RELATIVE CHRONOLOGY IS closely linked with stratigraphy, the branch of geology concerned with the superposition of deposits or strata.[1]* In studying stratigraphy, the order of superposition is first observed, then the sequence is subdivided into natural groups of beds. The order of appearance of new organic forms – fossils – is noted and, in the case of Quaternary stratigraphy, the appearance of new types of artifacts. Finally, having established the order of organic or cultural succession, the sequence can be used as a guide to the relative ages of newly encountered formations.

It has seldom been possible to observe superposition on any considerable scale in Quaternary deposits and the sequence has had to be established and subdivided largely without such aid. Successive glacial moraines, raised beaches and river terraces, for instance, are quite different phenomena which do not necessarily occur in the same areas. Only on the floor of the oceans, and there only in some places, has there been a continuous sedimentary record of the whole of this period, although deposits accumulated on lake-beds and in caves at some localities represent fairly extensive sequences. The ideal stratigraphical column of the Quaternary has for the most part to be pieced together by correlating deposits and events of very diverse kinds.

We should recall at this point the view of some geologists that the conception of a Quaternary era is illogical, that the Pleistocene period should be regarded as a continuation of

*There are notes at the end of each part.

the Tertiary, and that there is no justification for separating so-called Post-Glacial time as Recent or Holocene since it is possible that we are living in an interglacial. However, it is convenient and probably less confusing to follow accustomed usage:

$$\text{Post-Pliocene} = \text{Quaternary} \left\{ \begin{array}{l} \text{Holocene} = \text{Post-Glacial} \quad \text{or} \\ \text{Recent} \\ \text{Pleistocene or Great Ice Age}^2 \end{array} \right.$$

The Pleistocene period has been defined on a palaeontological basis: by the proportion of extinct to living mollusca in its marine faunas, and by the presence of *Elephas*, *Equus* and *Bos* in its land fauna. It has also been defined on the basis of certain changes of sea-level. Nevertheless, the most outstanding fact about the period is its broad coincidence with the Great Ice Age. Consequently the successive glaciations have provided the most obvious means of subdividing the period, particularly in the higher latitudes.

Chapter 2

The Glacial Chronology

THE FOUR MAIN advances of glaciers in the Alps recognized by Penck and Brückner (1909), have been widely adopted as providing a convenient subdivision of the period, at any rate as far as Europe is concerned. In discussions during the Second Congress of the International Quaternary Organization (INQUA) at Leningrad in 1932 it was agreed to group these glacial subdivisions in terms of Lower, Middle and Upper Pleistocene as follows:

Würm Glaciation

Riss-Würm Interglacial
} Upper Pleistocene

Riss Glaciation

Mindel-Riss Interglacial
} Middle Pleistocene

Mindel Glaciation

Günz-Mindel Interglacial
} Lower Pleistocene

Günz Glaciation

This scheme has become widely used in Europe,[3] but it does not fall into line with the classification used by vertebrate palaeontologists, which is based mainly on the succession of elephants. For example, *Elephas* (*Palaeoloxodon*) *antiquus*, regarded as typical of the Middle Pleistocene, had emerged and was spreading widely before the time of the Mindel glaciation. Following the decision of the International Geological Congress in 1948 to include the Villafranchian in the Pleistocene, a new classification of the Alpine stages was proposed in 1958 by the geologist, Paul Woldstedt (1958, p. 3), and as it is in full accord with the scheme favoured by vertebrate palaeontologists[4] it will probably now come into general use. It is adopted in this book:

$$\left.\begin{array}{l}\text{Würm} \\ \text{Riss-Würm} \\ \text{Riss}\end{array}\right\}\ \text{Upper Pleistocene}$$

$$\left.\begin{array}{l}\text{Mindel-Riss} \\ \text{Mindel} \\ \text{Günz-Mindel}\end{array}\right\}\ \text{Middle Pleistocene}$$

$$\left.\begin{array}{l}\text{Günz and Pre-Günz} \\ \text{(Donau) stages}\end{array}\right\}\ \begin{array}{l}\text{Lower Pleistocene} \\ \text{(Villafranchian)}\end{array}$$

In view of the widely held and long-standing conception of the Pleistocene as broadly equivalent to the Ice Age it is satisfactory to find that glaciers were already advancing in the high alpine valleys during the earlier part of the Villafranchian stage.

Glacial stages can be recognized far beyond the limits of the moraines and tills or boulder clays laid down by the glaciers and ice-sheets, for a region of glaciation is surrounded by a zone, sometimes several hundred miles wide, which is affected by intense frost and associated phenomena. This 'periglacial' area usually includes three main types of environment: *tundra*, with peat mosses and shrubs such as dwarf birch and dwarf willow; *taiga*,[5] with stunted forest, mainly coniferous; and *steppe*, dry grassland on which *loess* is liable to accumulate, that is to say the deposit of rock dust carried by wind from exposed glacial moraines and outwash deposits. Under periglacial conditions the subsoil is more or less permanently frozen, when it is termed *tjaele*,[6] or less elegantly permafrost. In spring time the top layer of the *tjaele* thaws and forms a sludge of disintegrated rock which tends to flow down sparsely vegetated slopes and to accumulate on lower ground, for example in valley bottoms. The unstratified tumultuous deposits known as *head*, in many parts of Britain, or as *coombe-rock* in the chalk valleys, were formed by this process of *solifluxion* during glacial stages. Solifluxion has frequently caused a characteristic disturbance of the upper layers of stratified river deposits and lake-beds (Fig. 1). Loesses and solifluxion layers are valuable indicators of glacial horizons in Pleistocene sequences outside the areas of glaciation. In their classic researches Penck and Brückner based their four-fold scheme partly on moraines but to a much greater extent on fans and terraces of outwash gravel deposited by the

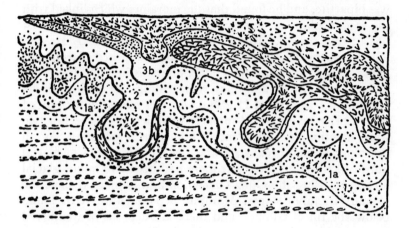

Figure 1 Section in 100-ft terrace gravels of the Thames, at East Burnham, Bucks, showing disturbance of the stratified gravelly sand by solifluxion and cryoturbation. *After Breuil.*

rivers flowing from the glaciers which occupied the Bavarian valleys during Pleistocene times, as follows:

Low Terrace	representing the Würm Glaciation
High Terrace	„ „ Riss „
Younger Deckenschotter	„ „ Mindel „
Older Deckenschotter	„ „ Günz „

Subsequently, researches by Eberl (1930) showed[7] that the Low Terrace was composite and comprised deposits of three glacial phases. The second phase (Main Würm or Würm II), marked the peak of the glaciation. The readvancing glaciers extensively eroded the deposits of the much weaker Early Würm or Würm I advance, and converted them into hog-back hillocks of the type known as drumlins. The third phase (Würm

III) is recorded by a belt of moraines which lie well within the limits of those of phase two. On the basis of terminal moraines, Penck and Brückner recognized a number of oscillations in the retreat of the Würm glaciers. The Laufen retreat (Fig. 12) in their classification has generally been identified with the main or Würm I/II interstadial of Eberl's classification.

Eberl confirmed earlier observations that the High Terrace was bipartite, and he found that the moraines which linked with the second phase of advance lay well within those of the first phase; that is to say Riss II was weaker than Riss I. He also found that the Younger Deckenschotter comprised two spreads of gravel but the second was much more distinct and linked up with the group of moraines representing the main Mindel Glaciation (= Mindel II). The Older Deckenschotter proved to comprise seven gravel-spreads, of which only the last two were identifiable with Penck's Günz-Deckenschotter. As all the older gravel-spreads showed the characteristics of glacial outwash, Eberl inferred that there had been five minor glacial advances before the Günz Glaciation and he named these the Donau (Danube) stages. Morainic deposits have been found below the till of Günz I, and there are deposits of weathered loess which can be correlated with the Donau stages.

Studies of the deposits of loess which overlie some of the glacial deposits and extend across the unglaciated Central European plain almost to the shores of the Atlantic (Figs. 2 and 4), have provided useful confirmation of the subdivision of the glacial stages into stadia and *interstadia*[8]. The latter are represented in the loesses by zones of weathering or 'fossil soils'. Thus, when the geologist Soergel (1928) reinvestigated the sections in the Mauer sand-pit he found that the Younger and Older Loesses, were subdivisable by levels of loamy weathering which represented mild intervals within the main glacial stages. In almost all areas where it is fully preserved the Younger Loess contains a well developed fossil soil horizon representing the main interstadial Würm I/II. In a few areas there is a second, less distinct soil horizon marking a climatic oscillation presumed to correspond with the Würm II/III interstadial in the Alps. Both these soil horizons have been recognized in Austria (Brandtner, 1954; Gross, 1956) and elsewhere in Central Europe where they have been closely dated and are

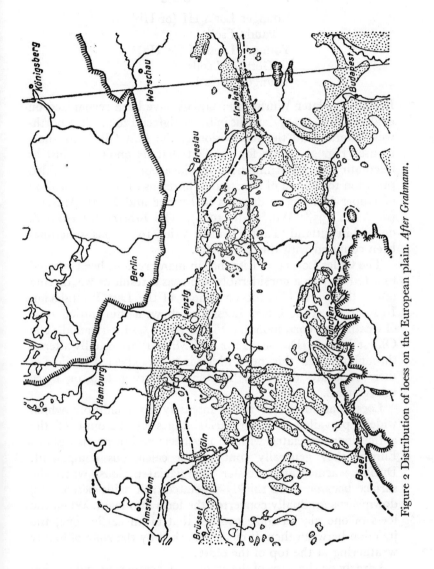

Figure 2 Distribution of loess on the European plain. *After Grahmann.*

provisionally known as the 'Göttweig[9] Interstadial' and the Paudorf Oscillation in the following sequence:

Younger Loess III (or IIb)
Paudorf soil
Younger Loess II (or IIa)
'Göttweig' soils
Younger Loess I

Earlier and later Würm interstadials have been recognized on evidence from peaty deposits in the periglacial zone of the north-west littoral, and the subdivision of the Last Glaciation now in use (Fig. 3) allows for the fact that its onset was just as fluctuating as its termination. Radiocarbon dating has added precision to the use of interstadial horizons in the classification of Upper Pleistocene deposits in Europe and North America (de Vries 1958; Woldstedt, 1960). The Brørup Interstadial, defined in Jutland (Tauber and de Vries, 1958), has sometimes been confused with the 'Göttweig'.

The Older Loess (= Riss) has in many regions been altered to a red clay to a considerable depth as a result of weathering under the warm climatic conditions of the Last Interglacial. In some areas the Older Loess also shows a thin buried zone of weathering corresponding to the Riss I/II interstadial. The Oldest Loesses (Donau, Günz and Mindel) are usually altered throughout their thickness, which is to be expected in view of their exposure to loamy weathering during two or three interglacials.

Loesses accumulated under intensely dry conditions which widely prevailed during glacial stages on account of the anticyclone associated with an ice-sheet; and in north-western Europe they generally contained a calcareous component. During warmer and moister interglacial periods, when the surface became more thickly vegetated, soil acids percolating downwards gradually converted the loess into loam. When the loess of one glacial stage overlies that of an earlier one, the junction between them is clearly marked by the zone of loamy weathering at the top of the older.

Largely on the basis of the amount of weathering and erosion which occurred between the formation of the Younger Decken-schotter and the High Terrace in the Bavarian valleys, Penck

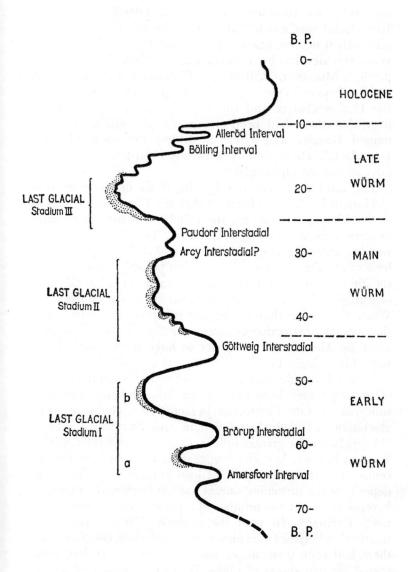

Figure 3 Schematic curve representing the undulations of the Last Glaciation in Europe, showing the main phases of loess deposition (stippled), the current terminology and radiocarbon chronology. *After Woldstedt.*

and Brückner considered that the Mindel-Riss or Second
Interglacial was much longer than the other two, and consequently it became known as the Great Interglacial. In recent
years, this view has been regarded as questionable (Flint, 1957,
p. 385). Moreover, P. Beck (1937) discovered in some of the
Swiss valleys evidence of two distinct glacial advances between
the Deckenschotter and the High Terrace, leading him to
infer that there had been two minor glaciations, which he
named Kander and Glütsch, during the so-called Great
Interglacial. These are now generally regarded as Pre-Rissian
advances of the alpine glaciers.

The total areas covered by the drifts of the four main
glaciations in the Alps indicate that the Riss advance was the
most widespread, although the Mindel was equally extensive
in some regions and less so in others. The Würm Glaciation
was less extensive than either Riss or Mindel, and the Günz
least of all. For reasons unknown, but possibly connected with
the intensity of cold rather than the extent of the ice, the fauna
of Europe suffered much greater changes in the course of the
Würm Glaciation than during the two preceding ones. As we
shall see, the extinction of Neanderthal man and his replacement by Modern man appears to have been closely linked
with this ecological crisis.

Although the glacial advances and recessions in the foreland
of the Alps have been used as the 'standard' for the glacial
subdivisions of the Pleistocene, in fact the Scandinavian area of
glaciation, which included Britain and Northern Germany,
(Fig. 4) had a far greater influence on the unglaciated parts of
Western Europe. As each advance of ice from the Scandinavian
centre tended to destroy or at least considerably disturb the
deposits of the preceding one, it has not been easy to establish
beyond all doubt the number of separate ground-moraines in
north Germany. In 1913 the geologist Gagel (1913), using
weathering horizons as evidence of interglacials, concluded that
there had been three major glaciations in that region, represented by two sheets of Older Drift (later called Elster and
Saale) and the much less weathered Younger Drift which
included the Baltic End Moraines. Further researches led to the
subdivision of the main drifts and correlation with the Alpine
stages as follows:[10]

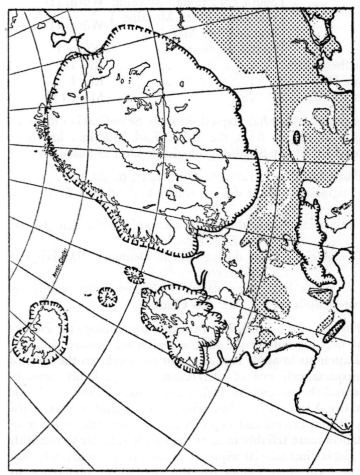

Loess ▨ Margins of land ice ⊥⊥⊥⊥ Margins of sea ice ⸻ Ancient coast line

Figure 4 Distribution of ice in Europe at the maximum stage of the Last Glaciation.

B

North Germany		*Alps*
	Baltic End Moraines	Minor readvances
Weichsel Drift	South Pomeranian Moraine	Würm III
	Frankfurt- Posen Moraine	Würm II
	Brandenburg Moraines	
	Stettin Stadium[11]	Würm I
Warthe Drift[12]	.. ..	Riss II
Saale Drift ..	.. ..	Riss I
Elster Drift ..	.. ..	Mindel II

The period which has elapsed since the Scandinavian ice-sheet began its retreat from the Baltic End Moraines has been subdivided by the Swedish geologist de Geer as follows:

4 Post-Glacial (arbitrary, see Flint, 1957, p. 385.).

3 Finiglacial – stage during which Finland was freed from ice.

2 Gotiglacial – stage during which southern Sweden (Gotia) was freed from ice.

1 Daniglacial – stage during which Denmark (Dania) was uncovered.

These stages have been dated chronometrically mainly by varve-analysis (p. 77). See also Chart A.

The use of the Penck and Brückner terminology for Pleistocene deposits outside the Alpine region has proved difficult, and attempts to apply it throughout the world on the basis of inadequate evidence of correlation have probably actually hindered the progress of Pleistocene geology. Professor I. M. van der Vlerk (1955) has wisely recommended that, until glacial and interglacial deposits can be correlated over long distances more reliably than at present, it is better to establish the glacial/interglacial sequence in each region separately and to use local stage names (*cf.* R.2 dating) in preference to hypothetical alpine correlates (*cf.* R.3 dating). Professor F. E. Zeuner also urged caution and recommended that the Penck and Brückner terminology should be replaced as follows:

Würm – Last Glaciation (LGl.)
Riss-Würm – Last Interglacial (LIgl.)
Riss – Penultimate Glaciation (PGl.)

Mindel-Riss – Penultimate Interglacial (PIgl.)
Mindel – Antepenultimate Glaciation (ApGl.)
Günz-Mindel – Antepenultimate Interglacial (ApIgl.)
Günz – Early Glaciation (EGl.)

The view is sometimes held that Zeuner's terminology is less committal than that of Penck and Brückner, but both assume the correctness of deducing that there were four main glaciations during the Pleistocene period – and 'a rose by any other name. . . .'[13] To put the matter in another way, it is really no easier to establish that a deposit in some remote part of the world is of 'Antepenultimate Interglacial' age than to prove that it is of Günz-Mindel age. In this book local stage names have been used as far as possible in conjunction with provisional R.3 dating in whatever is judged to be the most appropriate general terminology.

Chapter 3

Interglacial Correlation and Palynology

THERE ARE FEW who would deny that the accumulated evidence from many areas indicates that the Pleistocene climatic fluctuations culminated in the higher latitudes with the formation of continental ice-sheets on four occasions. On the other hand, cores from favourably situated localities on the ocean floors, providing a continuous record of climatic fluctuations throughout the greater part of the period, give a picture of very numerous and complicated temperature changes which can only be correlated with the latest phases of the known glacial sequence (Fig. 5). It is probable that on the land the glacial climaxes represented the summation of a complex succession of changes in the atmosphere and hydrosphere. The extent to which glaciers and ice-sheets advanced depended so much on local factors that whereas some areas bordering a centre of glaciation were overrun by ice-sheets during all four periods of glacial climax, other areas similarly situated were only glaciated during, say, one, two or three climaxes. In a number of regions, two advances or stadia of a single climax appeared as pronounced as two separate climax glaciations. In the latter circumstances, water-laid deposits between two boulder-clays or tills would not be truly interglacial, but *interstadial*[8]. Indeed the 'Fourth and Fifth Interglacials' recognized by James Geikie (1877, p. 393)[14] were based on just such occurrences in Scotland. The deposits in question are now known to represent interstadials of the Last or Fourth Glaciation.

To a considerable extent the problem of Pleistocene

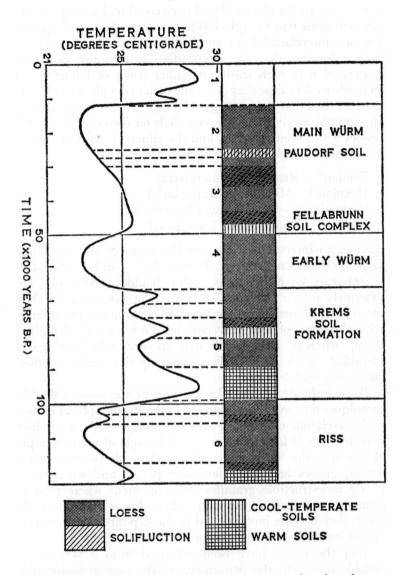

Figure 5 Correlation between palaeotemperature curve based on deep-sea cores, and loess/soil profiles in Austria and Moravia. *According to Emiliani.*

correlation in the glaciated and periglacial regions depends on distinguishing true interglacials from interstadials, and separating one interglacial from another. The interglacials were of longer duration than the interstadials and for the most part associated with high sea-levels (either rising or falling); and in north-west Europe they generally included a phase of climate warmer than that characteristic of the same areas today. During the comparatively shorter interstadials on the other hand, the sea-level was relatively low, and the climate remained cool. Four main interglacials have been distinguished:

4 Eemian[15] – Riss–Würm Interglacial
3 Hoxnian[16] – Mindel–Riss Interglacial
2 Cromerian[17] – Günz–Mindel Interglacial
1 Tiglian[18] – Donau–Günz Interglacial

The warm interval between the Donau stage and the Günz Glaciation has only come to be regarded as an interglacial in recent years. Glacial deposits, such as boulder clays or tills, are extremely difficult to correlate over long distances, for they are usually unfossiliferous and vary in character in accordance with the types of rock traversed by the ice which deposited them, whereas interglacial deposits are relatively easily identified, particularly if they contain pollen-grains (as they commonly do when *acid*).

Pollen-analysis[19] is undoubtedly one of the most valuable techniques now available as an aid in the stratigraphical dating and correlation of peaty layers and fine-grained, water-laid deposits such as lake muds or silts. Throughout many months of the year the air is laden with pollen, blown from trees, shrubs, grasses and other flowering plants, and when these nearly indestructible granules settle on areas where peat is forming or in relatively still water where clay or silt is accumulating, they become incorporated in the deposits and preserved almost indefinitely in the absence of lime.

After the grains have been extracted from a sample by suitable treatment the percentages of the various highly distinctive types of pollen (Figs. 7, 16) can be counted under a microscope, and analysis of the results makes it possible to work out the relative abundance of the various tree species and non-tree species prevailing in, and for some distance around, the area when the deposit was formed. One of the main uses of pollen-analysis is to find out what changes occurred in the flora of a region during the accumulation of a particular deposit or series of deposits. For this purpose samples are collected at closely spaced intervals in a column of the deposit, and the percentages of the different tree and non-tree pollen-grains plotted in the form of a diagram or sequence of pollen-spectra (Fig. 6). In all interglacials the vegetation followed a

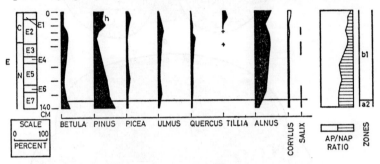

Figure 6 Pollen diagram prepared from 'zone E' of the Cromer Forest at West Runton, Norfolk. *After Duigan.*

similar sequence of change, corresponding to a regular cycle of climatic phases:

1 Late Glacial – Tundra vegetation
2 Early Temperate – Mixed–oak forest replacing birch forest
3 Late Temperate – Mixed–oak forest giving way to coniferous forest
4 Early Glacial – Park-tundra

However, when the pollen-diagrams of different interglacials are compared in detail each proves to have certain distinctive features, in the order of appearance and relative abundance of particular species, and these features are recognizable in widely separated localities. For example, all Tiglian diagrams show an abundance of the hemlock fir *Tsuga*, which is present as a rarity in Cromerian diagrams and absent from later ones. In Britain the silver fir (*Abies*) is absent from Cromerian diagrams, abundant in the Late Temperate phase of the Hoxnian and sparse at the corresponding horizon in the Eemian, when the spruce (*Picea*) predominated. The early rise to dominance of

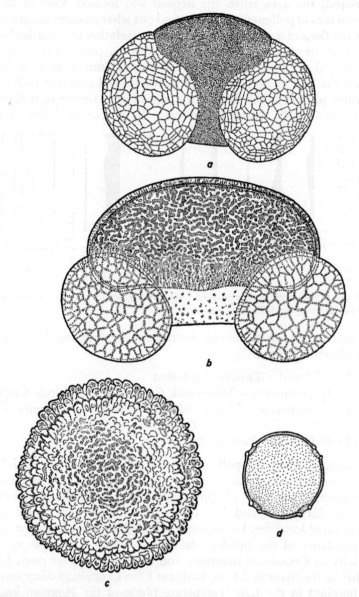

Figure 7 Interglacial pollen. *a Picea* (spruce); *b Abies* (silver fir); *c Tsuga* (hemlock fir); *d Carpinus* (hornbeam) x 450. *del John Shaw.*

hornbeam (*Carpinus*) after the mixed–oak phase is characteristic of Eemian diagrams in Britain and on the Continent, while a lengthier mixed–oak phase and absence of a distinct *Carpinus* zone distinguishes the Hoxnian (see Fig. 7).

Besides pollen-grains there are many other plant remains, microscopic and macroscopic, which occur as fossils in fresh-water Quaternary deposits, and which can be used for stratigraphic dating. For example, macrosporangia of the exotic water-fern *Azolla* (Fig. 8) have been found in Tiglian, Cromerian and Hoxnian deposits in north-west Europe and each of these interglacials had a distinct species (van der Vlerk, 1955, pp. 36–7).

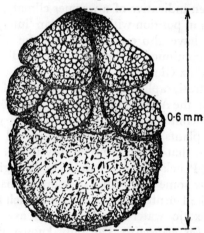

0·6 mm

Figure 8 Macrosporangium of *Azolla tegeliensis. After Florschutz.*

Azolla filiculoides (now only native in America) found in Hoxnian but not in Eemian or later deposits.
Azolla aff. *filiculoides* (not quite identical with the living species) in Cromerian deposits.
Azolla tegeliensis (extinct) in Tiglian deposits.

It is now recognized that interglacial horizons are far more useful than glacials as a basis for subdivision and correlation of Pleistocene sequences, at any rate in north-west Europe. Botanical differentiation is usually the most reliable but the mammalian and molluscan faunas of each interglacial were also quite distinctive; and there are indications that when better known the insect faunas will prove equally diagnostic.[20]

Ultimately the interglacials defined on the basis of pollen and fauna in north-western Europe will surely be identified in the Alpine region. Already some progress has been made in this direction. Nangeroni, Venzo[21] and others working on the Italian flank of the Alps have dated the earliest glacial/interglacial stages in terms of faunal and vegetational sequence. They investigated a succession of deposits in Lombardy, containing pollen and mammalian remains, ranging in date from Late Pliocene to the time of the Mindel Glaciation. The 'cold' levels corresponding with the Donau Glacial advances were found to be separated from the later Günz drift by sediments containing pollen indicative of a warmer climate. This 'warm' zone agrees well in position with the Tiglian 'interglacial'. The Italian workers have also established that the Villafranchian mammal fauna continued to the top of the 'cold' strata correlated with the Günz Glaciation.

The precise stratigraphic age of the two most famous interglacial deposits in the Alps is still uncertain. The Hötting breccia near Innsbruck contains leaves of *Rhododendron ponticum* and other southerly plants indicating a mean annual temperature 2° C higher than that of the same locality today. The deposit was referred by Penck to the Mindel–Riss Interglacial, but is now regarded by some authorities as more probably of Riss–Würm age.[22] The Dürnten peat-beds near Zurich have yielded traces of the exotic water-lily *Brasenia* in association with remains of *Elephas antiquus*.[23] The only known Post-Tertiary deposits in north-west Europe which contain *Brasenia* are Eemian, so the Dürnten 'lignites' are almost certainly of Riss–Würm age, but this requires confirmation by pollen-analysis.

Pollen-analysis sometimes serves as a valuable cross-check to faunal dating. The horizon of Peking Man has generally been considered interglacial on the basis of fauna, but pollen-analysis of the matrix of a cervid antler from the Upper Sinanthropus zone indicated that this deposit accumulated under cool conditions on the boundary between *taiga* forest and steppe, such as would have prevailed there during a glacial stage. Combining the two lines of evidence the stratigraphical dating of Choukoutien is now counted as Mindel II (Kurtén & Vasari, 1960).

Chapter 4

Dating and Correlation by Fauna

THE FAUNA OF a region changes in course of time in response to climatic oscillations, there is emergence and spread of new species, and the dying out of others. Some genera and species are more useful age-indicators than others, either on account of being subject to rapid evolutionary change (*eg* elephants), or on account of the speed and extent of their migrations (*eg* deer). Among mammalia, the most useful groups for correlating Pleistocene deposits are: elephants, rhinoceroses, bears, hyenas, certain small mammals (Microtine rodents, shrews, etc), pigs, bovids, deer and antelopes. The extent to which R.3 dating by means of Pleistocene mammalia approaches 'absolute' (in the sense of synchronic) dating, depends on the speed with which the 'dating' species migrated. Where unchecked the larger mammals spread at the rate of about 1,000 kilometres in a century, but with small mammals the rate is slower (Kurtén, 1957). Probably the main limitation to correlating deposits across the world by means of mammalia is the fact that some forms do not migrate far, and that even the most widespread species fail to cross certain boundaries.

The species or subgenera of elephant (see Fig. 9) which successively predominated in Europe have served as one of the main bases for the subdivision of the Pleistocene as follows:

Upper Pleistocene: *Elephas* (*Mammuthus*) *primigenius*
Middle Pleistocene: *Elephas* (*Palaeoloxodon*) *antiquus*
Lower Pleistocene: *Elephas* (*Archidiskodon*) *meridionalis*

There is an overlap in the time ranges of these species but the

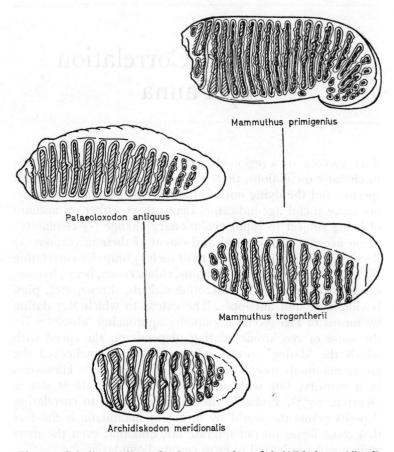

Figure 9 Grinding surfaces of 3rd upper molars of *Archidiskodon meridionalis*, *Palaeoloxodon antiquus*, *Mammuthus trogontherii*, and *Mammuthus primigenius*. ($\frac{1}{6}$).

time of first appearance of each serves to mark the base of a division. Attempts have been made to extend this system beyond Europe by correlation of equivalent or co-lateral species. Thus eastwards through Asia *E. meridionalis* gave place to *E. (Archidiskodon) planifrons*. In recent years the recognition of *E. hysudrindicus** as equivalent to *E. namadicus* in the Indian Pleistocene, and that in turn as closely comparable with *E. antiquus* in Europe, has contributed to the modern classification of the Trinil beds as Middle Pleistocene.

A complication in the use of elephants in the stratigraphical dating of Pleistocene deposits is that there were several independent lines of evolution. In Europe there were two lines (Fig. 10) leading from the *Archidiskodon* stock: to *Palaeoloxodon* (early, typical and late *antiquus*), adapted to the woodlands characteristic of interglacial conditions; and to *Mammuthus* (*trogontherii* or early mammoth, with transitions to the well-known Upper Pleistocene *primigenius*), adapted to steppe conditions, and represented in deposits laid down during glacial phases.

The dating of all fossil hominids of Europe has largely rested on the evidence of the associated elephant remains.

The predominant elephant in the Mauer Sands is an early form of *Palaeoloxodon antiquus*, whereas in the Süssenborn deposits of the succeeding Mindel (Elsterian) stage remains of the early mammoth *Mammuthus trogontherii* are common, so that Heidelberg Man can be confidently referred to the Günz–Mindel interglacial (see below.)

The Steinheim skull occurred in *antiquus*-bearing river gravels overlying *trogontherii* gravels and capped by gravels yielding mammoth teeth of the *trogontherii-primigenius* transition (Fig. 11). This hominid was therefore living in the Mindel–Riss or Hoxnian interglacial and was broadly contemporaneous with Swanscombe Man whose skull accompanied typical *Palaeoloxodon antiquus*. The early Neanderthal men of Weimar–Ehringsdorf on the other hand were living at the time of the late form of *P. antiquus* which was characteristic of the Riss–Würm or Eemian Interglacial.

Finally, the 'classic' Neanderthalers and Upper Palaeolithic

---

* In Oakley, 1964 (first impression) *E. hysudricus* was inadvertently listed in the Trinil fauna instead of *E. hysudrindicus*.

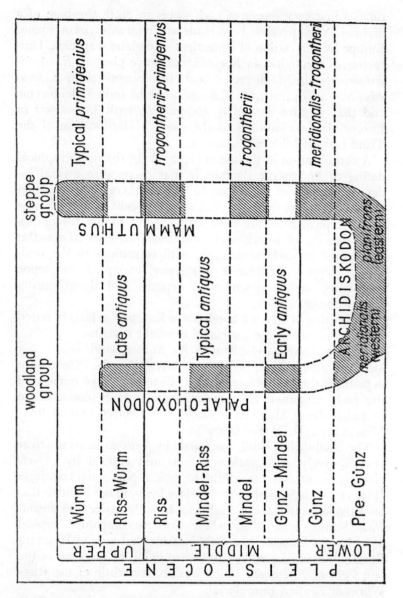

Figure 10 Diagram illustrating the two lineages leading from *Archidiskodon* stock to *Palaeoloxodon* and *Mammuthus. After Adam.*

races of *Homo sapiens* were contemporaneous with *Mammuthus primigenius*.

Hyenas have proved very useful for purposes of relative dating, particularly *Crocuta crocuta* which evolved out of a Villafranchian species in India and then spread rapidly through other parts of Asia and Africa replacing *Hyaena brevirostris* which had similar ecological requirements (Kurtén, 1957, 1957*a*). The immigration of *Crocuta crocuta* into Europe occurred at the beginning of the Mindel I glacial stage (Kurtén,

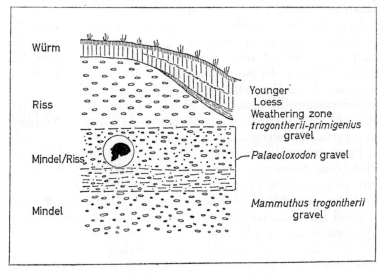

Figure 11 Position of Steinheim skull in the Palaeoloxodon Gravel.

1962). Its absence from the fauna of the Mauer Sands is, in my view, the definitive argument in favour of this formation dating from the Günz–Mindel or main Cromerian Interglacial, rather than from the Cortonian (Kurtén, 1960, p. 27) or Mindel Interstadial, which is a view held by many palaeontologists at the present time. The occurrence of a sub-species of *Hyaena brevirostris* in the Djetis Beds of Java has been quoted as suggesting that these deposits, which contain the oldest known remains of *Pithecanthropus*, date from late Villafranchian times (Kurtén, 1956, p. 42).

The time-ranges of some of the genera and species of mammalia which have proved most useful in stratigraphic dating of Pleistocene deposits in Europe have been published by van der Vlerk and Florschütz (1950, pp. 120–1). A few of these mammals have a more restricted 'vertical' distribution in certain regions, where their use for R.3 dating is therefore greater. For example, hippopotamus was present in Britain during the Cromerian and Eemian interglacials, but apparently absent during the Hoxnian (Sutcliffe, 1960, 1964).

Some fossil mammalia aid the dating of deposits through indicating a particular phase of climate, rather than through having a restricted time-range. Thus, in Britain it may be inferred that a deposit containing contemporaneous hippopotamus is of interglacial age, whereas a deposit with contemporaneous musk-ox is bound to date from a glacial stage. Other finds in the same deposit might narrow the dating to a particular interglacial, or glacial.

Fossil mammalia contribute much to the relative dating of Pleistocene deposits in Africa, but the use of European standards of comparison are misleading (Ewer, 1963). For example, in Africa *Archidiskodon* continued into the Middle Pleistocene.

Fossil invertebrates also have proved useful for correlating Quaternary deposits. Freshwater and land mollusca (*eg* snails) as well as insects, are valuable climatic indicators and as some species in these groups have very restricted time-ranges (either locally or universally) they are useful for R.2 and R.3 dating. Molluscan communities are on the whole more sensitive than the mammalia to changes in micro-climate,[24] so that the environmental evidence of mollusca and mammalia may sometimes appear conflicting.

As Lyell and others since his time have shown, the increasing percentage of Recent species in a sequence of marine molluscan faunas serves as a useful index of relative age. The following figures illustrate this increase in the Upper Pliocene to Lower Pleistocene marine series of East Anglia.[25]

Tentative correlation		East Anglian deposits	Percentage of living species
Günz		Weybourne Crag[26]	92
Tiglian		Norwich Crag	84
Donau	Villafranchian	{ Newer Red Crag	73
		{ Older Red Crag	66
Upper Pliocene		Coralline Crag	60

Attempts have been made to correlate Tertiary and Quaternary deposits in widely separated parts of the world by equating marine faunas with the same percentage of living species. This method has been used in an endeavour to date the Pleistocene deposits of Java in terms of the European relative chronology, but it is not generally considered reliable. Unless the specific determinations in the two regions compared are made by the same conchologist, the 'personal equation' is likely to affect the estimated percentages considerably (Davies, 1934, p. 57). Moreover, neither the rate of evolutionary change, nor the rates at which species are displaced, is likely to be the same in communities that are only remotely related and living under different conditions.

If the living species of mollusca in the Pliocene–Pleistocene marine deposits of north-west Europe are analysed on the basis of their present distribution, it is possible to form some idea of the changing temperature gradient in the North Sea in those times. The arrival of arctic species in the shallow waters which covered parts of East Anglia and southern England during the deposition of the Red Crag is believed to reflect the cooling effects of the incipient Scandinavian ice-cap. The arrival of new northern immigrants, accompanied by a decline in Mediterranean species, continued throughout Crag times. That this was due to the increasing coldness of the southern part of the North Sea is supported by other evidence. Far-travelled boulders occur in the 'Stone Bed' at the base of the Red Crag, and also scattered sporadically in the overlying shelly sands (Boswell, 1931, p. 87). These 'erratics' were evidently dropped by icebergs drifting from the north.[27] The sudden increase in the proportion of arctic species in the fauna of the Weybourne

Crag is consistent with the correlation of this deposit with the first main glaciation (Günz).[28]

	Partial Analysis of Crag Molluscan Faunas[29]	
	Arctic species	Mediterranean species
	%	%
Weybourne Crag	15	0
Norwich Crag	8	6
Newer Red Crag	6	11
Older Red Crag	1	15
Coralline Crag	<1	18

Once they were established, many cold-water species tended to persist after conditions had become warmer again. Apart from a few which apparently returned during the Hoxnian Interglacial,[30] Mediterranean species did not reappear in the North Sea after Tiglian times.

Chapter 5

Palaeotemperatures Recorded in Deep-sea Cores

RECONSTRUCTION OF PAST climatic fluctuations in low and high latitudes during Pleistocene and earlier times has become possible through the development of Kullenberg's device for deeply coring the bed of the ocean.[31] There are now not only means of determining the temperatures prevailing in the surface and bottom waters of the sea during the formation of many layers of deposit in deep-sea cores, but also means of estimating their chronometric ages. Although these researches are still in their infancy, it is already evident that a chronological framework will become available into which the fragmentary records of Pleistocene events on land will eventually be fitted. Thus, so long as the R.3 age of a fossil human skull is reliably established, it will be possible in time to date it in years by consulting a world-wide geochronological timetable based on ocean-core researches.

The possibility of establishing palaeotemperature-scales arose from the work of H. C. Urey (1947) on the properties of the isotopes of various elements. As isotope-fractionation of oxygen was theoretically dependent on temperature, he inferred that there should be measurable differences in the oxygen-18/oxygen-16 ratio in calcium carbonate ($CaCO_3$) deposited from water at different temperatures. Controlled experiments proved that this was true, not only when calcium carbonate was precipitated inorganically, but also in the case of biochemical secretion of lime by marine organisms. Extensive applications of the O_{18}/O_{16} method of reconstructing palaeotemperatures has been carried out by Cesare Emiliani and others during the last ten years.[32]

Although it was soon well established that in building calcareous shells all marine organisms use O_{18} and O_{16} in proportions determined by the temperature of the surrounding water, further studies showed that some lime-secretors are more suitable than others for reconstructing palaeotemperatures. Shells of foraminifera, particularly the pelagic (planktonic) ones: that is to say those living in the surface waters of the sea such as *Globigerina*, have proved to be the most sensitive indicators. The isotopic temperature of the water in which the shells grew is calculated from measurements made on the selected sample by means of a mass-spectrometer. When the technique has been applied to samples from a succession of layers of Globigerina Ooze in the ocean-bed core, a curve can be drawn showing the fluctuations in the isotopic temperature of the surface waters through the section of time represented by the core. After making certain corrections based on measurements in sea-water of the same level and latitude today, the isotopic temperatures obtained from shell beds in the cores can be converted into *true palaeotemperatures*.

Working on these lines, Pleistocene palaeotemperature curves have been drawn up on the basis of foraminiferal layers in Atlantic, Caribbean, Mediterranean and Pacific cores. For the most part pelagic foraminifera were used, but when Emiliani measured the isotopic composition of benthonic forms he found indications that the temperature of the bottom waters did not change much during the glacial and interglacial stages. On the evidence of the pelagic foraminifera in North Atlantic cores and their probable correlation he concluded that the contrasted climates during the Pleistocene were the effects of changed insolation in the high latitudes, and that there was a lag of about 5,000 years before the full effects were recorded in palaeotemperatures of the oceans. He found that cores from below equatorial waters were the most useful for building general palaeotemperature curves for the Pleistocene period, because seasonal variation there is only slight, so that the estimated palaeotemperatures are probably close to the annual mean.[33]

One of the first Caribbean cores showed seven complete temperature cycles through the glacial Pleistocene. Taking all the Caribbean core results now available into consideration with the equatorial and North Atlantic core records, Emiliani constructed a generalized palaeotemperature curve: and by extrapolating from radiocarbon dating of the later layers, and from protoactinium/thorium datings of layers up to 175,000 years old,[34] he combined it with a chronometric time-scale (Fig. 12). The reproduction of this time-scale and curve serves at any rate the purpose of showing the currently accepted names of the main glaciations and interglacial stages recognized in North America, and their probable European equivalents.

Although there is general acceptance of the importance of palaeotemperature studies of deep-sea cores, with its promise of eventual construction of a chronometric framework for the Pleistocene period, there is lack of agreement on the equation of the minima, or troughs in the curve, with the glaciations recognized on the continents.[35] Thus many authorities doubt the validity of Emiliani's inferred dating of the glaciations, which may be summarized as follows:

Years B.P.

Main Würm	12,000 to 30,000	Inferred equivalent core layers being dated by C_{14} to 30,000 years
Early Würm	50,000 to 65,000	
Riss	100,000 to 125,000	and by Pa_{231}/Th_{230} to 175,000 years.
Mindel	180,000 to 210,000	Dates obtained by extra-
Günz	265,000 to 290,000	polation.

One of the arguments against the above datings of the Mindel and Günz Glaciations is that they are in striking contrast to the potassium/argon datings of Early Middle Pleistocene (= Mindel) volcanics as *c* 400,000 years old, and of Late Villafranchian (= Günz) volcanics as more than 1,000,000 years old. Further work on ocean-bed cores is already indicating that none of the temperature minima so far recorded by Emiliani is as old as Günz.

Scientists at the Lamont Laboratory of Columbia University, New York, have studied over 3,000 cores of sediment from the bottom of the oceans since 1947. In 1963 Ericson, Ewing and Wollin reported that eight of the cores had penetrated deep enough into the deep-sea sediments of former ages to reveal the changes in the planktonic life throughout the Tertiary

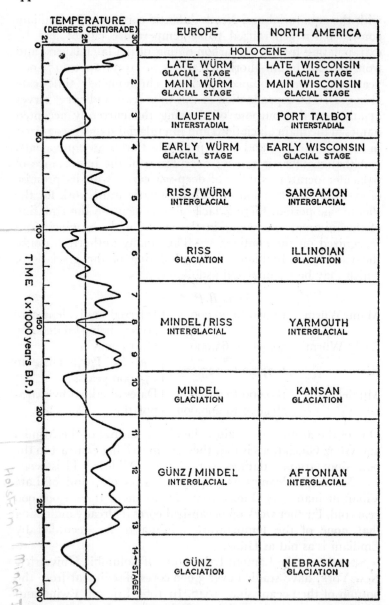

Figure 12 Generalized palaeotemperature curve with chronometric scale, correlated with European and North American glacial and interglacial stages, according to Emiliani, 1961.

era. Most important from the point of view of this book was the discovery by the Lamont scientists of the existence of a well-defined limit in the upward succession of discoasters which are abundant in all the Tertiary deep-sea sediments from the Paleocene through the Pliocene and then disappear. They interpreted this extinction of discoasters, occurring within 4–6 inches of sediment, as the result of a profound climatic change occurring over a period of not appreciably more than 5,000 years. The age of this event, possibly the Pliocene/Pleistocene boundary, can be estimated approximately as 1.5 million years.[36]

Chapter 6

Changing Levels of Sea and Land

THE SCRAPPINESS OF the stratigraphic record of the Pleistocene period is largely due to its having been a period of denudation and erosion rather than one of accumulation and sedimentation, except in certain ocean basins or *geosynclines*. One of the methods of subdividing the period and correlating the stages on a global basis depends on the fact that the land-masses have been slowly and intermittently rising in relation to sea-level throughout Upper Tertiary and Quaternary times.[37] As a consequence there have been phases of active down-cutting by rivers when the land was rising, and phases of lateral erosion by river and sea when the relative level was static. In the stable parts of Southern Britain there are three erosional platforms probably corresponding to prolonged pauses in the uplift of the land. These are, in descending order of age:

600-ft platform capped by Older Red Crag[38]
400-ft platform capped by the Pebble Gravel and oldest local
glacial drift (Günz?)[39]
200-ft platform capped by the Finchley Boulder Clay (Mindel
II?)[40]

In addition to the rising of the land-masses, throughout Quaternary times there has been an up and down movement of sea-level reflecting changes in the volume of the world's ice-sheets. Alterations of sea-level which are independent of any movement of the land are known as *eustatic*. According to the now widely held theory of *glacial eustasy*,[41] high sea-levels correspond to interglacial stages, when there was more or less complete deglaciation; while low sea-levels correspond to glacial stages, when much of the water had been withdrawn from the oceans and was locked up on the land as ice. The present heights above sea-level of 'fossil' shore-lines or raised beaches have been extensively used as a means of relative dating of deposits and human industries associated with them. However, this has proved difficult or unreliable in regions affected by any considerable local uplift or depression of the land. (Movements of the land independent of changes in sea-level generally compensate for a change in load or pressure, and are therefore grouped as *isostatic* movements.)

The systematic study of Pleistocene beaches was begun by General R. de Lamothe, working on the North African shore,[42] and continued by Depéret, working in the French and Italian Riviera. Depéret recognized that shore-line deposits occurred at four main altitudes on both sides of the Mediterranean and that this arrangement provided a useful means of subdividing the Pleistocene period. He applied names to the stages as follows:[43]

Stages	*Altitude of beach deposits*		
Monastirian	18–20 m above present sea-level		
Tyrrhenian	28–30 m ,,	,,	,,
Milazzian	55–60 m ,,	,,	,,
Sicilian	99–100 m ,,	,,	,,

Still higher shore-lines had been noted by L. de Lamothe, and these were eventually recognized as corresponding to the Calabrian stage, classified until recently as Upper Pliocene. Two lower-shore lines were also found, and named Late Monastirian and Epi-Monastirian.[44]

Each of these stages of accumulation of shore-line deposits was separated from the next by an interval during which the sea first withdrew to a lower level and then began rising again. The fact that during each rise or transgression the sea never quite regained the height lost during the preceding regression to a low level can only be accounted for by continual rising of the land superimposed on the up and down movement of sea-level.[45]

When similar studies were made along other shores[46] it was found that, apart from local variations in height due to isostatic warping, shore-lines of apparently similar age occurred at approximately the same heights almost throughout the world, strongly supporting the theory of glacial eustasy. According to data available at time of going to press, the relative heights of the mean sea-levels at the times of formation of the main shore-lines were as follows:[47]

Stages	Mean ht. above present sea-level	Correlated features in S. Britain
Epi-Monastirian[44]	2–4 m	10-ft raised beach
Late Monastirian	6–8 m	25-ft ,, ,,
Main Monastirian	15–18 m	50-ft ,, ,,
Tyrrhenian	30–45 m	100-ft ,, ,,
Milazzian	± 60 m	200-ft platform
Sicilian[49]	± 100 m	400-ft ,,
Calabrian[48]	± 200 m	600-ft ,,

Studies of the faunas of the Pleistocene marine deposits have provided some support for correlation of transgressive phases (high sea-levels) with interglacial phases, and regressive phases (low sea-levels) with glacial stages.

The foraminifera in the latest Pliocene deposits in Italy give indications of increasingly cool water, and it is therefore supposed that the regression of the sea which preceded the first Pleistocene transgression (Calabrian), corresponded to the onset of glacial conditions (Blanc, 1957, p. 100). The molluscan fauna of the Calabrian indicates warm temperate conditions, although it does include one northern form, *Cyprina islandica*. It has been suggested that this species may have entered the Mediterranean from the Atlantic as a 'northern visitor' during the preceding cold regressive phase, and then remained there (Blanc, 1957, p. 100).

The Sicilian fauna includes a number of northern species of mollusca, including *C. islandica*, but again these may have been adaptable 'hang-overs' from the preceding stage of regression. The 'Milazzian' fauna is indistinguishable from the Sicilian. The Tyrrhenian transgression on the other hand was distinguished by the absence of northern elements and by the entry of a new warm fauna which included the tropical gastropod *Strombus bubonius* (Fig. 13). The *Strombus* fauna persisted in the Mediterranean through the Main and Late Monastiriah stages.[50]

One of the most important events in the history of the Mediterranean shores was the 'Great Regression' sometimes known as the Roman or Romanian regression[51] which followed the 'Milazzian' (or as some prefer, Sicilian II) and preceded the Tyrrhenian stage of high sea-level. The fact that it coincided with a very striking change in the composition of the marine molluscan fauna is of considerable interest because the Mindel Glaciation, with which this regression probably corresponded, was a time of equally dramatic change in the continental mammalian fauna (Zeuner, 1959a, p. 285).

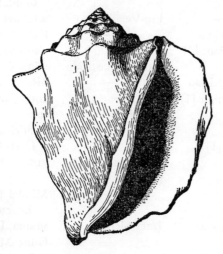

Figure 13 *Strombus bubonius*. (⅔).

There is very little direct evidence of the magnitude of the drop in sea-level which intervened between the various high sea-level stages, except in the case of the regression following the Late Monastirian.[52] Borings in Lower Versilia at the foot of the Appenines have revealed sands with land and freshwater molluscan shells overlying marine deposits at 90 m below present sea-level.[53] The fauna in these Versilian marine deposits indicates that they are 'post-*Strombus* beds', that is to say they mark the beginnings of a new transgression post-dating the Late Monastirian. There can be little doubt that the immediately preceding drop in sea-level by nearly 300 ft was eustatic, and that it reflected the withdrawal of water from the oceans during the Würm Glaciation. It may be called the Pre-Versilian regression.[54]

By using a combination of stratigraphical methods, the excursions of sea-level in the Mediterranean during Pleistocene times have now been correlated tentatively with the Alpine Glacial/Interglacial stages as follows:[55]

Mediterranean Stages		*Alps*
Transgressions	*Regressions*	*Probable Correlates*
Versilian[56] —	—	Late Würm interstadial to final Post-Glacial
—	Pre-Versilian	MAIN WÜRM
Late Monastirian[57]	—	Early Würm
(= Tyrrhenian III)		interstadial
—	Inter-Monastirian	WÜRM I
Main Monastirian	—	Riss–Würm
(= Tyrrhenian II)		Interglacial
—	Pre-Monastirian	RISS
		Mindel–Riss
Tyrrhenian (I)	—	Interglacial
—	Romanian	MINDEL II
	(Pre-Tyrrhenian)	
Sicilian II	—	Mindel I/II
(Milazzian)		interstadial
—	Inter-Sicilian	MINDEL I
Sicilian I	—	Günz–Mindel
		Interglacial
—	Pre-Sicilian	GÜNZ
Calabrian	—	Donau–Günz
		interstadial
—	Post-Astian	DONAU

Chapter 7

River Terraces

IN ONE PHASE of their history rivers may be laying down gravels, sands and clays on their flood-plain, in another they may be actively eroding through these deposits, leaving remnants of them along the valley sides in the form of terraces. Many of the main rivers of the world show a succession of terraces, and as these commonly contain relics of animals and men who frequented the river banks during the formation of the component deposits, their study has a useful bearing on the chronology of early man and his cultures.

Broadly one may say that river terraces are the result of the process of valley-erosion having been interrupted at intervals by valley-silting or aggradation. There are two main causes of such interruptions: changes in sea-level, and changes in the volume of the river or in the load it has to carry.

A river will actively erode until the slope of its bed or longitudinal profile (*thalweg*) has acquired a form known as a curve of equilibrium. This is roughly parabolic: steep near the source and flattening out towards the mouth, where the river meanders on its flood-plain. Erosion mainly in the upper reaches, and deposition mainly in the lower reaches, are by this stage balanced and minimal. The river is said to be graded to *base-level*. This last term requires a word of explanation. A river cannot of course erode its bed below the level of the body of water into which it flows (ultimately in most cases the sea) and this constitutes normally its base-level. If its base-level changes, the activity of a river is considerably affected. With a lowering of base-level, the fall or effective gradient is greater so the river becomes rejuvenated and erosion of its bed is renewed or increased. On the other hand, with a rising of base-level, it builds up or aggrades its bed. Terraces were formed in the lower reaches of rivers during Pleistocene times mainly as a result of the oscillation of sea-level consequent on the periodic withdrawal of water from the oceans as ice-sheets grew on land. Thus, during the glacial maxima, when there was regression of the sea, the rivers actively eroded their beds in response to the lowered base-level. The down-cutting began at their mouths and worked upstream. During interglacials when sea-level was rising again, the rivers became sluggish, silted up the new channels and built thick deposits on their valley floors – the process known as *aggradation*. Although changes in sea-level are not immediately registered in the upper courses of rivers, the 'head of rejuvenation'[58] due to each fall in base-level gradually travels upstream.

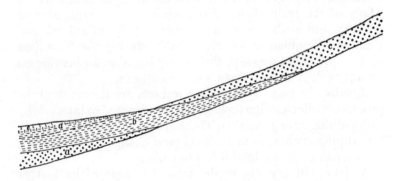

Figure 14 Sequence of river gravels from one glacial stadium to the next. *a* Cold-climate gravels in lower course of river accumulated while sea-level was low; *b* interglacial gravels during rising of sea-level; *c* glacial-climate gravels at beginning of next icing-up; *d* erosion in lower course of river during sinking of sea-level; *e* solifluxion of *b* gravels during glacial stage. *After Woldstedt.*

Alterations in volume of water and sedimentary load due to climatic changes were the factors mainly controlling erosion and aggradation in the middle and upper portions of European rivers during Pleistocene times (Fig. 14). Whereas aggradation was characteristic of interglacial stages near the mouths of rivers, it was characteristic of glacial stages higher up, where solifluxion from the valley sides commonly supplied loads of sediment in excess of the water to carry them under periglacial conditions. During interglacials on the other hand, the volume of water in the same stretch of river was adequate to carry the available sedimentary load, and erosion commonly prevailed.[59]

As with raised beaches, the higher river terraces are for the most part older than the lower. Alternate erosion and aggradation in river valleys could scarcely account for the occurrence of terraces in tiers, with the oldest at the top, unless on balance down–cutting through Pleistocene times had been in excess of aggradation. Since all the main terraces run into ancient sea-levels the explanation of their occurrence in tiers is clearly the same as that applying to the raised beaches: they all reflect the rise of the land masses which has continued throughout Quaternary times.

The aggradation surfaces of the main terraces of the Lower Thames are approximately at 10 ft, 25 ft, 50 ft and 100 ft above present river level, corresponding apparently to the Epi-Monastirian, Late Monastirian, Main Monastirian and Tyrrhenian sea-levels. Below the river bed in the Lower Thames valley (as in the valleys of many other rivers) there is a deep buried channel which was cut when the sea had sunk far below its present level, evidently during the main phase of the Last Glaciation, and then filled with gravels and alluvial muds during the subsequent Versilian or Flandrian transgression.[54] This buried channel serves as a reminder that although as a rule the stratified deposits on a low terrace are younger than those on a higher one, a low terrace may sometimes include patches of a deposit laid down in a deep channel broadly contemporary with or antedating the deposits formed on the terrace above.

In the Somme Valley the so-called 45 m, 30 m, 10 m and 5 m terraces show all the complexity of structure which one must expect in deposits accumulated not far from the mouth of a river, where the effects of major and minor changes in base-level are fully recorded. The Somme terraces are of special interest from the point of view of relative chronology because they also contain evidence of the main cold-climate oscillations, in the form of solifluxion deposits and loesses, and a sequence of early palaeolithic industries which has been taken as the standard for north-west Europe.

Chapter 8

The Somme Terraces

RIVER TERRACES CAN be grouped either according to the
height of the erosional surface or bench underlying the deposits
or according to the maximum height attained by the fluviatile
deposits on it. Both systems have been used in classifying the
Somme Terraces. V. Commont (1910) studied the terraces
in the region of Amiens, and defined them on the basis of the
height of their benches *measured from the floor of the buried channel*
at that locality:

> High or 45-m Terrace
> Middle or 30-m Terrace
> Low or 10-m Terrace

General de Lamothe (1918) studied them in the light of his
experience of sea-levels in the Mediterranean. Plotting the level
of the highest fluviatile deposits on each terrace, he reconstructed
the profile of the river at the end of each of the main aggradations. The surfaces of these sheets of aggradation have a gradient
diminishing seawards and running into the former high sea-
levels as follows (Zeuner, 1959*a*, p. 126):

Sheet of La Ferme de Grace (at Amiens resting on 45-m bench)
graded to sea-level 57–58 m above OD.

Sheet of St Acheul (at Amiens resting on 30-m bench) graded
to sea-level 32–33 m above OD.

Sheet of Montières (resting at Amiens on 10-m bench) graded
to sea-level 18–19 m above OD.

It is sometimes wrongly assumed that the rock-benches of the
terraces slope seawards parallel to the surfaces of the aggradation sheets, but in fact their gradient is much steeper. The

rock-benches represent the levels to which the Somme cut down during low sea-level stages, and these did not last long enough for the river to become graded to base-level by erosion.

It is worth noting that the basal deposit in each of the Somme terraces was formed under cold conditions, whereas the succeeding deposits (representing aggradation through rising sea-level) were mainly formed under warm conditions. In terraces of Central European rivers the converse is generally true: the lower horizons represent warm phases, the upper horizons cold phases (Zeuner, 1959a, p. 126).

The sequence of events represented by the Somme terraces may be summarized as follows:[60]

1. Erosion of bench of HIGH TERRACE at 45 m above floor of Buried Channel at Amiens.

2. Solifluxion, forming clayey coombe rock and angular gravel on bench of High Terrace usually correlated with Günz Glaciation, now tentatively correlated with Mindel I.

3. Aggradation of fluviatile sand and gravel, and deposition of white marl (carrière Carpentier, Abbeville) with Cromerian fauna: *Elephas (Archidiskodon) meridionalis, Rhinoceros (Dicerorhinus) etruscus* and earliest Palaeolithic industries: Abbevillian hand-axes mainly below the white marl, Clactonian I flakes and cores mostly above it.[61] The terminal surface of aggradation of these High Terrace deposits graded with the 60-m or Milazzian sea-level.

4. Down–cutting, possibly in two stages: the river cut the bench of MIDDLE TERRACE at 30 m above floor of Buried Channel at Amiens, and then possibly cut down to the bench of the Low Terrace.

5. Solifluxion formed coombe rock at base of 30-m terrace, with derived Abbevillian and Clactonian I artifacts. Correlated with Mindel II Glaciation.

6. Aggradation of sands and gravels as sea-level rose to 32 m above OD. The gravels of this important interglacial aggradation contain remains of *Elephas (Palaeoloxodon) antiquus*, and the Rhinoceros *Dicerorhinus kirchbergensis* syn. *merckii*;[62] also Acheulian I–III and Clactonian II industries. In places these deposits overlap the High Terrace. Correlated with Mindel–Riss Interglacial.

c

7. Solifluxion (= Pre-Riss?)[63] produced chalky-coombe rock (locally known as *presle*) during occupation of the 30-m terrace by Acheulian III tool-makers and before termination of the aggradation.

8. Down–cutting, ultimately to below level of 10-m bench. Meanwhile, at St Acheul for instance, sandy hill-washes (*sables roux*) accumulated in hollows on the Middle Terrace. Associated industry Acheulian IV (famous '*Atelier de Commont*').

9. Solifluxion gravel with cold fauna, *Mammuthus primigenius*, *Coelodonta antiquitatis* and *Megaceros*, accumulated on 10-m bench of LOW TERRACE during early wet phase of the Riss Glacial Stage. Derived Acheulian and Levalloisian I–II of Breuil.[64]

10. Deposition of OLDER LOESS, mainly on north-east facing slopes, forming cover to solifluxion gravels on 45-m and 30-m terraces (Older Loess is *not* found on the 10-m terrace). Cold dry phase of Riss Glacial Stage. Contemporaneous industry: Acheulian V.

11a. Weathering of Older Loess under warm interglacial conditions, forming *argile rouge*, or where redeposited *limon rouge fendillé*, with Acheulian VI industry at base and Acheulian VII at top. These Late and Final Acheulian industries are grouped by some authorities as Micoquian.

11b. Contemporaneously with weathering of Older Loess, aggradation of fine gravels and sands forming upper part of 10-m terrace (Low Terrace No. 1) at Montières, graded to sea-level 18–20 m above OD. These deposits contain flakes and flake-blades classified by Breuil as Levalloisian III and IV, at one time grouped with 'Warm Mousterian' for they are associated with the last appearance in north-west Europe of *Hippopotamus* and *Elephas* (*Palaeoloxodon*) *antiquus*. Correlated with Riss–Würm Interglacial.

12. Down–cutting to 5-m bench (Low Terrace No. 2) or lower.

13. Solifluxion gravel and chalky coombe-rock spread out from slopes: associated *Mammuthus primigenius*, *Coelodonta antiquitatis* and reindeer; Levalloisian V industry (with heart-shaped hand-axes) on surface, covered by Younger Loess. Early phase of Würm.

14a, b. Deposition of YOUNGER LOESS, with one conspicuous interstadial break (Würm I/II). Mousterian, Levalloisian VI, VII; Upper Palaeolithic in uppermost layer.

15a. Erosion of Buried Channel during low sea-level correlated with Main Würm Glaciation (Würm II).

15b. Aggradation filling Buried Channel and covering 5-m bench of Low Terrace with silts. Final Levalloisian elements and Upper Palaeolithic industries.

Chapter 9

The Glacial Stages in Latium

STUDIES OF THE Pleistocene sequence in Central Italy, particularly in the Rome area, led the late Professor Alberto Blanc to establish a new scheme of relative chronology for local application.[65] The framework of the scheme consists of the five main cold phases in the sequence, which are assumed to represent glaciations. These were provisionally named by Blanc to provide a terminology independent of theoretical correlations.

Although these new names may pass out of use when correlation with the Alpine stages has been established beyond all doubt, they are at the present time being used extensively in discussion of evidence bearing on the antiquity of early types of man and palaeolithic cultures in the Mediterranean region. The glacial stages recognized by Blanc are as follows:

1 *Acquatraversan Glaciation* (= Alpine Donau?)
The regression of the sea marked by the unconformity between the Astian deposits (Upper Pliocene) and the Calabrian deposits (= Villafranchian[66]) is believed to correspond to the onset of glacial conditions, for reasons already outlined (p. 48). The Astian/Calabrian unconformity is well exposed at the site of Acquatraversa, a valley near Monte Mario to the north of Rome.[67] Although Calabria is in Southern Italy, the recent identification of the Pliocene–Pleistocene boundary in a continuous series of marine clays and diatomaceous earths at Le Castella in Calabria is important enough to interpolate here. The boundary is clearly marked by the appearance of *Anomalina baltica* and other northern foraminifera, but no major change in temperature of the sea has been detected by oxygen-isotope analysis of shells on either side of the boundary.

Presumably the first glaciation was appreciably later. (Emiliani *et al.*, 1961.)

2 *Cassian Glaciation* (= Alpine Günz?)

The temperate Calabrian stage was followed by regression of the sea, indicated by erosion to below the present flood-plain in the valley of the Tiber. Peat interstratified with gravels which were deposited after the erosive phase has yielded land shells of types now living in mountainous areas, and pollen of pine (*Pinus*), silver fir (*Abies*) and spruce (*Picea*) associated with survivors of the Pliocene flora, such as *Tsuga* and *Carya*, not known in Europe after the time of the Mindel Glaciation.

The fluviatile gravels of this stage are devoid of volcanic material (indicating that the local Sabatino volcanoes were not yet erupting), but near the Via Cassia they contain sharp-cornered blocks of clay which were evidently transported in a frozen condition.

A layer of cryoturbation (frost-disturbance) intercalated between Calabrian and Sicilian deposits at one site in the Rome area is attributed to the cold conditions which accompanied the Cassian Glaciation.

3 *Flaminian Glaciation* (= Alpine Mindel II?)

The beginning of eruptive activity of the Sabatino group of volcanoes coincided with a cold period, and with the earliest dated evidence of Palaeolithic man in Italy. The evidence may now be briefly summarized. In the Agro Cerite area of Torre in Pietra the first granular tuffs of these volcanoes overlie Upper Sicilian deposits. In the small valley known as Fosso del Tavolato a layer of peat occurs amidst the lower layers of the Sabatino granular tuffs, and contains pollen of pine and silver-fir and land and freshwater molluscan shells of species now occurring in more northerly or higher altimetric situations. In a pit on the Via Flaminia in Rome, river gravels containing the first indications of activity of the Sabatino volcanoes have yielded bones of a swan which now nests in the Arctic and is rarely found in Italy (*Cygnus bewicki*), and shells of terrestrial mollusca which have a mountainous and northern distribution. These gravels also contain sharp-edged blocks of clay which must have been transported by the river in a frozen condition.

Early Palaeolithic (Clactonian) flakes have been found below the early Sabatino tuffs at an exposure in Via Flaminia, but the 'floor' of Acheulian hand-axes found at Torre in Pietra is probably post-Flaminian.

4 *Nomentanan Glaciation* (= Alpine Riss?)

A period colder than the present, probably comprising two distinct phases, occurred *after* the paroxysm of the Sabatino volcanoes which resulted in the formation of the famous 'tuff with black pumices' of Cervetteri,[68] and *before* the Last Inter-glacial. The evidence for this includes the occurrence at Torre del Pagliaccetto near Torre in Pietra of cryoturbation in two fluviatile layers both containing derived black pumice and both antedating the Last Interglacial. The older frost-dis-turbed layer contains advanced Acheulian hand-axes, the upper contains a primitive Levalloiso–Mousterian industry. The intervening lacustrine deposits indicate that frost action was rather prevalent throughout their formation. A similar Levalloiso–Mousterian industry, associated with a fossil human metatarsal bone and remains of the arctic swan (*C. bewicki*), occurs in gravels exposed near the Via Nomentana in the Aniene Valley.

5 *Pontinian Glaciation* (= Alpine Würm)

There is good evidence for the effects of the Last Glaciation in the Rome area, comprising:

Phase I (cool oceanic climate) represented by levels of peat with 100 per cent silver fir (*Abies*) overlying beach deposits with *Strombus bubonius* in the Canale Mussolini (Pontine Marshes). During this phase Neanderthal Man occupied the caves of Monte Circeo. The warm fauna with *Hippopotamus*, *Dicerorhinus kirchbergensis* and *Elephas* (*Palaeoloxodon*) *antiquus* persisted through this cool-climate phase in Central Italy.

Phase II (cold continental climate) represented by fluviatile sands with *Mammuthus primigenius* and *Equus hydruntinus*, over-lying the peat with *Abies*. Neanderthal man was at this time being replaced by Aurignacian man (*H. sapiens*) simultaneously with the replacement locally of a warm fauna by a cold steppe fauna. Although there is no doubt that the 'Pontinian' glaciation can be equated exactly with the Alpine Würm Glaciation, a local name has been introduced so that the terminology for cold periods in central Italy is complete.

Chapter 10

Pleistocene Subdivisions in Holland

FOR A NUMBER of years Dutch geologists were very doubtful about the application of the Alpine glacial names to the climatic fluctuations recorded in the Pleistocene deposits of Holland (or more strictly the Netherlands) and accordingly they introduced a number of local stage-names for use until successful correlation could be established with neighbouring countries. The scheme as a whole was devised by Professors I. M. van der Vlerk and F. Florschütz (1950, 1953), although some of the stage-names which they used had been proposed by other authors. The basis of the Dutch subdivision of the Pleistocene is palaeontological, and therefore more in keeping with the classification of deposits of earlier periods. The stratigraphy of the Pleistocene has usually been an exception to the general rule, and based on geomorphological events (*eg* glaciations) to a greater extent than on fossil contents.

The following stages were proposed by van der Vlerk and Florschütz in 1950.

Tubantian
Eemian
Drenthian
Needian
Taxandrian
Tiglian
Praetiglian

Although several of these terms have now been superseded, the fact that they have been used in a number of important papers on Pleistocene geology and on the dating of fossil bones makes it desirable to outline their original diagnoses in this book.

Praetiglian is the name given to the interval between the beginning of the Pleistocene, as defined by the International Geological Congress in 1948, and the commencement of deposition of the Tegelen Clay. On the basis of their foraminiferal, bryozoan and molluscan faunas, the Poederlian[69] and Amstelian[69] marine deposits of the Netherlands are referred to this stage, generally regarded as equivalent to the Donau Glacial Stage in the Alps and to the Red Crag in the East Anglia.[70] The Poederlian deposits, which include gravels at the base, were laid down in the relatively shallow waters of a transgressive sea. The contemporaneous Amstelian clays were deposited in deeper water and are distinguished from the underlying Pliocene (Reuverian[71]) clays by their content of cold-water mollusca and foraminifera (*eg Elphidiella arctica*). Information about the mammalian fauna on the land bordering the sea at this time is supplied by highly mineralized black bones dredged from the sea-floor off the coast of Walcheren and from the bottom of the Scheldt estuary. The 'Black Bones' fauna[72] includes *Elephas* (*Archidiskodon*) *planifrons*, *Mastodon* (*Anancus*) *arvernensis*, *Cervus falconeri* and *Equus* cf. *stenonis*, as well as remains of whales and walruses related to types now confined to more northerly waters. The pollen-spectra of freshwater clays capping the Reuverian clays at Belfeld[73] show that in Praetiglian times the Dutch flora included beech (*Fagus*), while Tertiary forms such as *Tsuga* were becoming rare.

Tiglian is the name now widely used for the first or Villafranchian Interglacial represented by the Tegelen Clay[18] of the Limburg district. The pollen diagrams from the Tegelen Clay with diabolo-form of the 'pine-block' and ellipsoidal form of the 'spruce-block' show that the climate changed from cool at the beginning of the stage,[74] through moderately warm conditions in the middle, to cool at the close. Beech had disappeared. Among the macroscopic plant remains the most striking fossils in the Tegelen Clay are macrosporangia of *Azolla tegeliensis* (Fig. 8). Mammalia represented in this deposit include mice of the extinct genus *Mimomys*, beavers, mainly the large extinct *Trogontherium* although the existing form *Castor fiber* occurred as a rarity; *Elephas (Archidiskodon) meridionalis, Equus robustus* (zebra), *Dicerorhinus etruscus* and a monkey, *Macaca florentina*.

The Tiglian is represented in Britain by the Norwich Crag. *Taxandrian* is derived from the name of a tribe which Pliny tells us occupied the province of Noord Brabant in south-east Netherlands during Roman times. This stage was recognized as a result of a study of samples from bore-holes in this province which revealed a succession of sediments, comprising marine glauconitic[75] sands of Reuverian age at the base, followed by marine and freshwater deposits of Tiglian age and an overlying series of sands[76] and gravels some 90 m thick which included at a low level a bed with macrosporangia of *Azolla filiculoides* in addition to small numbers of the declining Tiglian species. The top layer of the fine fluviatile sediment containing these remains of *Azolla* had been disturbed by cryoturbation indicating that the climate oscillated considerably within the Taxandrian stage. Pollen-analysis of deposits in the same stratigraphical bracket at other sites showed that during the deposition of the lowest part of the Taxandrian, the so-called Kedichem Series, the climate was prevailingly cool with predominance of pine, although it did include a temperate oscillation or interstadial (the *Azolla* horizon). Further research,[77] mainly on sections in the Westerhoven area, led to the subdivision of the Kedichem Series as follows:

> Menapian Glacial Stage
> Waalian Interglacial
> Eburonian Glacial Stage

Voles in the Kedichem Series include the earliest examples of *Microtus*, together with species of the now extinct *Mimomys*.

During the accumulation of the lower part of the overlying Sterksel Series of the Taxandrian, conditions became essentially interglacial and supported mixed-oak forest. The evidence from the Westerhoven sections established that these deposits were equivalent to the Cromer Forest Bed in England, but that the overlying uppermost beds of the Sterksel Series represented the Elster Glaciation of North Germany.

Whereas pollen of the extinct conifer *Tsuga* and other survivors of the Tertiary flora occur in the Kedichem Series, they are absent from the Sterksel (Cromerian–Elsterian) zones.

The increasing 'modernization' of the Dutch flora, judged by decreasing percentage of exotic species (as compared with species indigenous to the Netherlands) serves as a useful rough index of the relative age of plant-bearing deposits (van der Vlerk and Florschütz, 1953, pp. 17–18):

	% Exotic species
Eemian	9
Needian	17
Tiglian	42
Reuverian	82

Needian is the stage represented by brick-clays at Neede in the province of Gelderland. *Azolla filiculoides*, in the form of macro-sporangia, is the most characteristic fossil in these clays. The pollen-diagrams at the type site indicate the early predominance of pine and alder, followed by scattered mixed-oak woodland, and then a marked influx of silver fir. Comparison with pollen-diagrams from sites in Britain led to the identification of the Needian with the Hoxnian, and as the sections in the brick-pits at Hoxne can be studied more easily than those at Neede, the Dutch geologists (van der Vlerk *et al.*, 1957, p. 312) proposed that the name Needian should stand down in favour of Hoxnian (p. 28, note 16). The mammalian fauna of this interglacial is well known in the Netherlands: it includes species of *Microtus* and *Arvicola* but not of *Mimomys* which was now extinct; and among the larger mammals, *Elephas (Palaeoloxodon) antiquus, Dicerorhinus kirchbergensis, Equus* aff. *caballus*, and possibly *Hippopotamus*, although this is only an inference based on the application of a method of relative dating of bones.[78]

Although there is no undoubted evidence that the sea made inroads on Holland during the Needian stage, North Germany was invaded by the 'Holstein Sea' at this time. In Germany this interglacial has generally been known as the Holsteinian.

Drenthian, named after the province of Drenthe in the northern part of the Netherlands, is a stage with three subdivisions. The earliest stage was marked by deposition of gravel fans by the rivers Rhine and Maas, and also by the formation of the oldest loess in the Netherlands, preserved near Limburg. The onset of cold climatic conditions during early Drenthian times is also indicated by the palaeontological evidence. *Elephas antiquus* was replaced by mammoth (*Mammuthus primigenius*), and lemmings entered the country for the first time on record. The middle phase of the Drenthian, represented by peaty layers in the so-called High Terrace gravels, was an interstadial in which pine and birch temporarily declined while oak, alder and hazel again began to spread until this sequence was reversed by the onset of the third phase, when ice advanced and covered the whole of the northern part of the Netherlands. This Upper Drenthian phase is clearly the time of the main Saale Glaciation of North Germany, and presumably the Lower and Middle Drenthian represent an earlier advance and interstadial of the same glaciation.[79]

Eemian: This stage derives its name from the small river Eem[15] in the province of Utrecht. Melt-water gravels of the Late Drenthian (Saalian II) Glaciation are here overlain by shelly clays marking a transgression of the sea ('Eem Sea'). Apart from occurrences of *Cervus elaphus* (red deer), there are no records of the mammalian fauna on land in the Netherlands at this time. Plant remains from the Eemian deposits show that the marine transgression occurred during the phase of maximum temperature (see p. 28) of the interglacial. In contrast to the rather monotonous Needian pollen-diagrams, those of the Eemian are complex (see pp. 29–30). The Eemian is generally considered to be equivalent to the Riss–Würm interglacial of the Alps.[80]

Tubantian: The word is derived from the old name for the district now known as Twenthe. In 1930 excavation of the Rhine–Twenthe canal provided much fossil material including remains of sub-arctic plants and a typical Late Pleistocene mammalian fauna. This periglacial stage, equivalent to the Weichsel Glaciation of North Germany, includes the Younger Loess of the Netherlands, various of fluvio-glacial deposits, glacial-lake beds, and many classic examples of cryoturbation. Pollen-diagrams and macroscopic plant remains from these deposits show that the Tubantian flora, although it includes many tundra elements such as *Dryas*, dwarf birch and dwarf willow, was not devoid of trees such as pine, spruce and alder, which probably formed clumps or stretches of woodland like those along the courses of the large rivers flowing through the mainly frozen wastes of Siberia and Alaska today.

The Tubantian has been subdivided into three phases[81] corresponding to Early Glacial, Main or Pleniglacial and Late Glacial of other regions. The main elements of the Late Pleistocene mammalian fauna of Europe, *Mammuthus primigenius*, *Coelodonta antiquitatis* (woolly rhinoceros), *Bison priscus* and *Rangifer tarandus* (reindeer), were present during the early phase, with the addition of elk (*Alces*) during the middle phase; but mammoth, bison and less certainly woolly rhinoceros disappeared from the Netherlands before Late Tubantian times.

In revisions (1957, 1959) of the Pleistocene stage-names applicable in the Netherlands and neighbouring countries, Professor van der Vlerk has suggested that the local names Tubantian, Drenthian, Needian and Taxandrian should in future be dropped, since with the growth of knowledge and better correlation they have proved superfluous. He has proposed that the following sequence of stages set out in the left-hand column of the Table below, alternately glacial and interglacial (inset relative to succeeding stage), should be taken to constitute a general subdivision of the Pleistocene in Western Europe. Those stages named in italics are not yet widely recognized and are still grouped by some authors as early Taxandrian.

General Subdivision in Western Europe	*Probable Alpine Equivalents*
Weichselian	Würm
Eemian (Ipswichian, *auctt.*)	Riss–Würm
Saalian	Riss
Hoxnian (formerly Holsteinian)	Mindel–Riss
Elsterian	Mindel
Cromerian	Günz–Mindel
Manapian	Günz III
Waalian	Günz Interstadials (and Günz II stadial)
Eburonian	Günz I
Tiglian	Günz–Donau Interglacial (and Donau III stadial)
Praetiglian	Donau II

Villafranchian (brace spanning Manapian through Praetiglian)

It is particularly noteworthy that not only in the Netherlands but also in Poland and the USSR no less than six glacial stages have been recognized.

Chapter 11

Post-Glacial Chronology and Palynology

THERE HAVE BEEN a number of important changes in climate since the Last Glaciation, and these have been reflected in alterations in composition and distribution of vegetation. These vegetational changes were first recognized in the last century by Blytt in 1881 and by Sernander (1910) as a result of studying assemblages of macroscopic plant remains in successive Post-Glacial deposits in Norway and Sweden. Their subdivisions of Holocene time have since been confirmed and more closely studied by *pollen-analysis* (p. 70), mainly in Denmark. When Professor H. Godwin (1940, 1941, 1956) worked out the Post-Glacial forest history in Britain by this method (Fig. 15), he found that the successive tree associations were almost identical with those in Denmark, and accordingly he adopted, with slight modifications, the system of numbering the pollen-zones which had been devised there by Jessen.

As these vegetational changes prove to be broadly consistent throughout north-west Europe, the stages named by Blytt and Sernander and numbered by Jessen (and Godwin) have provided a most useful relative chronology for the Post-Glacial period. In so far as the changes could be tied in with de Geer's varve chronology (p. 77), pollen-dating acquired a chrono-metric aspect. The identity of the main vegetational changes throughout north-west Europe led to these stages and zones being regarded as synchronous. This of course would be broadly true if the changes were due to widespread climatic changes; but forest trees do require time to migrate, and it has therefore been debated whether the zone boundaries are actually synchronous or only 'metasynchronous' in the various regions. For example, it seemed quite possible that the sudden expansion of hazel (*Corylus*) at the end of the Boreal stage began earlier in Southern Europe than in northern latitudes. However, the development of radiocarbon dating has made it possible to test the extent to which the pollen-zones are synchronous. The datings of pollen-zoned peats so far reported have indicated a fair degree of synchronism throughout north-western Europe.[82]

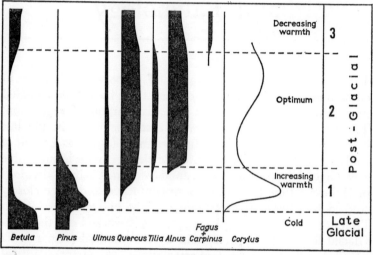

Figure 15 Generalized profile of Post-Glacial pollen sequence in East Anglia.

In the table opposite the Late Glacial and Post-Glacial vegetational stages have been dated on the basis of the available radiocarbon age-estimations (see also Chart A). In books published before 1959 the dating of these stages was based on the less exact varve-chronology.

In the *Late Glacial* Stage (originally named Sub-Arctic phase), tundra conditions were widespread; apart from dwarf birches and dwarf willows, trees were lacking over extensive areas, and the most characteristic plant was the creeping Mountain Avens or *Dryas* (Fig. 17). Studies in Denmark led to the recognition of two warmer intervals within the Late Glacial Stage, and these were named the Bølling and Allerød oscillations. The Allerød was the more important, for although only of short duration (about 1,000 years) it has been identified in many

Pollen Zones* (British) Usage)	Characteristic Trees	Stages		Commencing dates BC	Climate
VIII	Beech; birch returning	Sub-Atlantic		500	Cool, moist
VIIb	Less elm	Sub-Boreal		3000	Drier[83]
VIIa	Oak, alder, elm	Atlantic		5600	Warm, moist
VI	} Pine, hazel	Boreal { Late	7000		{ Warm,
V		{ Early	7700		{ dry
IV	Birch, pine	Pre-Boreal		8300	Cool
I–III	(tundra vegetation)	Late Glacial		c13000	Cold

* See Fig. 16.

parts of Europe including the Alps and in North America, [84] and it has been accurately dated by radiocarbon methods. It may prove to be a synchronic 'marker' horizon traceable at any rate throughout the northern hemisphere, in some degree comparable with the Climatic Optimum (p. 75) of Atlantic times. For attempted correlation of all these stages see Chart A.

Pollen-Zones	Late Glacial Sub-Stages	Commencing date BC
III	Younger *Dryas* Phase	8900
II	Allerød Oscillation	c 10000
I c	Older *Dryas* Phase	c 10300
I b	Bølling Oscillation	c 11000
I a	Oldest *Dryas* Phase	c 13000

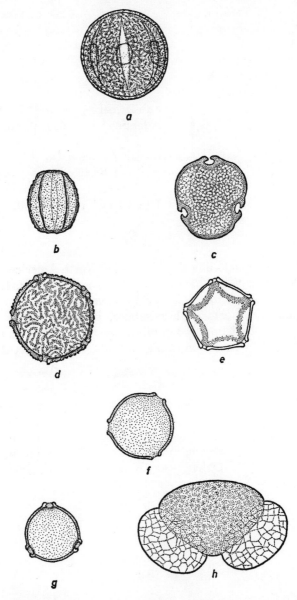

Figure 16 Post-Glacial pollen. *a Fagus* (beech); *b Quercus* (oak); *c Tilia* (lime); *d Ulmus* (elm); *e Alnus* (alder); *f Corylus* (hazel); *g Betula* (birch); *h Pinus* (pine). x 500.   *del John Shaw.*

Figure 17 Mountain Avens (*Dryas octopetala*).

del R. Powers.

Chapter 12

Post-Glacial Baltic
Geographic Stages

THE GEOGRAPHICAL EVOLUTION of the Baltic region during Post-Glacial times has also been used as a basis of relative chronology (see Chart A).[85] With the melting of the Fennoscandian[86] ice-sheet at the end of the Pleistocene period, the land was relieved of a great load which had been pressing it down in accordance with the principle of *isostasy*.[87] Released from its load the Fennoscandian land-mass began to rise, more in the centre where the depression had been greatest, and decreasingly towards the margins. Meanwhile the sea-level was rising on account of the enormous volume of water added to the oceans by the melting of ice-sheets in many parts of the world. The geography of the Baltic region thus underwent a rather complicated evolution, determined by the interplay of the uneven rising of the land and the simultaneous rising of sea-level.

The earliest stage was marked by the *Baltic Ice Lake*, the shores of which were frequented by Late Palaeolithic hunters and fishers in the ninth millennium BC. With the retreat of the ice from the Central Swedish Moraines, the Ice Lake was rapidly drained and sea-water entered the Baltic region, carrying with it a sub-arctic fauna which included the bivalve mollusc *Yoldia*. The *Yoldia Sea* was contemporary with the earliest Mesolithic hunters and fishers. As a result of the isostatic uplift of the land proceeding faster at this time than the rise of sea-level, this sea became cut off and converted into a freshwater lake, called the *Ancylus Lake* after the name of the small limpet-shaped univalve mollusc *Ancylus*, found in its deposits. Later, as the rise of sea-level overtook the elevation of the land, connection with the ocean was re-established and the Baltic area was occupied by the *Littorina Sea*, so called after the common periwinkle *Littorina littorea*, whose shells abound in its deposits. The sea-level continued to rise, causing a series of transgressions, that is to say progressive submergences of the land, between 5000 and 3000 BC. There is therefore a succession of Littorina strand-lines. Their spacing and heights above present sea-level vary from place to place owing to the fact that differential uplift of the land continued after the sea-level had become stabilized about 3500 BC (Godwin *et al.*, 1958). The dwelling places of the people of the shell-mound or Kitchen–Midden culture are found along the earlier shore lines of the Littorina Sea; but its later beaches were frequented by the Neolithic farmers. The deposits of the 25-ft raised beach on the coasts of Northern Britain were laid down contemporaneously with the Littorina Sea.

In summary, the stages in the evolution of the Baltic region have been dated approximately as follows:

Baltic Sea	Began *c* 2000 BC	
Littorina Sea	„ *c* 5000	„
Ancylus Lake	„ *c* 7800	„
Yoldia Sea	„ *c* 8300	„
Baltic Ice Lake	„ *c* 9000	„

The maximum extent of the Littorina Sea in Atlantic times closely followed what has been called the Post-Glacial CLIMATIC OPTIMUM – the time when, judging from the distribution of warmth-loving animals and plants in Europe, the mean annual temperature was as much as 2° C higher than at present. This short period of extended distribution of thermophilic species was named the Climatic Optimum on the basis of plant studies in the Baltic region, although its discovery was due to R. Lloyd Praeger who found the evidence for it in the molluscan fauna of Post-Glacial estuarine clays in north-east Ireland.[88] In North America it has been called the THERMAL MAXIMUM and was within the Altithermal stage of Antev's classification.

There is world-wide evidence of the Climatic Optimum, and although the maximum temperature may have been reached earlier or later in a few exceptional areas, it is probably true to say that this was a synchronic episode, that is to say, occurring everywhere at about the same time and is therefore of great importance from the point of view of absolute dating. Evidence from ocean-bottom cores studied by the oxygen isotope method indicates that the peak of the Climatic Optimum was at c 4000 BC (Emiliani, 1955).

CHART A

DATES IN THOUSANDS B.C.		EVENTS IN BALTIC REGION WITH VARVE DATINGS IN YEARS B.C.	PROBABLE CORRELATION WITH ALPS		N.W. EUROPEAN CLIMATIC CHANGES	POLLEN ZONES	DATES IN YEARS B.C. REVISED (1960) BY C14.	CULTURAL PERIODS
1	BALTIC SEA			POSTGLACIAL.	SUBATLANTIC	VIII	500	IRON AGE
2					SUB-BOREAL	VIIb		BRONZE AGE
3	LITTORINA SEA	[CLIMATIC OPTIMUM*]					3000	NEOLITHIC
4					ATLANTIC	VIIa	c.4000*	
5							5500	MESOLITHIC
6	ANCYLUS LAKE				LATE BOREAL	VI		
7		BIPARTITION OF ICE 6923					7000	
8	YOLDIA SEA / BALTIC ICE LAKE	FINIGLACIAL RETREAT / DRAINING OF BALTIC ICE LAKE 7912			EARLY BOREAL	V	7700	
9		BALTIC FENNOSCANDIAN ICE LAKE MORAINES	Daun Stadium?		PRE-BOREAL	IV	8300	
					YOUNGER DRYAS	III	8800	
10	RETREATING ICE SHEET	GOTIGLACIAL RETREAT	Gschnitz Stadium?	LATE GLACIAL	ALLERØD INTERSTADIAL	II	10,000	UPPER PALAEOLITHIC
11					OLDER DRYAS	Ic	c.10,300	
					BØLLING INTERSTADIAL	Ib	c.11,500	
12		BALTIC END MORAINE	Bühl or Ammersee Stadium					
13					OLDEST DRYAS	Ia		
14		DANIGLACIAL RETREAT						
15			Würm III or Schlieren Stadium	PLENIGLACIAL (FULL GLACIAL)			c.15,000	
16	HALTED ICE SHEET	SOUTH POMERANIAN MORAINE						
17								
18								

Chapter 13

Dating by the Varve Method

ALTHOUGH THIS BOOK is not primarily concerned with the methods of chronometric dating, no account of Post-Glacial chronology in the Baltic region would be complete without some account of varve analysis, developed by Baron de Geer in Sweden.[89] As early as 1878 he noticed the regularity of the lamination of glacial clays exposed in sections around Stockholm, and came to the conclusion that the laminae, which were paired, marked the annual melting of the ice as it receded across Sweden at the end of the Ice Age. If the paired laminae or *varves*[90] could be counted they should, he deduced, provide a record of the number of years that elapsed between one halt in the recession and the next. He organized systematic counting of the varves in sections all across Sweden from the Scanian moraines in the south to the shores of Lake Ragunda in the north. Only a small fraction of the total number of annual layers is preserved in any one section, but by plotting the variation in varve-thickness in each section and then matching identical sequences in different sections de Geer and his coworkers were able to combine the records and thus construct a reasonably complete chronology of the recession. Sections were measured at intervals of about one kilometre along a series of mainly south-north traverses; individual varves could be traced for distances of up to more than 50 km, and proved to overlap one another in the direction of ice-retreat like tiles on a roof.

De Geer took as zero-point in his varve chronology the division of the dwindling Scandinavian ice-cap into two parts. The point of bipartition was close to Lake Ragunda. Sections in north central Sweden show one unusually thick varve layer, attributable to the exceptional run-off of ponded melt-water which occurred when the ice-cap divided. In the Angerman Valley, the deposition of varve clays has continued up to the present day, and by counting the varves in sections there it has been possible to date de Geer's zero-varve as 6923 BC.[91] Most authorities, however, now prefer to count the draining of the Baltic Ice Lake (the beginning of the *Finiglacial phase* of retreat) as marking the commencement of 'Post-Glacial' time. With the opening of its ice dam the level of water in the Baltic Ice Lake dropped to sea-level, and the varves subsequently deposited were thicker and browner than the preceding ones, on account of the additional sediment flocculated by the inflow of salt water. According to varve chronology the draining of the Baltic Ice Lake took place in 7912 BC. If this date is accepted, 8000 BC may be taken as a convenient date to choose for the Pleistocene/Holocene boundary (*ie* the arbitrary end of the Ice Age), for it coincides almost exactly with the breakdown of the glacial anticyclone over Fennoscandia, which had widespread effects (Zeuner, 1959, p. 28). This is the first stratigraphical horizon to be defined in years, but there is little doubt that with the fuller development of new chronometric methods of dating, such as the potassium/argon technique, most major stratigraphical boundaries will be defined eventually in this way.

The finiglacial retreat began from the line of halt marked by the Central Swedish–Salpausselkä (Finnish) moraines. The preceding phase of retreat, which began from the Scanian belt of moraines at the south end of Sweden was called by de Geer the *Gotiglacial* phase, for it uncovered the region of Gotia. The varve dating of this phase is full of uncertainties. Thus the published estimates of its date of commencement based on varve counts vary from 11500 to 16000 BC. According to Antevs (1947) the earliest Scanian moraines which can be dated by varve chronology are 13,500 years old. This is probably the best date to accept for the beginning of the Gotiglacial phase. It is nearly coincident with the onset of the Bølling interstadial in the pollen sequence dated by radiocarbon. The higher estimates for the beginning of the Gotiglacial published by de Geer may be nearer the mark for the age of the earliest of the Pomeranian moraines[92] in Northern Germany, with which de Geer correlated the Scanian moraines.

The retreat of ice preceding the halt marked by the Scanian moraines is difficult to follow in detail because the sea interrupts the sequence. It has been called the *Daniglacial* phase, for it was during this time that Denmark was finally freed from ice. There is no direct evidence of its duration.

The stages in the retreat of the Fennoscandian ice-sheet may be summarized as follows:

	Commencing date, BC
'Post-Glacial' (de Geer)	6890
Finiglacial	7912
Gotiglacial (Antev's revision of de Geer)	11500
Daniglacial	c 15000 (?)

As the chronology of Late Pleistocene and Early Holocene times has been based almost entirely until recently on these and other varve counts and estimates, it is worth while considering the method in a little more detail. (Indeed, the term *geochronology* itself, which now of course has a much wider meaning – covering the whole history of the earth – was first used to mean dating by varves).

Typical varves are pairs of laminae, the lower member consisting of coarser sediment (silt) grading upwards into finer material (clay) constituting the upper lamina. The top of this is sharply defined by contact with the overlying coarser lamina of the next pair. Varves are formed when glaciers discharge their melt-water into a lake or other body of relatively still water. The inflowing melt-water, at a temperature close to $0°$ C, is generally lighter than the body of standing water (with a temperature closer to $4°$ C), and therefore spreads its suspended sediment over the whole area of the lake, instead of depositing it all in a delta near the point of entry. The coarser fraction of the sediment settles to the bottom of the lake almost at once, but the finer part remains in suspension throughout the summer months, and only reaches the bottom when the water begins to freeze in wintertime. Each spring the cycle is repeated. The lower, coarser lamina is usually light in colour, whereas the upper lamina containing more decayed vegetable matter is darker. The thickness of a varve depends on the extent of the spring and summer melting of the ice.

Varve dating has been criticized on the ground that several laminations sometimes occur within an annual unit, either through short cycles of abnormal weather with phases of winter melting of the ice. Many such anomalies have been detected in Denmark.[93] However, they appear to have been very rare in the classic Swedish area of varve chronology. In Switzerland, Max Welten (1944) took the trouble to analyse the pollen and diatom contents of successive laminae of the varve clays of Faulenseemoos near Interlaken, and showed that the light coloured (more calcareous) layers represent the summer season, the darker ones autumn, winter and spring.

De Geer and his co-workers considered that it was possible to correlate varve-series over immense distances. For example, they used their method of long-distance correlation or *tele-connection* (de Geer, 1927) in an attempt to date varve-clays in South America on the Swedish time-scale. But this method of teleconnection assumes a much closer parallelism in the fluctuations of summer weather in different continents than is justified by recent meteorological observations.

Antevs attempted to apply de Geer's method of varve analysis to dating the stages of glacial recession in North America. He measured and attempted to correlate sections of varves along traverses between New York and Northern Ontario. The North American varve chronology (Antevs, 1932) is much less reliable than that worked out by the workers in Sweden because there are many gaps in the series available for counting, and these have had to be filled by estimates, for example the duration of time represented by one gap had to be estimated by calculating the rate of recession of the Niagara Falls. Largely on the basis of Antev's varve chronology it was estimated that the earliest human occupation in North America was between 15,000 and 25,000 years ago. Radiocarbon dating, however, has now shown that the gaps in the varve series are really much shorter than Antevs had estimated, and that the age of the earliest securely dated sites of human occupation in the New World are closer to 10,000 than to 20,000 years.

Chapter 14

Pluvials and Interpluvials

IN THE COURSE of geological investigations in the region of the Dead Sea during the last century, Louis Lartet (son of the discoverer of the fossil ape *Dryopithecus*) found deposits which he recognized as having been left by that lake when its water stood at a much higher level than at present. In 1865 (Lartet, 1865) he published the view that the former expansion of the Dead Sea coincided with the glacial period. Evidence of raised lake levels in Pleistocene times was later found in many of the drier parts of the world, while studies in eastern California provided proof that the rise of lake waters in that region was essentially contemporaneous with the advance of glaciers in the neighbouring mountains (Russell, 1887). These periods of higher lake-levels became known as *pluvial*[94] *ages* because it was inferred that they represented times of increased rainfall. Since glaciers and ice-sheets can only form and grow if there is an increase in precipitation, it seemed reasonable enough to correlate pluvial conditions in tropical and subtropical lowlands with glacial conditions in higher latitudes and mountains. In 1914 the English meteorologist C. E. P. Brooks (1914, 1926, p. 315) formulated this general theory of pluvial-glacial correlation, with its implication that interglacial periods arc represented in the tropics and subtropics by dry or *interpluvial*[95] *ages*. If pluvial phases were synchronic throughout Africa, for example, and contemporaneous with glaciations in Europe we should have an invaluable means of relative dating, and for that reason it is important to examine the theory of glacial-pluvial correlation in some detail. Unfortunately, although a great deal of factual data has been cited in support of it, recent researches (Flint, 1959) have thrown considerable doubt on the validity of much of the evidence counted as proof of climatic change in low latitudes.

There is undoubtedly some evidence that there have been major climatic changes in various parts of Africa during the Pleistocene period. For instance glaciers on the high mountains of equatorial Africa were formerly more extensive; there are traces of lakes in regions which are now desiccated; fossil soils occur which can only have formed under conditions wetter or drier than those prevailing today; and accumulations of windblown sand (dunes) occur under a protective cover of vegetation; and so on. There is scarcely any doubt that these climatic changes were directly or indirectly effects of the same general cause as that responsible for the Ice Age; but the view that pluvials in low latitudes and glacials in high latitudes were contemporaneous is still largely in the realm of theory.

On the theoretical side, pluvial-glacial correlation has been considerably influenced by the various attempts to explain the Ice Ages – of which there have been at least eight during the 4,000 million years of the earth's existence. Geological, mainly palaeontological, evidence has indicated that throughout long periods the earth had a generally mild, equable climate and lacked polar ice-caps (Holmes, 1944, p. 250)[96]: indeed the extent of ice on the earth today is sufficient to justify the conclusion that we have not yet fully emerged from the Pleistocene Ice Age. That is to say, we may be now in an *interglacial* phase. The evidence that indicates an increasing desiccation of large areas of Africa might be regarded as supporting the theory that interglacials in the higher latitudes correlate with arid or inter-pluvial phases in the lower latitudes. This subject is of immense practical importance to man, but it is one of great complexity and urgently requires much fuller study. It should be noted that some authorities maintain that desiccation in Africa is to a large extent the outcome of man's interference with the vegetation.

There are two main groups of theories to account for Ice Ages[97]: geographical and astronomical. The first group includes the theory that the north and south poles with their ice-caps have wandered as a result of 'continental drift'; and the more widely held view that uplift of continents and mountain ranges has favoured the growth of glaciers and ice-sheets. These geographical theories fail to account for the glacial-interglacial fluctuations that are such a marked feature of the Pleistocene Ice Age.

In the second group of theories it is supposed that Ice Ages owe a great deal to alterations in the radiation received from the sun, and these theories more readily account for interglacial fluctuations. Some authors have assumed that the energy emitted by the sun has remained constant throughout geological time (apart from the 11-year sun-spot cycle which apparently reflects a rhythmic change in the sun's magnetism). These authors assume that some geographical factor produces an ice age in the first place, but they explain the oscillations by appealing to variations in the proportion of the *insolation* or energy received on the earth's surface through the seasons. The difference in insolation between summer and winter has varied through long-term changes in the eccentricity of the earth's orbit with the precession of the equinoxes and changes in tilt. These minor changes in the positional relation of earth to sun have been going on throughout geological time, and cannot possibly explain the rare commencement of an Ice Age; but given an Ice Age they may explain its fluctuations. Other authors, rather in the minority, believe that the *emission* of energy from the sun has varied considerably in course of time, and that this variation may have been adequate to account for the origin of Ice Ages as well as their oscillatory character. The British astronomer Fred Hoyle (1950, p. 58[98]) has suggested that at long intervals the whole solar system tunnels through clouds of cosmic dust which stimulates solar activity and indirectly causes ice ages.

The theory that variation in solar emission has caused Ice Ages agrees with the views of the British meteorologist, Sir George Simpson, who has stressed that the total energy received annually from the sun is more important in determining the climate of a zone than its distribution through the year. He has pointed out that glaciation requires a balance between increased atmospheric circulation and precipitation on the one hand, and decreasing mean annual temperature on the other. Neither decreasing temperatures nor increasing precipitation on its own can maintain the growth of an ice sheet. For example, Siberia, the coldest continental area on earth, is not glaciated, simply because there is insufficient precipitation to nourish an ice-sheet. In 1930, Simpson showed that by postulating two complete cycles of solar radiation (emission) during the Pleistocene period, it was possible to account for *four* advances of ice in Europe separated by alternately cold-dry and warm-wet interglacials; and at the same time to account for *two* pluvial periods in the warmer parts of the world. Simpson's argument[99] ran as follows:

With increase in solar radiation there is a general rise in temperature, an increase in winds, cloudiness and precipitation. At first the increased precipitation gives greater accumulation of snow in winter, and the increased cloudiness reduces the melting in summer, causing glaciers and snow fields to spread. But the continuing rise in temperature eventually prevents further advance and leads to retreat and disappearance of ice. Thus the peak of radiation corresponds with a warm interglacial phase. With the subsequent decrease in solar radiation there is a reverse sequence of changes: the mean temperature falls and the annual variation in temperature decreases so that although it declines it does not decline so rapidly as the winter temperature, with the result that snowfields increase and glaciers re-advance. This continues until the reduction in precipitation becomes the deciding factor, when glaciers dwindle through lack of nourishment, leading to a cold dry interglacial phase which lasts until increasing solar radiation marks the beginning of a new cycle. Simpson correlated the minima of radiation with cold dry interglacials, and the maxima with warm wet interglacials.

While at first this theory seemed to agree fairly well with the available evidence, it agreed less well as new evidence came to light.

In 1929, E. J. Wayland[100] had concluded on the basis of field work in Uganda that there were two main pluvials in East Africa during the Pleistocene period. When the records of pluvial phases in the Pleistocene sequences of other countries were re-examined they appeared to be reducible to two main pluvials with minor oscillations.[101] These findings strongly supported Simpson's hypothesis. However, further researches by Nilsson[102] in Kenya led to the inference that there had been three major pluvials in East Africa, with intervening inter-pluvial phases. At one time Leakey (1950) considered that there were four pluvials represented in East Africa as set out in the following table (but see also note 112):

4. *Gamblian Pluvial*[103]
   Third Interpluvial
3. *Kanjeran Pluvial*[104]
   Second Interpluvial
2. *Kamasian Pluvial*[105]
   First Interpluvial
1. *Kageran Pluvial*[106]

Leakey working with Solomon at an earlier stage had also recognized two Post-Pluvial wet phases named:

ii. Nakuran[107]
i. Makalian[108]

Palaeontological and archaeological evidence appeared to favour broad correlation of four main pluvials with four glaciations in the Alps, a conclusion that received approval from the meteorologist C. E. P. Brooks (1949, p. 271), although it ran counter to the requirements of Simpson's theory. The correlation between world-wide climatic changes, pluvials, and glaciations has been recently reviewed by Rhodes Fairbridge (1961).

The four pluvial stage-names became widely adopted for application throughout Africa as stratigraphical units, and the names were applied wherever correlation with the type-area was regarded as well attested by palaeontological, archaeological or geological evidence.[109] The fact that these stages were originally defined on a climatic basis led to the tacit assumption that their recognition in some other region implied that the climatic sequence there was comparable. In other words, the pluvial-interpluvial sequence described in equatorial Africa became regarded, quite unjustifiably, as applicable throughout the greater part of the continent. Re-appraisal of the evidence in 1957 by two Pleistocene geologists, Professor R. F. Flint of Yale[110] and Dr H. B. S. Cooke (1958), led to some questioning of the basis of the existing four-fold pluvial scheme. Flint agreed that there was good evidence in the type-area for moister and probably cooler conditions within the general bracket of

Gamblian time (*ie* Late Pleistocene), and for the two Post-Pluvial wet phases. He also found moderate support for a late Pre-Gamblian pluvial at Olorgesailie (correlated archaeologically with 'Kanjeran' deposits); but in the type-area he found no acceptable evidence for any of the other Pre-Gamblian climatic phases from Kageran to the Third Inter-pluvial.

Meanwhile, Simpson (1957) had reconsidered the application of his solar radiation theory to Pleistocene world climate, taking into account recent trends in the interpretation of the geological evidence, particularly the international agreement in 1948 to enlarge the Pleistocene to include the Villafranchian, and the use of tool-traditions as dating-lines.[111] He noted that the existence of glacial phases before the Günz Glaciation had to be taken into account; and reconstructing a curve of solar radiation based on there having been, most probably, six glacial maxima within the enlarged Pleistocene (Fig. 18), he deduced that there should have been three periods of heavy precipitation in equatorial Africa during that period coinciding with interglacials:

> III. Kanjeran-Gamblian[112] (Upper Pleistocene)
> II. Kamasian (Middle[113] Pleistocene)
> I. Kageran (Lower Pleistocene)

Although Simpson's scheme accords well with some of the evidence from low latitudes, particularly in Africa, factual data derived from pollen-analysis of interglacial peats in Europe appear to be entirely contrary to it. The pollen evidence indicates that each of the interglacials included a phase of climate which was as warm as or warmer than that prevailing at the same locality today; whereas Simpson's radiation theory

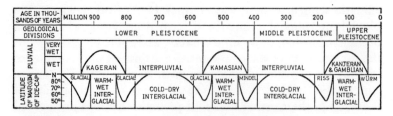

Figure 18 Correlation between glacial and African pluvial stages according to Simpson on the basis of his solar radiation theory.

demands that alternate interglacials should be cold and dry. One possibility appears to have been neglected. It would be inappropriate in a general book to examine it thoroughly; but it is perhaps worth asking this question: is it not possible that the radiation-maxima coincide with true interglacials in the pollen-analysts' sense, and that the 'cold dry inter-glacials' of Simpson are masquerading under the name of inter-stadials?

If only to underline the uncertainties that still exist, it should be recalled that some climatologists hold very different views from Simpson, and consider that world climatic changes are due to variations in the proportion of solar energy received on the earth's surface in summer and in winter. This *insolation* varies, as already noted, with the inclination of the earth's axis of rotation, with the eccentricity of its orbit and with the chang-ing position of perihelion at autumn equinox. These variations have different effects of course in the different latitudes. Dr E. A. Bernard, who is one of those holding the view that these are the factors which account for the Pleistocene climatic changes, has recently (Bernard, 1959) calculated on this basis that when the obliquity of the earth's axis is at a maximum, interglacial conditions will exist in high latitudes and pluvial conditions in low latitudes. Owing to the poleward spread of the tropical deserts during this phase, the middle or subtropical latitudes, which now have winter rainfall, then became increasingly arid. On the other hand, when the obliquity of the earth was minimal there were glacials in high latitudes, and increased winter rainfall in the subtropical belt, while the tropical deserts expanded equatorwards.

Bernard has done a great service to palaeoclimatology in recognizing that the term *pluvial* involves an oversimplification; because it does not make any distinction between an increase in total annual rainfall and an increase in seasonal rainfall. He has proposed that the term *isopluvial* should be used for increased rainfall distributed throughout the year (as in equatorial regions), and *displuvial* for increased summer rainfall (accom-panied by excessive aridity in winter).

The term pluvial has been used widely to include not only phases of increased tropical and equatorial rains, but for the winter rainfall which in the higher latitudes is closely associated

D

with the genesis of glaciation. Bernard has grouped these under *'pluviaux de front polaire'*. Furthermore, when Europe was extensively glaciated it was largely covered by a permanent anticyclone which deflected depressions far to the south of their normal west-east track, and brought regular cyclonic rains to the Mediterranean countries including the North African littoral. All these increases of rainfall closely linked with glaciation should perhaps be distinguished as *glacio-pluvials*.

Fig. 19 reproduces the pattern of climatic changes in Africa during the last 100,000 years according to Bernard's calculations. If there is any degree of truth in this scheme, the use of pluvial stages as means of synchronic dating throughout Africa, will have to be abandoned. Fortunately we shall soon be in a position to test it objectively, because the radiocarbon method will in due course enable us to date deposits in the various latitudes absolutely, throughout about half of this time span. Indeed it is already possible to plot the climatic changes in some parts of Africa on a time chart for the last 60,000 years. Using the results of pollen-analysis as a means of determining changes in vegetation and therefore of climate in the radiocarbon dated sequence at Kalambo Falls, Zambia, Professors Desmond Clark and van Zinderen Bakker (1964) showed that there was a remarkably close synchronic parallelism with the temperature curve of the Würm glaciation in Europe. Thus at 57,000 years B.P. (Late Acheulian horizon) the conditions at Kalambo were relatively warm, corresponding to the Brørup interstadial in Europe (Fig. 3), and were followed by a considerable decrease in temperature during the times of Sangoan and Middle Stone Age cultures. Two warm interludes in this period of cooling, at about 43,000 years B.P. and at about 27,000 B.P., apparently corresponded with the 'Göttweig' and Paudorf Interstadials in Europe.

During the coldest of the three cool phases indicated at Kalambo (altitude 1200 m.) there was a downward shift in vegetation belts of 600–900 metres, corresponding to a decrease in mean annual temperature of 3°–5° C.

A pollen-diagram of a peat-bog on the tree-line of the Western Kenya Highlands has recently been studied with the aid of radiocarbon dating of a key sample. This indicated a cold treeless horizon about 12,650 years old, corresponding with the

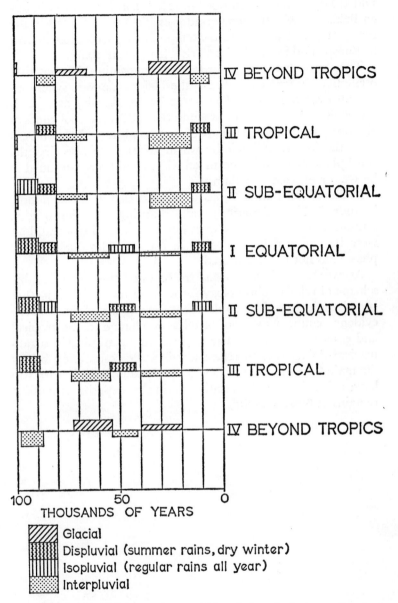

Figure 19 The climatic changes in Africa during the last 100,000 years according to Bernard, 1959.

Oldest Dryas phase in Europe (p. 71). According to van Zinder-
en Bakker (1962) the temperature oscillations indicated in the
diagram are identical and contemporaneous with those known
in Europe and in the Andes since 'Pleniglacial' times.

These recent studies go far towards confirming the view that
oscillations in *temperature* during the Pleistocene were synchronous all over the Earth. There was less conformity as regards
increases and decreases in precipitation. All three cool zones at
Kalambo contain indications of wet conditions, but whereas
both the lower, and middle warm zones were also dry, the
third phase of warming occurred while conditions continued to
be wet or at least very damp.

Radiocarbon dating[114] has confirmed that lakes in middle
latitudes in North America expanded during glaciation in high
latitudes; but the crucial question as to whether conditions
were becoming drier or wetter in *low* latitudes during these
phases has not been answered.

As we have already seen, the construction of a reliable
scheme of relative chronology for the Pleistocene in Africa has
been handicapped by doubts about the validity of much of the
evidence counted as proof of climatic change in the tropical
and equatorial realms. (The same is true of tropical and subtropical Asia.) It is therefore worth while considering briefly
the main lines of evidence now in use because each in turn will
have a bearing on the relative dating of deposits containing
remains of fossil hominids.

Chapter 15

African Pleistocene Climatology

(a) *Ancient Lake-levels*

Climatic control of Pleistocene lake-levels in East Africa has been favoured by many investigators from J. W. Gregory (1921) onwards, but doubts have been expressed from time to time, for example Solomon at one time wholeheartedly supported this idea, but as a result of further work in Uganda he thought later (1939) that crustal movement had been a major factor in forming and in draining lakes in the Rift Valley basins.

The levels of some of the lakes in Africa have undoubtedly been affected by earth-movements and volcanic dams. But even where tectonic and volcanic agencies can be excluded other climatic factors besides rainfall are liable to control the levels of lakes. It has been estimated for example that 85 per cent of the water entering Lake Victoria annually is lost by evaporation (Brooks, 1925). A general lowering of temperature with consequent reduction in the rate of evaporation in this part of Africa would therefore result in a rising of the level of the lake without there being any increase in rainfall.

After re-examining the data obtained by Nilsson in the Naivasha sector of the Kenya Rift Valley, Flint (1959, p. 355) concluded that although earth-movement and volcanic activity may have formed the basins, the sequence and extent of the horizontal strand-lines seem to demand a climatic control of lake-levels in Late Pleistocene and early Post-Pleistocene times.

(b) *Fossil Spring Deposits*

Calcareous tufas formed by springs in regions now relatively arid are probably the most reliable of all the indicators of rainfall in the past, because such deposits require for their formation a fairly constant supply of water, only possible if the annual rainfall remains high. Dr Gertrude Caton-Thompson (aided by Miss E. W. Gardner) has described the freshwater tufas formed around extinct springs in the Kharga Oasis in the Egyptian Desert ($25\frac{1}{2}°$ N.) (in Caton-Thompson and Gardner, 1932). In outline the sequence they discovered was as follows (beginning with the earliest event recorded):

1. Formation of crystalline *Plateau Tufa*, containing reed impressions, but no industry or fauna.
2. Period of major erosion by streams, forming the main valleys.
3. Heads of valleys filled by accumulations of angular breccia; no evidence of water action. Arid period.
4. Cellular *Wadi Tufas* containing leaves of figs, palms and ferns; in two successive sheets, each overlying a spread of gravel, the earlier with Upper Acheulian, the later with Acheulio-Levalloisian 'floors'.
5. Erosion in upper reaches of Wadis.
6. Formation of the last *Wadi Tufas* in two successive terraces or sheets covering respectively Lower and Upper Levalloisian 'floors'.
7. Progressive desiccation with humid oscillations: cutting and filling of narrow stream channels, forming a series of low terraces contemporaneous with the Levalloiso–Khargan, Khargan and Aterian industries and leading on to the relatively dry conditions of the present day.

These events clearly represent two major pluvial phases (1–2 and 4–6). The tufas unquestionably record times of raised watertable, reflecting increased rainfall on the catchment area. The episodes of intense erosion (2 and 5) have been interpreted as representing rainfall maxima; but it is conceivable that they correspond in each case to a decline in pluvial conditions, which may well have been marked by a more sharply seasonal distribution of the rainfall.

The four aprons of spring-deposited tufa or travertine in front of the Kaap escarpment at Taung in Bechuanaland are probably the best available evidence of relatively wetter climates in Southern Africa during Pleistocene times. They have an important bearing on the dating of the type-specimen of *Australopithecus africanus* (Oakley, 1954, pp. 79, 82; Peabody, 1954).

(c) Erosion, Alluvium and Colluvium

In the great river valleys of Southern Africa there are terraces indicating alternate cutting and filling (aggradation) by the rivers during the Pleistocene period – processes probably controlled there in the absence of tectonic movement, mainly by climatic changes. In country of that type, lacking a continuous cover of vegetation, increased rainfall or increased length of rainy season results in headwater and gully erosion on unprotected slopes, but on account of the augmented transporting power of the rivers, gravels and sands are eventually deposited in the bottoms of the main valleys. Thus, the Older and Younger Gravels of the Vaal Valley probably correspond to periods oı increased rainfall, or pluvial phases. In regions where the cover of vegetation is continuous, on the other hand, heavy rains produce relatively little alluvial deposition, but the rivers continue to erode their beds in adjustment to base-level which has been falling continually through the gradual rise of the African continent relative to sea-level since Tertiary times. In regions which are marginal, from the point of view of vegetation, alluvial deposition will be reduced either through the vegetation becoming continuous (*eg* under isopluvial conditions), or through the rainfall declining (*ie* under interpluvial conditions).

Erosion, aggradation and changes in grade of river-borne sediment have often been used as criteria of climatic change, but the factors involved are obviously so complex and delicately balanced, that valley-formation and alluvial phenomena in general are easily misinterpreted.

The study of hill-washes (colluvium) sometimes provides more useful information about rainfall in Pleistocene times than does the study of alluvium. For example, Professor G. Bond (1957) studied the weight-distribution of feldspar grains in successive layers of Late Pleistocene hill-wash at Khami near Bulawayo, and from the data he was able to calculate the volume of run-off and to deduce the possible former rainfall maxima and minima. Dr C. K. Brain (1958, p. 121) has also attempted to make estimates of rainfall in early Pleistocene times in the Transvaal by studying the colluvial components of breccias in the dolomite caves of that region. The results of his work contributed to the dating of the Australopithecines in terms of the regional pluvial-interpluvial sequence.

(d) Fossil Soils

Soils formed during Pleistocene times sometimes give useful indications of former climates. If they have been preserved intact under more recent accumulations they are called *fossil soils*, and where these can be dated stratigraphically they provide valuable palaeoclimatic data.

Recent researches have established the fact that red soils are formed in tropical and subtropical regions where the annual rainfall is more than 40 ins per annum. At one time the mistaken idea was prevalent that fossil red soils represent interpluvials, whereas in fact their formation is usually linked with pluvial conditions.

The formation of concretions of iron sesquioxides (ferricrete) in tropical soils has been attributed by some authors to high, markedly seasonal rainfall, but new observations in South Africa (Mason *et al.*, 1959) have now shown that the formation of ferricrete is commonly related to ground-water conditions rather than to the rainfall or atmospheric humidity. Even when the rainfall is not high, impeded drainage can give rise locally to the formation of ferricrete.

Under hot dry climates where the rainfall is less than about 18 inches per annum, and provided there is lime in the parent rocks, olive-grey to whitish concretions of calcium carbonate known as *kunkar* are commonly formed in the soil a few inches below the surface.[115] Sometimes the carbonate is deposited in massive layers (surface-limestones or calcrete).

(e) Aeolian Sands

Relatively dry periods or interpluvials are represented in some parts of Africa, notably in Rhodesia and in the Transvaal, by aeolian or wind-blown sands of the so-called Kalahari type, mainly reddish in colour. The true Kalahari Sand (Cooke, 1958) constitutes the top member of the Kalahari System which covers an immense area in the western half of Africa from 20° S to 1° N. Since it is truncated by the 'end-Tertiary peneplain' or erosional surface the upper part of this system is evidently of Pliocene age. Although a high proportion of the grains in the Kalahari Sand are of the well-rounded form with frosted surface indicating wind-transport, they are usually red in colour on account of a coating of ferric oxide (haematite). This suggests that following their accumulation under extremely dry conditions the prevailing climate was semi-arid, with seasonal rainfall. Similar sands accumulated in various parts of Africa during Pleistocene times are distinguished as *Kalahari-type* sands. Some of these are probably re-deposited Kalahari Sand. Except where they occur in the form of 'fossil' dunes, it is difficult to be sure on superficial inspection whether they have been wholly accumulated (in one or more stages) by wind transport, or whether they originated as aeolian sands but have been re-deposited by water. Red sands in the Pleistocene succession near the Victoria Falls have recently been studied microscopically by Bond (1957*a*) who has shown that some layers consist wholly of *polished* grains, typical of river sand, whereas other layers contain a very high proportion of *frosted* grains characteristic of wind-blown sand.

(f) *Palaeontological Evidence of Climatic Change*

Pollen in peaty deposits (unfortunately rare in Africa) and other fossil plants sometimes provide useful evidence of former climates. The plant remains in the Kharga tufas have already been quoted. Pollen-analysis of the peaty clays associated with the Florisbad Skull in the Orange Free State indicated that Florisbad Man dated from a relatively dry phase preceding the commencement of the Gamblian pluvial (van Zinderen Bakker, 1957). Pollen-analysis, combined with radiocarbon dating, is now beginning to provide a palaeoclimatological framework for African Palaeolithic cultures, and thus adding a new, ecological dimension to their definition. The recent studies of the Kalambo sequence by J. D. Clark and van Zinderen Bakker (1964) suggest that as warm dry conditions gave way to the wet, cooler conditions, so Acheulian hand-axe culture, suited to open grassy country, was supplanted by Sangoan chopper-tool culture suited to woodland.

The fossil vertebrates in African Pleistocene deposits have yielded little evidence of former climatic conditions. It may be recalled that the fossil beds at the top of the Kaiso Beds in Uganda were interpreted by Wayland as having been laid down in large discontinuous pools under conditions of desiccation, but it is now regarded as quite possible that the draining of Lake Edward was due to crustal disturbance rather than to a change in climate.

In Palestine, on the other hand, Pleistocene mammalia have been used as climatic indicators. The late Miss Dorothea Bate plotted the relative frequency of remains of gazelle (a steppe animal) and fallow deer or *Dama* (a woodland form) in successive layers in the Mount Carmel Caves, and showed that climatic fluctuations were thereby clearly demonstrated. She interpreted the evidence as indicating three maxima of forest development, representing pluvial phases. The first maximum occurrence of *Dama* remains coincided with Micoquian culture (=advanced Upper Acheulian), the second with the Upper Levalloiso–Mousterian, and the third (fairly closely linked with the second) coincided with Antelian culture (p. 157). These results are of great importance in considering the chronology of the fossil men of the Mount Carmel Caves, but some mammal specialists in interpreting similar faunal assemblages consider that the preponderance of *Dama* or *Gazella* reflects changes in the dietary preferences of the Palaeolithic hunters, rather than general climatic oscillations between moister and drier.

Chapter 16

Pleistocene Subdivisions in the Maghreb

ALL OF NORTH AFRICA west of Egypt was called the Maghreb, or 'The Western Land' by geographers in the Middle Ages, although the term is now restricted to the part comprising Tunisia, Algeria and Morocco. This region, also known as Barbary, is largely a plateau which rises into mountain ranges and is bounded on the north and west by sea, and on the south by the Sahara Desert.

The stratigraphical framework of Pleistocene events and sites in Barbary has been built mainly on the succession of ancient marine transgressions recorded in beaches along the Mediterranean coast (mainly Algeria) and along the Atlantic littoral (Morocco).

The Algerian beaches partly formed the basis of the Pleistocene Mediterranean sea-level chronology already outlined (pp. 47–50); but the Moroccan beaches (Choubert, 1962) are important because of their association with a sequence of marine molluscan and terrestrial mammalian faunas, with a sequence of palaeolithic industries and of clearly defined terrestrial episodes.

There has been difficulty in using parallelism with the classical beaches of Italy as a reliable basis for Quaternary chronology applicable throughout the Maghreb. Earlier workers who thought that a simple parallelism could be traced did not take sufficient account of the part played by tectonic deformations which altered the original heights of the beaches.

George Lecointre (1952) made a thorough study of the mollusca in the Moroccan beaches, and recognized three main faunas:

Molluscan Fauna III: warm with *Purpura haemastoma* present in the 30-m and 7–8-m beaches.

Molluscan Fauna II: cold with *Purpura lapillus* and *Littorina littorea* present in the 20-m beaches at Casablanca which are regarded by some authors as part of the transgression forming 60-m beaches.

Molluscan Fauna I: subtropical with a species of *Trochatella* now living in Chilean waters, and other species regarded as typically Senegalese. Present in 70–100-m beaches.

It is clear enough that the 30-m beaches of Morocco can be correlated with the 30-m or Tyrrhenian I beaches of the Mediterranean, and the 7–8-m beaches of Morocco with the Late Monastirian. On the other hand, the more ancient levels and beaches are discordant. Thus the 70–100-m beaches correspond *in height* with the Sicilian, but their subtropical fauna is far more compatible with their being pre-Sicilian, *ie* Calabrian. In this case the 60-m beaches of Morocco are the counterpart of the Sicilian beaches in the Mediterranean. For discussion of these problems of correlation of beaches see Choubert (1962).

The most important terrestrial episodes in the Morocco sequence were extensive formations of sand dunes, of which there are two main series. The more ancient dunes constitute what is known as the Great Dune of Casablanca which over-lies deposits containing the cold Molluscan Fauna II and was accumulated during the time of lowered sea level known as the *Romanian* regression. The beginning of the next big regression (post 30-m beach) was the time of accumulation of the coastal sand dunes known as the Little Dune of Casablanca.

Red soils, *Tirs*, were widely formed in Morocco except during unusually arid phases. The earlier series of red soils cover a long period of time and both antedate and cover the Great Dune. The later red soils overlie the calcareous crust which seals the older series. *Crusts*, of which there are several in the Moroccan sequence, were formed mainly as a result of semi-arid conditions drawing to the surface and then evaporating lime-charged water.

Four main Quaternary mammalian faunas have been recognized in the terrestrial succession of the Maghreb (Arambourg, 1962):

Upper Pleistocene phase 2: disappearance of *Elephas jolensis* (and more gradually of *E. atlanticus*); local disappearance of hippopotamus and rhinoceros.

Upper Pleistocene phase 1: declining numbers of species characteristic of M. Pleistocene; incoming of Eurasiatic elements: *Dicerorhinus kirchbergensis*, *Megaceroides*, *Elephas jolensis* and *Ursus*.

Middle Pleistocene fauna: *Archidiskodon recki* (gradually replaced by *E. atlanticus*); *Homoioceras*, *Dicerorhinus simus* (white rhinoceros), *Notochoerus*, *Equus mauritanicus* (large zebra) and *Epimachairodus*.

Lower Pleistocene fauna: *Anancus*, *Archidiskodon africanavus*, *Leptobos*, *Stylohipparion*, *Libytherium* and *Epimachairodus*.

The climatic cycles, terrestrial and marine transgressive, which constitute the broad stratigraphic framework in the Maghreb, have been studied by many authorities, and the terminology has been somewhat confusing to students.[116] The position has recently been clarified by Pierre Biberson (1961). The stage-names in general use and their archaeological and alpine correlations, are set out in the following Table.

Alpine correlates	*Marine Transgressions*	*Continental cycles ('Pluvials')*	*Cultures in Maghreb*
Post-Würm	—	Rharbian	Neolithic
	Flandrian	—	Oranian
Würm	—	Soltanian	Aterian
	Ouljian	—	Final Acheulian
Riss	—	Tensiftian	Upper Acheulian
	Anfatian	—	Middle Acheulian
Mindel	—	Amirian	Lower Acheulian
	Maarifian	—	Chellean (Clacto-Abbevillian)[117]
Günz	—	Saletian	Late Oldowan
	Messaoudian	—	Oldowan
Donau	—	Moulouian	Oldowan
	Moghrebian (Calabrian)	—	None

Notes to Part One—
Stratigraphical Dating

1 The principles of stratigraphy were outlined by Geikie, (1885, p. 626).

2 Earlier Ice Ages are known, for example in Pre-Cambrian and in Late Carboniferous–Early Permian times.

3 This classification of the Alpine stages has been used by Zeuner (1946). Although in later editions (1950, 1952, 1958, p. 133) the base of the Pleistocene had been lowered to include the Villafranchian stage (formerly classed as Upper Pliocene), the top of the Lower Pleistocene was drawn by Zeuner at the end of the Mindel stage.

4 Haug (1911, p. 1767) pointed out that new types, of Asiatic origin, appeared abruptly in the Villafranchian stage: 'Ces immigrés sont les genres *Elephas*, *Equus* et *Bos*. Leur introduction soudaine dans la faune européene constitue un évenement assez important pour justifier l'établissement d'une coupure de premier ordre. Aussi placerons-nous à la base du Quaternaire le Villafranchien'.

5 It is probable that *taiga* was much more extensive than *tundra* in periglacial Europe.

6 For discussion of the term *tjaele* meaning frozen ground see Bryan (1951, p. 69) and Paterson (1940). Each time the water-gorged subsoil in periglacial regions is re-frozen after the seasonal thaw, the pressure of growing ice-crystals tends to rotate stones and arrange them in positions which simulate convexion currents in a boiling liquid. This process, which Dutch geologists have called cryoturbation (from κρόνς ice, and τυρβάζω I stir) leads to the formation

of stone polygons on flat surfaces. In vertical sections through ground affected by this process the stones have been 'up-ended' and arranged in loops or festoons (Fig. 1).

7 For useful summary of Eberl's researches see Zeuner 1959, pp. 65–68.

8 An interstadial is a mild interval, whereas an interglacial is a much larger interval when glacial conditions had passed away in the region concerned and relatively hot summers caused the weathering of the underlying loesses to proceed much further, with the production in some areas of red soils. Thus the Last Interglacial weathering of the Older Loess in France converted it to a considerable depth into red clay (*argile rouge*); whereas the weathering during the inter-Riss and inter-Würm Interstadials produced relatively thin layers of brown soil.

9 The 'Göttweig Interstadial' has been defined in years by Flint and Brandtner (1961, pp. 321–28), as 35–48,000 B.P., but identification of its flora is difficult. As some of the 'Göttweig soils' are proving to be Eemian, the name of the main Würm Interstadial will have to be replaced.

10 For a summary of recent work on the North German glacial succession see Woldstedt, 1958. It should be noted that the term Baltic End Moraine is sometimes used to include the Pomeranian.

11 The Stettin moraines are placed in this position on the authority of Woldstedt, 1956, p. 82.

12 For a number of years it has been debated as to whether the Warthe Drift represented a re-advance of the Saale ice (this was Woldstedt's interpretation of the evidence), or whether it marked an early advance of the ice of the Last Glaciation (this was originally Zeuner's view). Recently evidence has been found that the Eem Sea (note 15 below) broke through the Warthe drift, confirming Woldstedt's interpretation (see van der Vlerk *et al.*, 1957, p. 312).

13 Confusion has undoubtedly arisen through attempting to correlate the *stadia* of the Alpine glaciations. For reasons briefly discussed in the next chapter (Interglacial Correlation), these are sometimes only of local significance. Some authorities hold that there were three stadia of the Riss

glaciation, but others would identify Jungriss with Würm
I (see Zeuner, 1954).

14 James Geikie (1914) later published a revised classification and correlation with the Alpine stages of Penck
and Brückner (1909).

15 The Eemian stage was named after the Eem, a small river
flowing from Utrecht, past Amersfoort into the Ijsselmeer
(Netherlands). This valley has for long been known as the
type locality of the Eem marine deposits which are
widespread in the Netherlands, Denmark and the Baltic
fringe of North Germany, and which mark an invasion
of this region by the sea during the Last Interglacial.
These marine beds are sandwiched between glacial
deposits, and contain a molluscan fauna including many
species which now have a more southerly distribution.
See Nordmann 1928. The Eemian Interglacial is represented by numerous peaty lake and river deposits in
north and north-western Europe, and these have provided the basis for working out the characteristic Eemian
pollen profile. See Jessen and Milthers (1928).

The Eemian Interglacial is equivalent to the Ipswichian
interglacial recognized in East Anglia (West, 1957, 1958,
1960).

16 Dr R. G. West's studies of the pollen in the lake-beds at
Hoxne in Suffolk revealed a sequence of changes in the
vegetation closely matching those indicated by pollen
diagrams of Elster-Saale interglacial deposits in North
Germany and adjoining countries. This interglacial stage
had been named Needian in the Netherlands (van der
Vlerk, 1955 and references); but in view of the complete-
ness of the record at Hoxne it was agreed in 1957 that the
name Hoxnian proposed by West should be substituted.
See West 1955, and 1956, pp. 265–6, van der Vlerk,
et al. 1957, p. 312. In North Germany the Elster-Saale
interglacial was marked by invasion of the 'Holstein Sea'
and this stage is commonly known as Holsteinian (see
Woldstedt, 1958, pp. 17–19, 64), van der Vlerk (1957,
p. 312).

17 The Cromer Forest Bed was for long regarded by British
geologists as 'pre-glacial', for it is overlain by the oldest

known glacial deposits in East Anglia – the North Sea Drift. The underlying Weybourne Crag is a marine deposit containing shells of a cold-water molluscan fauna. In 1950 Woldstedt published Thomson's pollen-diagram of the Cromer Forest Bed which showed that it was undoubtedly interglacial in character, beginning with a cool pine-birch phase at the base, passing through a mixed-oak forest phase in the middle to a top phase dominated by conifers. The pollen profile of this deposit was later studied in more detail by Miss S. L. Duigan. Woldstedt correlated the 'Cromer–Warmzeit' with the Günz–Mindel Interglacial (1954, p. 231). The term Cromerian Interglacial was introduced by West (1955, p. 49; 1958, 1960) but 'Cromerian' has also been extensively used by palaeontologists in a much wider sense as a faunal stage, without any climatic implication.

18 The earliest 'interglacial' flora is that represented in the Tegelen Clay of the Limburg region in the Netherlands. The name Tiglian is derived from the Latin name for this locality, where the clay was used for making tiles (*tiglia*: Latin, *tegels*: Dutch) in Roman times as it is today. For list of the Tiglian flora see van der Vlerk and Florschütz (1953, pp. 36–37).

19 The study of pollen is known as palynology. For an account of the application of pollen-analysis to Quaternary geology see Godwin 1941, 1956. For a summary of the results of the application of this technique to interglacial deposits see West (1955, 1960). Pluvial lake beds in western North America have been shown to contain a pollen record revealing major changes in Pleistocene vegetation zones (Martin and Gray, 1962, pp. 110–11).

20 Researches by G. R. Coope have shown that insect faunas, particularly the Coleoptera, which are often abundant in some Pleistocene deposits, are very sensitive in their response to environmental or climatic changes, and studies of their remains have therefore proved a valuable asset in elucidating Quaternary ecologies (Coope 1959, 1962). See also Zeuner (1961).

21 Nangeroni (1950), Venzo (1955). See also useful summary in R. F. Flint (1957, p. 385).

22 R. F. Flint, 1957, p. 387. On the other hand F. E. Zeuner (1959, p. 205) accepted the Hötting breccia to be of Mindel–Riss Age.

23 James Geikie named the Third Interglacial 'Durntenian' on the basis of this occurrence (Geikie 1914, pp. 239, 262).

24 The term micro-climate refers to any situation where temperature and humidity are distinct from those prevailing in a particular region. For example, the south-facing slopes of a sheltered valley in a periglacial zone might enjoy conditions resembling those of an interstadial.

25 The figures are based on Boswell (1931, p. 88). The correlation is based on opinion expressed at a symposium on Pleistocene correlations between the Netherlands and adjacent areas (*eg* Zagwijn in van der Vlerk *et al.*, 1957, pp. 240–1).

26 Crag is a Suffolk dialect term for the shelly marine sands of Upper Pliocene and Lower Pleistocene age which occur extensively in East Anglia. The term probably came from the Celtic word *cregga* meaning a shell (Arkell and Tomkieff, 1953, p. 31).

27 We may recall Hazzledine Warren's view that the 'eolithic' flaking observed on nearly 50 per cent of the flints in the 'Stone Bed' was mainly due to the grounding of pack-ice which jammed together patches of stones strewn on the floor of the shallow Crag sea (Warren, 1948).

28 Boswell (1931, p. 89) argued against regarding the influx of northern species in the Weybourne Crag as evidence for equating it with a glacial episode; but he was writing before pollen-analysis had established that the overlying Cromer Forest Bed represented an interglacial, now recognized as Günz–Mindel.

29 Based on Boswell, 1931, pp. 88, Table I.

30 Baden-Powell, 1953. The deposits classified as belonging to the Corton stage are in part at least Hoxnian.

31 The Kullenberg piston-corer allows cores of more than 36 ft in length to be raised intact from the sediments resting on the ocean floors (for description see Kullenberg, 1947).

32 In addition to the papers by Emiliani, the book by Nairn and Thorley 1961, contains a useful general account of these researches.

33 One general inference from palaeotemperature research on deep-sea cores is that the maxima and minima reached the same values repeatedly through Pleistocene times, indicating that the mean temperature during the main glacial stages were alike, and similarly those of the inter-glacials. Moreover, the present time is equivalent in part to an interglacial, so that we may reasonably infer that there were residual ice-sheets in the polar regions during interglacial stages, in contrast to the Tertiary era, when so far as we know there was no polar ice (Flint, 1957, pp. 438–9).

34 The Pa/Th technique of dating and its application to deep-sea sediments has been described by Rosholt *et al.* 1961.

35 Frye (1962) has pointed out the wide diversity in correlations of the ocean-bottom layers dated to the 300,000–350,000 years-span: equated with the Nebraskan Glaciation by Emiliani (1958), but with the Illinoian Glaciation by Hough (1953) and by Eardley and Gvosdetsky (1960).

36 From rates of accumulation of Pleistocene sediments on the sea-floor determined by radioisotope datings, and from the known thickness of sediment above the extinction-level of discoasters, Ericson, Ewing and Wollin (1963) began to estimate the age of the boundary. Developing the results further they later dated the beginning of the Pleistocene (counting Donau within enlarged Günz) as 1.5 million years BP. See book forthcoming, D. B. Ericson & G. Wollin, *The Deep and the Past* (Knopf, Nov. 1964).

37 For brief discussion of this, see note 45.

38 Fossiliferous sands of Red Crag Age occur, for example, at Netley Heath in Surrey at *c* 600 ft above sea-level. The much lower level of the Red Crag itself in East Anglia is due to the fact that whereas Britain as a whole has been rising since Pliocene times, land adjoining the North Sea (a geosynclinal area) has been affected by downwarping.

39 Wooldridge, 1958, p. 2.

40 The relation of 200-ft platform to the boulder clay of the Thames Valley Glaciation (presumably Mindel) and to the Milazzian sea-level, has been discussed by Zeuner (1959*a*, p. 153).

41 For an account of glacial eustasy see Zeuner, 1959*a*, p. 276.

42 General de Lamothe recognized in Algeria early sea-levels at 325, 255, 204, 148, 103, *c* 60, *c* 30 and 18–20 m above present sea-level. He regarded the first five as Pre-Pleistocene. See R. de Lamothe 1911.

43 In naming the four stages Depéret used two terms which had already been used as faunal stages: *Sicilian* (Doderlein in 1872) and Tyrrhenian (Issel in 1888); and introduced two new names: *Milazzian* (after Milazzo in Italy), and *Monastirian* (after Monastir in Tunisia). See Depéret, 1918. The use of the term Milazzian has been disputed but see Howell (1962).

44 C. Depéret recognized a shore-line in the Riviera at 7–8 m (Depéret, 1906, p. 223), but did not attach a name to this stage. It was called Late Monastirian by Zeuner (1959*a*, p. 283) who introduced this term in 1945. The transgression from minus 8 to plus 10 m, named *Ouljian* by M. Gigout on the basis of his work on the Atlantic Coast of Morocco, appears to be equivalent (see Biberson, 1955, p. 145). More recently Zeuner (1959*a*, pp. 350–5) has recognized evidence of an 'Epi-Monastirian' shore-line at 2–4 m, which he correlated with the first interstadial of the Würm Glaciation. At Gibraltar this is the 5-m shore-line which notches deposits accumulated after the Late Monastirian (8-m) beach, but elsewhere the distinction from the latter is not very clear. There is also a possibility of confusion with the *post*-glacial beach which occurs at 2–3 m above present sea-level at a number of localities (Zeuner, 1959*a*, p. 378–9, Flandrian beach).

45 The first person to explain the regression of sea-level as causally connected with glaciation was A. Tylor (1868, p. 576). His theory failed to explain why the shore-lines representing transgressive phases were in tiers. One suggested explanation of this is that there had been continual uplift of the continents in response to their unloading by erosion which carries away, on average about 0·11 mm each year (100 m in 1 million years). This is an example of isostatic uplift. See Arambourg, 1954. An attractive alternative explanation has recently been advanced. If the earth is expanding, as some geo-physicists now believe, the ocean basins are probably increasing in area and this

would result in the sea-level falling relative to land (Arthur Holmes in letter to *The Sunday Times*, 20 September, 1959). There seems to be an accumulation of evidence agreeing with the idea that the core of the earth is growing (Girdler, 1962, p. 521).

46 For example, E. Chaput (1928) showed that the four main shore-lines are well displayed on the west coast of France.

47 For general summary see Zeuner, 1959a, chapter IX. Fairbridge, 1958, pp. 471–82, Garrod, 1962, p. 249, Fleisch, 1962.

48 The term Calabrian has been used to cover marine deposits formed in Italy contemporaneously with the continental deposits known as Villafranchian, formerly counted as Upper Pliocene, but now classed as Lower Pleistocene.

49 It must be borne in mind that according to the terminology of some authors, following discussions at the INQUA Congress in Rome, 1953, the 100-m shore-line is classified as Calabrian, and the 60-m shore-line as Sicilian. For clarity it seems desirable to modify the new terminology as follows:

Older terminology	New terminology
Milazzian	Sicilian II
Sicilian	Calabrian II or Sicilian I
Calabrian	Calabrian I

50 The warm fauna with *Strombus bubonius* in Pleistocene deposits of the Mediterranean was termed Tyrrhenian by Issel. Depéret restricted the stratigraphic use of this term to the highest shore-line deposits containing the fauna, and this usage has recently been advocated by Zeuner (1959a, p. 284). However, the persistence of the *Strombus* fauna into the Main and Late Monastirian stages is considered by some authors as a good reason for regarding these as substages of Tyrrhenian. See Blanc, 1936.

51 Biberson (1955, pp. 141, 145). The drop in sea-level between Sicilian I and Sicilian II ('Milazzian') is regarded by this author as the first part of the Great or Romanian Regression (p. 142).

52 According to D. T. Donovan erosion features and terrace deposits of the river Severn and Bristol Channel, taken with

radiocarbon dates, indicate that from 24,000 to 45,000 years ago the sea was not more than a few metres above or below its present level. Donovan, 1962.

53 Blanc, 1936, pp. 140–56, 1937. For summary see Zeuner, 1959a, pp. 227–32.

54 Blanc (1936, p. 133) originally termed the 'Pre-Versilian' regression 'Pre-Flandrian'. Flandrian and Versilian are generally regarded as synonymous, but there is now some doubt about this. Flandrian was the name applied in northern France by G. Dubois to a transgression which began in Upper Pleistocene times and apparently continued there throughout Post-Glacial times up to the Middle Ages. See Dubois, 1924. In view of the recent evidence indicating that the Post-Glacial rise of sea-level was complete before Bronze Age times (Godwin *et al.*, 1958, p. 1518) it now appears probable that the later part of the Flandrian transgression was due to local subsidence. In any case it would seem wiser to use Versilian for the last Pleistocene transgression (interstadial?) and to restrict the term Flandrian to the *Post-Glacial rise of sea-level* (Biberson, 1955, p. 141). There is some slight evidence suggesting that a brief regression separated the Versilian from the Flandrian (Post-Glacial) transgression.

55 It is historically interesting that in 1921 Depéret attempted to correlate the Mediterranean sea-level stages with the main terraces of European rivers and these in turn with the Alpine glaciations. He concluded that the upper parts of the terraces could be equated with glaciations (we would now say that their formation terminated with the onset of glaciation). His correlation was as follows:

$$18–20 \text{ m} = \text{Würm}$$
$$30 \text{ m} = \text{Riss}$$
$$55–60 \text{ m} = \text{Mindel}$$
$$100 \text{ m} = \text{Günz}$$

He considered that the horizon of the Heidelberg jaw was at the base of the 30-m terrace which he equated with the Mindel–Riss Interglacial. See Depéret, 1921.

56 Blanc, 1957, p. 104.

57 See note 44.

58 This takes the form of a 'nick-point', in the longitudinal profile. See Zeuner, 1959*a*, pp. 42–9 for account of formation of river terraces (nick-point, p. 43).

59 Zeuner, 1959*a*, p. 46. In the middle reaches of a river it is probably true to say that gravels were laid down in *glacial* stages, but re-sorted in interglacials.

60 For detailed account of the terraces of the Somme and their palaeolithic contents see Breuil and Koslowski, 1931, 1932. The outline of the sequence now presented is based mainly on H. Breuil, 1939*b*. Some account has been taken of the revision by F. Bordes, 1957.

61 This is apparently the only acceptable evidence in Europe for contemporaneity of a palaeolithic industry with Cromerian fauna, although in China the industry of Peking Man is associated with a fauna which was for long identified as Cromerian, whereas new evidence indicated that it is of Mindel II age (Kurtén and Vasari, 1960). It is therefore most important to distinguish between a horizon of Cromerian *age* (*ie* dating from the Günz–Mindel Interglacial) and one containing elements of Cromerian *fauna*. Much of the Cromerian fauna persisted until the final phase of the Mindel Glaciation. Indeed it is quite probable that the horizon with type Abbevillian industry belongs to an interstadial within the Mindel period, rather than to the true Cromerian or Günz–Mindel Interglacial. This conclusion is in accord with correlation of the 45-m terrace with the Sicilian II or Milazzian sea-level. For an account of the industries in the 45-m terrace of the Somme, see Breuil 1932, p. 173; 1939*a*; 1939*b*, p. 334).

62 The name *D. kirchbergensis* (Jäger, 1839) takes priority over *D. merckii* (Jäger in Kaup, 1841) by two years and although the latter name has been most generally adopted in the past, an attempt is now being made by some workers to substitute the earlier name. See Adam, 1961.

63 The evidence for this 'Pre-Riss' solifluxion, contemporanous with Middle Acheulian industry of Levalloisian facies, was seen in a section of the 30-m terrace at Cagny, S.E. of Amiens, noted by Bordes (1957, p. 1).

64 Flake-tools known as '*le type Levallois*' were already

recognized at the end of the last century (G. and A. de Mortillet, 1900, p. 166), and then regarded as belonging to the transition from Acheulian to Mousterian. With the abandonment of the idea of single-line evolution of the Palaeolithic, and the adoption of the concept of parallel cultures, the Levalloisian became regarded as a distinct flake-culture related to the Mousterian. In the Somme Valley, for example, Breuil (1932, p. 127) recognized artifacts or assemblages of artifacts ('industries') representing seven stages of this culture (Levalloisian I to VII). Discoveries in other parts of the world, and researches elsewhere in France, later led to the view that the Levalloisian represented a technique of preparation of the core before detachment of the flake which was practised by various palaeolithic groups, some Acheulian, others Mousterian. The name Levalloisian is derived from Levallois–Perret, a suburb of Paris, where examples of this type of flake-tool have been found.

65 The scheme was outlined in 1955 and developed more fully in 1957. Blanc, 1955, 1957.

66 The Villafranchian (and its approximate marine equivalent, Calabrian) probably represents a period of time almost equal to the whole of the remainder of the Pleistocene. It can be subdivided as follows:

Upper Villafranchian = Pre-Sicilian regression = Günz
Middle Villafranchian = Calabrian (*part*) Donau-Günz = Tiglian
Lower Villafranchian = Post-Astian regression = Donau = Praetiglian

In the faunal sense Calabrian had a wider significance than being the marine equivalent of the Middle Villafranchian. Thus, Lagaaij (1952) showed that the bryozoan fauna of the Walton Crag (= Praetiglian) is essentially 'Calabrian'.

67 In 1953 members of the Rome meeting of INQUA visited a section which has been chosen as the type-section for the Pliocene-Pleistoene boundary. It is situated in the via Cortina d'Ampezzo on the north-eastern outskirts of Rome, where the marine Astian is overlain conformably

by the marine Calabrian, the time-gap between the two appearing short or even non-existant. Full details are given in the handbook of the 1953 INQA meeting and were discussed by King (1955).

68 The 'tuff with black pumices' has been named *necrolite* because it is the rock in which many Etruscan tombs were cut, for example those of Cervetteri (Blanc, 1957, p. 103).

69 The Poederlian, originally regarded as Upper Pliocene, was named in 1889 after Poederle in Belgium; the Amstelian after the Amstel River in the Netherlands.

70 At the time of the 18th International Geological Congress (1948) it was believed that the Older Red Crag (Walton horizon) and the contemporaneous Poederlian deposits should still be classified as Upper Pliocene; but work on their foraminiferal and bryozoan faunas showed that they must be regarded as basal marine Pleistocene (Calabrian, equivalent to Villafranchian). See for example Lagaaij, 1952.

71 Reuverian is named after Reuver in the Netherlands. At the type locality the deposits are freshwater plant-bearing deposits.

72 This fauna has been investigated by the methods of analytical dating described by van der Vlerk, 1959.

73 The Praetiglian has sometimes been known as Belfeldian.

74 It has been suggested that the cool phase at the commencement of the Tiglian stage is represented in Britain by the uppermost or Butleyan division of the Red Crag, but this is generally classified as Praetiglian. The cool termination of the Tiglian stage is probably represented by the Chilles-ford Beds in Suffolk and Norfolk which contain shells of cold water mollusca (*eg* species of *Yoldia* and *Mya*).

75 Glauconite is a green mineral, essentially a hydrated silicate of iron and potassium, formed only under marine conditions. It is datable by the potassium/argon method. The fauna in the glauconitic sands reached at minus 150 m in the Noord Brabant indicate much warmer conditions than in the Tiglian stage, but appropriate to the Upper Pliocene.

76 Judging from their heavy minerals (garnet predominating) the Tiglian sands were laid down by the Rhine, whereas

the overlying Lower Taxandrian sands (with abundant staurolite grains) were deposited by small rivers from the south. Mineral analysis of the Middle and Upper Taxandrian sands in the type area indicate alternating influence of the Rhine and Maas rivers. Van der Vlerk and Florschütz, 1953, p. 11.

77 Zagwijn and Zonneveld, 1956, Zagwijn, 1957. See also Kortenbout van der Sluijs, 1956.

78 Analysis of hippopotamus bone dredged from the bottom of the Scheldt estuary suggests but does not prove that it may have been derived from a Needian horizon. Van der Vlerk and Florschütz, 1953, p. 12.

79 According to current interpretation of the evidence, the re-advance of Saale (or Saalian II) can be equated with Warthe (see p. 24). Van der Vlerk et al., 1957, p. 312.

80 A few Austrian and German geologists distinguish 'Late Riss' in addition to Riss II. If the Eemian Interglacial is between Riss II and Late Riss, as some authorities have claimed, it is quite possible that the interval 'Riss-Würm' in the type area of the Alps is *not* the time equivalent of the Eemian. See Zangwijn, 1957, p. 287 (discussion). Establishing the relation of the Dürntentian beds to the 'Late Riss' moraines should help to settle this question which is bound up with the unsolved problem of which moraine was originally identified by Penck and Brückner as Riss.

81 The main phases of the Tubantian stage have been correlated with the German Glacial succession as follows:

Late Tubantian		Baltic End Moraines
	Pleniglacial C	South Pomeranian Moraines
	Interstadial II	2nd Weichsel interstadial
Middle	Pleniglacial B =	Frankfurt ⎫ Brandenburg ⎭ Moraines
Tubantian	Interstadial I	1st Weichsel interstadial
	Pleniglacial A	Stettin Moraines
Early Tubantian		Fruhwürm (Alps)

The Drenthian is probably subdivisible in a similar way. See Florschütz, 1957, pp. 245–9.

82 For radiocarbon dating of the Post-Glacial Stages see Godwin, Walker and Willis, 1957; Wright, 1957.

83 Although this phase is generally considered to have been relatively dry it is difficult to find evidence to support this view in Ireland where conditions appear to have been cooler than in the Atlantic stage but not drier. Mitchell, 1951.

84 Radiocarbon dating has led to the identification of the *Two Creeks Interval*, in the Late-Glacial sequence of central North America, with the Allerød Oscillation in Europe.

85 For fuller account see Wright, 1937, ch. 19, also Zeuner, 1959, pp. 47–55.

86 Fennoscandia comprises Scandinavia and Finland.

87 The concept of isostasy was introduced by T. F. Jamieson in 1865. The earth's crust is in a state of hydrostatic equilibrium; if an additional load is imposed on a portion of its surface that area will sink and the remainder of the surface will rise in compensation; and conversely if a load is removed (Wright, 1937, p. 404).

88 The discovery of The Climatic Optimum has usually been attributed to R. Lloyd Praeger (1892, p. 212) who demonstrated in 1892 a phase of climate 'if anything, milder than the present' in the Post-Glacial estuarine days of County Antrim, but he quoted a similar observation by T. F. Jamieson, History of The Geological Changes in Scotland, 1865. See Mitchell, 1954.

89 Bailey, 1943. For summary and useful evaluation of de Geer's work see Zeuner, 1959, pp. 20–45.

90 The term varve (Swedish *varv* meaning periodic repetition) was used by de Geer for layers representing an annual rhythm. See de Geer, 1912, p. 242.

91 The original estimate gave 6839 BC as the date of de Geer's zero-varve, but according to a revision by Nilsson, 1960, p. 147 it has now been determined as 6923 BC.

92 There are a series of 'Pomeranian' moraine-belts, and these were studied in relation to varve clays by Vierke, 1937. The Middle and Northern Pomeranian Moraines of this author from part of the Baltic End moraine complex,

which links with the South Scanian moraines. The earliest,
or South Pomeranian moraine, is the 'Pomeranian
moraine' of most authors. See Zeuner, 1959, pp. 30–1.

93 Hansen, 1940. Summarized in Zeuner, 1959, p. 31.

94 The term *pluvial* was first used by Blanckenhorn (1901,
p. 393), and brought into general use by Brooks (1914). A
pluvial has been defined by Sir Frank Dixey (in Clark,
1950, p. 11) as 'a climate of long extent, consistently wetter
(although allowing for minor fluctuations within the
whole) than the climate prevailing today'.

95 The term *interpluvial* was introduced by Wayland (1934,
p. 347), and defined by Dixey (1950), as a major climatic
phase drier than the climate today.

96 Ice Ages were probably initiated by uplift and mountain-
building orogeny but controlled by astronomical factors
(*cf.* Emiliani and Geiss, 1957).

97 The main theories are conveniently summarized by
Holmes, 1944, pp. 249–51. Among theories referring to
the atmosphere he includes the now rather discredited
view that in some periods dust blown into the air by
volcanic eruptions may have reduced the amount of solar
radiation reaching the earth's surface sufficiently to cause
a lowering of the mean annual temperature. More
plausibly it has been suggested that volcanic dust 'triggered-
off' pluvial rains in semi-arid regions in much the same way
that clouds can be made to precipitate by seeding artificial
nuclei into them. See Fuchs and Paterson, 1947.

98 Hoyle, 1950, p. 58, points out that at certain times the sun
must have been considerably warmer than it is at present
to account for coal being found at Spitsbergen within 12°
of the North Pole. Moreover, meteorologists suggest that
an increase, not a decrease, of the sun's heat is needed to
produce an Ice Age, although the necessary increase in
that case was less than that required for plants to grow at
the poles. He considers that 'the excess of radiation
necessary to produce the climatic changes. . . . just
described' cannot have been due to any alteration in the
internal structure of the sun, but 'was due instead to the
infall of interstellar gas on the solar surface'.

99 G. Simpson, 1930, 1934. One difficulty in applying the

radiation theory was to explain why the glaciated area is not symmetrical about the North Pole: in north-east America it extends to latitude 40° and only to latitude 60° in north-east Asia. In the first paper Simpson followed Wegener and Koppen in assuming that through continental drift there had been a shift in the position of the continents in relation to the north pole during this period. In his later paper (1934) he showed that the asymmetry of the glaciated area was easily accountable in terms of the present distribution of sea and land.

100 E. J. Wayland (1929, 1931), tentatively correlated his Pluvial I with the Günz and Mindel, and Pluvial II with the Riss and Würm glaciations.

101 C. E. P. Brooks (1931), shows that the two major pluvials recognized in the Pleistocene deposits of Uganda and Kenya may be subdivisible.

102 Between 1929 and 1949 the Swedish geologist E. Nilsson studied the ancient moraines on the slopes of Mt. Elgon, Mt. Kenya and Kilimanjaro and the Abyssinian Highlands and also the ancient beaches of lakes in the Eastern Rift Valley and on the Abyssinian plateau. He concluded from the incidence of these that there had been three pluvials which he named: The Great or Kafuan Pluvial, The Little Pluvial (= Kamasian) and Last Pluvial (= Gamblian). Nilsson, 1952.

103 The name *Gamblian* is derived from Gamble's Cave, Elmenteita. See Leakey and Solomon, 1929, Solomon in Leakey, 1931, p. 246. The Gamblian was subsequently divided into (a) Upper Gamblian (= Gamblian in the original sense, as used in 1929), represented by Layers 9–14 in Gamble's Cave II (Leakey 1931, p. 93) and by a strand-line 510 feet above Lake Nakuru; and (b) Lower Gamblian (termed Enderian in 1929), represented by Layer 15 in Gamble's Cave II, and by a strand-line 700 ft above Lake Nakuru. The two Gamblian high lake levels were separated by an oscillation during which the lake dropped by 300 ft. The pumiceous beach sediment with shells forming Layer 15 in the cave has been traced widely, marking a time when the lake was very extensive, and the climate appreciably wetter and probably cooler

than at present. The Gamblian pluvial was later considered to include three maxima, but no details have been published (Leakey, 1950, p. 63).

Palaeolithic cultures contemporaneous with Gamblian: Final Acheulian; Proto-Stillbay to Final Stillbay; Lower to Upper Sangoan; Lower Kenya Capsian.

104 The name *Kanjeran* was introduced by Leakey in 1948 (Leakey, 1950, p. 63) for the presumed Third Pluvial represented by deposits called 'Upper Kamasian': the lake beds with Acheulian industry at Kanjera in the Kavirondo gulf and at Olorgesailie in the Kenya Rift Valley, and Bed IV in the Olduvai Gorge, Tanganyika with similar industry. Contemporaneous cultures include Lower to Upper Acheulian, Fauresmith and earliest Sangoan.

105 The *Kamasian* pluvial was recognized on the basis of researches carried out in the Kenya Rift Valley by Leakey and Solomon between 1926 and 1929. Solomon demonstrated that the series of deposits described by the late Professor J. W. Gregory as laid down in what he had called 'Lake Kamasia' were not Miocene as he had supposed, but Pleistocene. At first Leakey and Solomon (1929) used the name Eburrian for these early Pleistocene lake beds, which they regarded as representing the 'First Major Pluvial' in Kenya, but later (Leakey, 1931) they substituted the name Kamasian, In the type area, close to the Kamasia Plateau between Nakuru and Eldoret, the sediments are white diatomites and sands composed of volcanic (tuffaceous) material. Palaeolithic cultures regarded in 1931 as contemporaneous with the Kamasian as then defined included Chellean, Acheulian and some Sangoan; but after the Upper Kamasian was re-named Kanjeran (in 1948), the cultures that proved to be contemporaneous with the Kamasian in the restricted sense were late Pre-Chellean (Oldowan) and Chellean. Some authors doubt the validity of the evidence for recognizing the Kanjeran as distinct from the Kamasian (Posnansky, 1961).

106 The term *Kageran* was proposed in 1947 largely on the basis of Wayland's Pluvial I, which, it was inferred,

preceded the Kamasian: see Leakey (editor), 1952, p. 7. Wayland (1934) considered that the gravels forming the 270 ft and 200 ft terraces in the Kagera Valley in Uganda were deposited at a time when the rivers of Central Africa were larger than their modern counterparts. On the evidence of their containing flaked pebbles, supposed Pre-Chellean pebble-tools (known as the 'Kafuan culture'), he had deduced that these deposits represented a pluvial period earlier than the Kamasian (Pluvial II of his scheme). Leakey (1950, p. 63) referred the Kanam Beds (Kenya) and other deposits in Tanganyika containing 'Early Oldowan' pebble-tools to the Kageran pluvial. The Oldowan is the oldest unquestioned human industry in Africa, whereas the 'Kafuan' is now rejected (p. 172). Many authors have referred to the first pluvial as the Kafuan Pluvial. E. J. Wayland has claimed that there is evidence in Uganda not only for the 'Kageran Pluvial' (the Kagera River being the type locality) but also evidence of Pre-Kageran Pluvials, the main one being covered by his name *Ibandan*. However, this work is largely unpublished, and as neither the pluvial origin nor the Lower Pleistocene age of the 'type' Kagera deposits has been established it is at present unwise to use these terms as though they had been generally accepted by geologists in the African field.

107 The Nakuran, second of two quite distinct post-pluvial wet phases recognized in Kenya by Leakey and Solomon (1929). This phase is represented by a strand-line 145 ft above the present Lake Nakuru, linked with Layer 3 in Gamble's Cave II (Leakey, 1931, pp. 32–3, 116 and 247). The contemporaneous cultures were Gumban and Njorowan (both, at that time, considered to be phases of the East African Neolithic). The Nakuran was preceded by a very dry phase which Brooks (in Leakey, 1931) correlated with the Climatic Optimum.

108 The *Makalian*, first post-pluvial wet phase, was named after the Makalia River south of Lake Nakuru (Leakey and Solomon, 1929; Solomon in Leakey, 1931, p. 246), and is represented by a strand-line 375 ft above Lake Nakuru. Contemporaneous cultures: Elmenteitan and

Wilton, also probably Upper Kenya Capsian (p. 197).

109 In the Proceedings of Third Pan-African Congress on Prehistory (Livingstone, 1955), London, 1957, p. xxxi, it was recommended that the terms Kageran, Kamasian, Kanjeran, Gamblian, Makalian and Nakuran should be used only in a *climatic* sense in the type area, and only applied as stratigraphic units outside East Africa when correlation is well established on at least two lines of evidence, geological, palaeontological, or archaeological. It was proposed that each division should have its upper limit defined in the type area by the onset of the next pluvial or wet phase.

110 R. F. Flint, 1959a, throws doubt, for instance, on the inference that the Kamasian deposits in the type-area represent a pluvial. In the first place they may lie in a series of small lake basins rather than forming the floor of one vast lake. In the second place, since the deposits have in some places been downfaulted nearly 2,000 ft, they may have been formed at an altitude which even under present-day conditions would receive a much higher rainfall than that appropriate to their situation today. In this region of Africa the rainfall increases by one inch for every 150–200 ft rise in elevation. This author also questions the validity of much of the evidence on which the 'interpluvials' are based. He admits that the red wind-blown sand in Layer 8 in Gamble's Cave II may mark a phase of desiccation following a pluvial stage; but he shows that the development of red soil in Olduvai Bed III (so-called interpluvial deposit) is more likely to record a damp seasonal climate than a dry one.

111 Oakley, 1961, chart opp. p. 92.

112 Simpson's conclusion (1957) that the Kanjeran and Gamblian are phases of a single pluvial were of course simply based on deductive logic following the application of meteorological theory. After he had published this paper, Dr L. S. B. Leakey admitted that the break between the Kanjeran and the Gamblian had never been very clearly demonstrated. He wrote: 'It now begins to appear possible that we in East Africa only had three major pluvials, the

Kageran, the Kamasian and a combined Kanjeran–Gamblian.' Leakey in Simpson, 1957, p. 481.

113 In Simpson's new chart the Kamasian is classified with the Kageran under Lower Pleistocene, but according to the classification adopted here it falls mainly within the Middle Pleistocene.

114 During interpluvial stages the near desiccation led to the precipitation of evaporites (including sodium carbonates and chloride). Carbonates are datable by the radiocarbon method. Flint and Gale, 1958.

115 Flint, 1959, pp. 366–7. The word *kunkar* is of Hindu origin and was applied to gravel.

116 Useful general works on the prehistory of the Maghreb in relation to regional Pleistocene stratigraphy and sea-levels have been published by Balout (1955), Biberson (1961), Howell (1962, including some of the preceding papers in symposium arranged by him) and Vaufrey (1955).

117 See Refs. II note 53.

References to Part One

ADAM, K. D. 1961. Die Bedeutung des pleistozänen Säugetier-Faunen Mitteleuropas für die Geschichte des Eiszeitalters. *Stuttgarter Beiträtge zur Naturkunde*, Stuttgart, No. 78, 34 pp.

ANTEVS, E. 1932. Late–Glacial Clay Chronology of North America. *Rep. Smithson. Inst.*, Washington (1931): pp. 313–24.

    1947. Dating the Past (Review). *J.Geol.*, vol. 55, pp. 527–30.

ARAMBOURG, C. 1954. Les 'Plages Souleveés' du Quaternaire. *Quaternaria*, vol. 1, pp. 55–60.

    1962. Les faunes mammalogiques du Pleistocène circum-méditerranéen. *Quaternaria*, vol. 6, pp. 97–109.

ARKELL, W. J. & TOMKEIEFF, S. I. 1953. *English Rock Terms*. Oxford. 139 pp.

BADEN-POWELL, D. F. W. 1953. Correlation of Pliocene and Pleistocene Marine Beds. *Nature, Lond.*, vol. 172, p. 762.

BAILEY, E. B. 1943. Gerard Jacob de Geer, 1858–1943. *Obit. Notices, Roy.Soc. Lond.*, vol. 4, no. 12. pp. 475–81.

BALOUT, L. 1955. *Préhistoire de L'Afrique du Nord*, Paris. 544 pp.

BARKER, H. & MACKEY, J. 1961. British Museum Natural Radiocarbon Measurements III, *Radiocarbon*, vol. 3, pp. 39–45.

BECK, P. 1937. Vorläufige Mitteilung über eine Revision des alpinen Quatärs. *Eclog.Géol.Helv.*, vol. 30, pp. 75–85.

BERNARD, E. A. 1959. Les Climats d'insolation des latitudes tropicales au Quaternaire. *Bull.Acad.Roy.Sci.Colon*, (NS) vol. 5, pt. 2, pp. 344–64.

BIBERSON, P. 1955. Nouvelles Observations sur le Quaternaire côtier de la Région de Casablanca (Maroc). *Quaternaria*, vol. 2, pp. 109–49.

1961. Le Cadre Paleogéographique de la Préhistoire du Maroc atlantique. *Service des Antiquités de Maroc*. Rabat., fasc. 16, 235 pp.

BLANC, A. C. 1936. La Stratigraphie de la plaine côtière de la Bassa Versilia (Italie), et la transgression flandrienne en Méditerranée *Rév.Géogr.Phys.*, vol. 9, pp. 131–2; 140–56.

1937. Low Levels of the Mediterranean Sea during the Pleistocene Glaciation. *Quart.J.Geol.Soc.*, Lond., vol. 93, pp. 621–51.

1955. Richerche sul Quaternario laziale, III. *Quaternaria*, vol. 2, pp. 187–200.

1957. On the Pleistocene Sequence of Rome: Palaeoecologic and Archaeologic Correlations. *Quaternaria*, vol. 4, pp. 95–109.

BLANCKENHORN, M. 1901. Das Pliocän und Quatärzeitalter in Aegypten ausschliesslich des Rothen Meergebietes. *Zeit. Deutsch.Geol.Gesell.*, vol. 53, pp. 307–502.

BOND, G. 1957. The Geology of the Khami Stone Age Sites. *S.Rhod.Nat.Mus. Occ. Papers*, vol. 3, pp. 44–55

1957a. Quaternary Sands at the Victoria Falls. *Proc. Third.Pan. Afr.Congr. Prehist.* (1955), London, pp.115–22.

BORDES, F. 1957. Some observations on the Pleistocene Succession in the Somme Valley. *Proc.Prehist.Soc.*, Lond. (NS) vol. 22 (1956), pp. 1–5.

BOSWELL, P. G. H. 1931. The Stratigraphy of the Glacial Deposits of East Anglia in relation to Early Man. *Proc. Geol.Ass. Lond.*, vol. 42, pp. 87–111.

1932. The Oldoway Human Skeleton. *Nature, Lond.*, vol. 130, pp. 237–8.

BOWLER-KELLEY, A. 1937. *Lower and Middle Palaeolithic Facies in Europe and Africa* (privately published), 31 pp.

BRAIN, C. K. 1958. See Refs to Part II.

BRANDTNER, F. 1954. Jungpleistozäner Löss und fossile Böden in Niederösterreich. *Eiszeit. u. Gegenw.*, vol. 4/5, pp. 49–82.

BREUIL, H. 1932. Les Industries à Éclats du Paléolithique Ancien: Le Clactonien. *Préhistoire*, Paris, vol. 1, pt. 2, pp. 125–90.

1934. De l'importance de la solifluxion dans l'étude des terrains quarteraires de la France et des pays voisins. *Rev. Géog.Phys. Géol.* vol. 7, pp. 269–331.

1939. Le Gisement de Chelles; ses Phénomènes, ses Industries. *Quartär*, vol. 2, pp. 1–21.

1939*a* Le vrai niveau de l'industrie Abbevillienne de la Porte du Bois (Abbeville). *L'Anthropologie*, vol. 49, pp. 13–34.

1939*b*. The Pleistocene Succession in the Somme Valley. *Proc.Prehist.Soc., Lond.*, (NS) vol. 5, pt. 1, pp. 33–8.

BREUIL, H. & KOSLOWSKI, L. 1931–32. Études de Stratigraphie paléolithique dans le nord de la France, la Belgique et l'Angleterre. *L'Anthropologie*, vol. 41, pp. 449–88; vol. 42, pp. 27–47, 291–314.

BROOKS, C. E. P. 1914. The Meteorological Conditions of an Ice Sheet and their bearing on the Desiccation of the Globe. *Quart.J.Roy.Met.Soc.*, vol. 40, pp. 53–70.

1925. The Fluctuations of Lake Victoria. *J.E.Africa & Uganda Nat.Hist.Soc.*, vol. 22, pp. 47–55.

1926. *Climate through the Ages.* London. 439 pp.

1931. In Leakey, L. S. B., *The Stone Age Cultures of Kenya Colony.* Cambridge. pp. 267–70.

1949. *Climate through the Ages.* 2nd edn. London. 395 pp.

BRYAN, K. 1951. The erroneous use of *Tjaele* as the Equivalent of Perennially Frozen Ground. *J.Geol.*, vol. 59, pp. 69–71.

CATON-THOMPSON, G. 1952. *Kharga Oasis in Prehistory.* London. 213 pp.

CATON-THOMPSON, G., & GARDNER, E. W. 1932. The Prehistoric Geography of Kharga Oasis. *Geogr.J., Lond.*, vol. 80, no. 5, pp. 369–406.

CHAPUT, E. 1928. Les terrasses des régions atlantiques françaises. In *First Report of the Commission on Pliocene and Pleistocene Terraces* (ed. by K. S. Sandford). Oxford. pp. 69–94.

CHOUBERT, G. 1962. Reflexion sur les parallélismes probables des formations quaternaires atlantiques du Maroc avec celles de la Méditerranée. *Quaternaria*, vol. 6, pp. 137–75.

CHURCHILL, D. M. 1963. A Report on the Pollen Analyses of the Muds from the Medulla Tissues of two Fossil Human Skeletons: Tilbury Man and Thatcham Man. *Proc.Prehist.Soc., Lond.* (NS), vol. 29, pp. 27–8.

CLARK, J. D. 1950. *The Stone Age Cultures of Northern Rhodesia*, Capetown. 157 pp.

1950a. The Associations and Significance of the Human Artifacts from Broken Hill, Northern Rhodesia. *J.Roy. anthrop.Inst.*, vol. 77, pp. 13–32.

CLARK, J. D. & VAN ZINDEREN BAKKER, E. M. 1964. Prehistoric Culture and Pleistocene Vegetation at the Kalambo Falls, Northern Rhodesia. *Nature Lond.*, vol. 201, pp. 971–5.

COMMONT, V. 1910. Note préliminaire sur les terraces fluviatile de la Vallée de la Somme. *Ann.Soc.Géol.Nord.*, vol. 39, pp. 185–210.

COOKE, H. B. S. 1958. Observations relating to Quaternary Environments in East and Southern Africa. *Geol.Soc.S. Africa*, Annexure to vol. 60, 73 pp.

COOPE, G. R. 1959. A Late Pleistocene Insect Fauna from Chelford, Cheshire. *Proc.Roy.Soc.* (B), vol. 151, pp. 70–86.

1962. A Pleistocene Coleopterous fauna with arctic affinities from Fladbury, Worcestershire. *Quart.J.Geol.Soc.*, vol. 118, pp. 103–23.

DAVIES, A. M. 1934. *Tertiary Faunas.* vol. 2, London 252. pp.

DEPÉRET, C. 1906. Les anciennes lignes de rivage de la côte française de la Mediterranée. *Bull.Soc.géol.France*, (4), vol. 6, pp. 207–30.

1918. Essai de coordination chronologique général des temps quaternaire. *C.R.Acad.Sci.*, Paris, vol. 167, pp. 418–22.

1921. La classification du Quaternaire et sa correlation avec les niveaux préhistoriques. *C.R.Soc.Géol.France* (1921). Paris. pp. 125–7.

DIXEY, F. 1950. In Clark, J. D. *The Stone Age Cultures of Northern Rhodesia.* Claremont. pp. 9–29.

DONOVAN, D. T. 1962. Sea Levels of the Last Glaciation. *Geol. Soc.Amer.Bull.*, vol. 73, pp. 1297–8.

DUBOIS, G. 1924. Recherches sur les terrains quaternaires du Nord de la France. *Mém.Soc.Géol.Nord.*, Lille, vol. 8. Mem.I., pp. 1–356.

DUIGAN, S. L. 1963. Pollen analyses of the Cromer Forest Bed Series in East Anglia. *Phil.Trans.R.Soc.Lond.* (B), vol 246, pp. 149–202.

EARDLEY, A. J. & GVOSDETSKY, N. 1960. Analysis of Pleistocene core from Great Salt Lake, Utah. *Geol.Soc.Amer.Bull.*, vol. 71, pp. 1323–44.

EBERL, B. 1930. *Die Eiszeitenfolge im nördlichen Alpenvorlande.* Augsburg. 427 pp. For useful summary of Eberl's researches see Zeuner, F. E., 1959. *The Pleistocene Period.* 2nd edn., London. pp. 65–8.

EMILIANI, C. 1955. Pleistocene Temperatures. *J.Geol.*, vol. 63, pp. 538–78.

1958. Palaeotemperature Analysis of Core 280 and Pleistocene Correlations. *J.Geol.*, vol. 66, pp. 264–75.

1961. Cenozoic Climatic Changes as indicated by the Stratigraphy and Chronology of Deep-sea Cores of Globigerina-ooze Facies. *Ann.N.Y.Acad. Sci.*, vol. 95, pp. 521–36.

EMILIANI, C. & GEISS, J. 1957. On Glaciations and their Causes. *Geolog. Rdsch.*, vol. 46, pp. 576–601.

EMILIANI, C., MAYEDA, T. & SELLI, R. 1961. Paleotemperature Analysis of the Plio-Pleistocene Section at Le Castella, Calabria, S. Italy. *Bull.Geol.Soc.Amer.*, vol. 72, pp. 679–88.

ERICSON, D. B., EWING, M. & WOLLIN, G. 1963. Pliocene-Pleistocene Boundary in Deep-Sea Sediments. *Science*, vol. 139, pp. 727–37.

EVERNDEN, J. F. & CURTIS, G. H. in press. The Present Status of Potassium-Argon Dating of Tertiary and Quaternary Rocks. *INQUA Conference Warsaw* (1961).

EVERNDEN, J. F., CURTIS, G. H. & KISTLER, R. 1957. Potassium-Argon dating of Pleistocene Volcanics. *Quaternaria*, vol. 4, pp. 13–17.

EWER, R. F. 1956. The Fossil Carnivores of the Transvaal Caves. *Proc.Zool.Soc.Lond.*, vol. 126, pp 259–74.

EWER, R.F. 1963. The Contribution made by Studies of the Associated Mammalian Faunas. *S.Afr.J.Sci.*, vol. 59, pp. 340–6.

FAIRBRIDGE, R. W. 1958. Dating the Latest Movements of Quaternary Sea Level. *Trans.N.Y.Acad. Sci.*, (2), vol. 20, no. 6, pp. 471–82.

1961. Convergence of evidence on climatic change and ice ages. *Ann.N.Y.Acad.Sci.*, vol. 95, pp. 542–79.

FLEISCH, H. 1962. La Côte Libanaise au Pléistocene ancien et moyen. *Quaternaria*, vol. 6, pp. 497–521.

FLINT, R. F. 1957. *Glacial and Pleistocene Geology*. New York. 2nd edn. 553 pp.

— 1959. Pleistocene Climates in Eastern and Southern Africa. *Bull.Geol.Soc.Amer.*, vol. 70, pp. 343–74.

— 1959a. On the basis of Pleistocene Correlation in East Africa. *Geol.Mag.*, vol. 96, pp. 265–84.

FLINT, R. F. & BRANDTNER, F. 1961. Climatic Changes since the Last Interglacial. *Amer.J.Sci.*, vol. 259, pp. 321–8.

FLINT, R. F. & GALE, W. A. 1958. Stratigraphy and Radiocarbon Dates at Searles Lake, California. *Amer.J.Sci.*, vol. 256, pp. 689–714.

FLORSCHÜTZ, F. 1957. The Subdivisions of the Middle and Younger Pleistocene up to the Late-Glacial in the Netherlands, England and Germany. *Geol.en Mijnb.*, (NS), vol. 19, pp. 245–9.

FRYE, J. C. 1962. Comparison between Pleistocene deep-sea temperatures and glacial and interglacial episodes. *Bull. Geol.Soc.Amer.*, vol. 73, pp. 263–6.

FUCHS, V. E. & PATERSON, T. T. 1947. The Relation of Volcanicity and Orogeny to Climatic Change. *Geol.Mag.*, vol. 84, pp. 321–33.

GAGEL, C. 1913. Die Beweise für eine mehrfache Vereisung Nord-deutschlands in diluvialer Zeit. *Geol.Rdsch.*, vol. 4, pp. 319–62, 444–502, 588–91.

GARROD, D. E. 1962. The Middle Palaeolithic of the Near East and the Problem of Mount Carmel Man. *J.Roy.anthrop. Inst.*, vol. 92, pt. 2. pp. 232–59.

GEER, G. DE. 1912. A Geochronology of the last 12,000 years. *C.R.Int.Geol.Cong.XI.* Stockholm (1910), vol. 1, pp. 241–58.

— 1927. Late Glacial Clay Varves in Argentina, measured by Dr. Carl Cladenius, dated and connected with the Solar Curve through the Swedish Time-scale. *Geogr.Ann. Stockh.*, pt. 1–2, pp. 1–8.

GEIKIE, A. 1885. *Text-book of Geology*. 2nd edn., London. 992 pp.

GEIKIE, J. 1877. *The Great Ice Age*. 2nd edn., London. 624 pp.

— 1914. *The Antiquity of Man in Europe (Munro Lectures)*. Edinburgh. 328 pp.

GIRDLER, R. W. 1962. Initiation of Continental Drift. *Nature, Lond.*, vol. 194, pp. 521–4.

GODWIN, H. 1940. Pollen Analysis and Forest History of England and Wales. *New Phytol.*, vol. 39, pp. 370–400.

— 1941. Pollen Analysis and Quaternary Geology. *Proc. Geol.Ass., Lond.*, vol. 52, pp. 328–61.

— 1952. Dutch Quaternary Investigations. *New Phytol.*, vol. 51, pp. 417–9.

— 1956. *The History of the British Flora.* Cambridge. 384 pp.

GODWIN, H., WALKER, D. & WILLIS, E. H. 1957. Radiocarbon dating and post-glacial vegetational history: Scaleby Moss. *Proc.Roy.Soc.* (B), vol. 147, pp. 352–66.

GODWIN, H., SUGGATE, R. P. & WILLIS, E. H. 1958. Radiocarbon Dating of the Eustatic Rise in Ocean level. *Nature, Lond.*, vol. 181, pp. 1518–9.

GRAHMANN, R. 1932. Der Löss in Europa. *Mitt.Ges.Erdk. Lpz.*, vol. 51, (1930–1) pp. 5–24.

GREGORY, J. W. 1921. *The Rift Valleys and Geology of East Africa.* London. 479 pp.

GROSS, H. 1956. Das Göttweiger Interstadial ein zweiter Leithorizont der letzten Vareisung. *Eiszeit u.Gegenw.*, vol. 7., pp. 87–101.

— 1958. Die bisherigen Ergebnisse von C14-Messungen und paläontologischen für die Gliederung und Chronologie des Jungpleistozäns in Mitteleurpa und den Nachbargebieten. *Eiszeitalter Gegenw.*, vol. 9, pp. 155–87.

HANSEN, S. 1940. Varves in Danish and Scanian Late-Glacial Deposits. *Danm.Geol.Unders.*, (2), vol. 63, 778 pp,

HAUG, E. 1911. *Traité de Géologie*, vol. 2, pt. 3. Paris pp. 1760–1921.

HOLMES, A. 1944. *Principles of Physical Geology.* London. 532 pp.

HOUGH, J. L. 1953. Pleistocene climatic record in a Pacific Ocean core sample. *J.Geol.*, vol. 61, pp. 252–62.

HOWELL, F. C. 1962. Results of Conference on Early Man and Pleistocene Stratigraphy in the Circum-Mediterranean Regions. *Quaternaria*, vol. 6, pp. 547–9.

HOYLE, F. 1950. *The Nature of the Universe.* Oxford. 121 pp.

JACOBSHAGEN, V., MÜNNICH, K. O. & VOGEL, J. C. 1962. Das Alter des Schädels von Rhünda III: C14 – Datierung der Fundschicht. *Eiszeitalter Gegenw.*, vol. 13, pp. 138–40.

JESSEN, K. & MILTHERS, V. 1928. Stratigraphical and Palaeontological Studies of Interglacial Fresh-water Deposits in

Jutland and North-west Germany. *Danm.Geol.Unders.*, (2), no. 48, 379 pp.

KING, W. B. R. 1955. The Pleistocene Period in England, *Quart.J.Geol.Soc.*, vol. 111, pp. 187–208.

KOENIGSWALD, G. H. R. VON. 1962. Das absolute Alter des *Pithecanthropus erectus* Dubois. *Evolution und Hominisation.*, pp. 112–19. Ed. G. Kurth. Stuttgart.

KORTENBOUT, VAN DER SLUIJS, G. 1956. The Cryoturbations in the Tegelen Region. *Geol. en Mijnb.*, (NS), vol. 18, pp. 421–2.

KORTENBOUT VAN DER SLUIJS, G. & ZAGWIJN, W. H. 1962. An Introduction to the Stratigraphy and Geology of the Tegelen clay-pits. *Meded.Geol.Sticht.*, (NS), no. 15, pp. 31–7.

KULLENBERG, B. 1947. The piston coresampler. *Svenska Hydr. Biol.Komm.*, *Skr.*, (3), vol. 1, pt. 2, 46 pp.

KURTÉN, B. 1956. The status and affinities of *Hyaena sinensis* Owen and *Hyaena ultima* Matsumoto. *Amer.Mus.Novit.*, no. 1764, 48 pp.

— 1957. Mammal Migrations, Cenozoic Stratigraphy and the Age of Peking Man, and the Australopithecines. *J. Palaeont.*, vol. 31, pp. 215–27.

— 1957a. The Bears and the Hyenas of the Interglacials. *Quaternaria*, vol. 4, pp. 69–81.

— 1960. Chronology and faunal evolution of the earlier European glaciations. *Comment.Biol.*, *Helsingf.*, vol. 21, no. 5, pp. 1–62.

— 1962. The spotted hyena (*Crocuta crocuta*) from the middle Pleistocene of Mosbach at Wiesbaden, Germany. *Comment.Biol.*, *Helsingf.*, vol. 24, no. 3, pp. 1–9.

— 1963. Villafranchian faunal evolution. *Comment.Biol.*, *Helsingf.*, vol. 26, pp. 3–18.

KURTÉN, B. & VASARI, Y. 1960. On the date of Peking Man. *Comment.Biol.*, *Helsingf.*, vol. 23, no. 7, pp. 1–10.

LAGAAIJ, R. 1952. The Pliocene Bryozoa of the Low Countries and their bearing on the Marine Stratigraphy of the North Sea Region. *Meded.Rijks.Geol.Gienst.(Sticht).*, (C), vol. 5, no. 5, 233 pp.

LAMOTHE, L. DE. 1918. Les anciennes nappes alluviales et lignes de Rivage du Bassin de la Somme et leurs Rapports avec celles de la Méditerranée occidentale. *Bull.Soc.géol.Fr.* (4), vol. 18, pp. 3–58.

LAMOTHE, R. DE. 1911. Les anciennes de rivage du Sahe d'Alger et d'une partie de la côte algérienne. *Mém.Soc. Géol.Fr.*, (4), vol. 1, 288 pp.

LARTET, L. 1865. Sur la formation du bassin de la mer morte ou lac asphaltite, et sur les changements survenus dans le niveau de ce lac. *C.R.Acad.Sci., Paris*, vol. 60, pp. 796–800.

LEAKEY, L. S. B. 1931. *The Stone Age Cultures of Kenya Colony.* Cambridge. 288 pp.

— 1950. The Lower Limit of the Pleistocene in Africa. *Rep.* XVIII *Int.Geol.Congr.* (London, 1948), pt. 9, pp. 62–5.

LEAKEY, L. S. B. (editor). 1952. *Proc. 1st Pan-African Congress on Prehistory.* Nairobi (1947), Oxford. 239 pp.

LEAKEY, L. S. B., EVERNDEN, J. F. & CURTIS, G. H. 1961. See refs. II.

LEAKEY, L. S. B. & SOLOMON, J. D. 1929. East African Archaeology. *Nature, Lond.*, vol. 124, p. 9.

LEAKEY, L. S. B. *et al.* 1933. The Oldoway Human Skeleton, *Nature,Lond.*, vol. 131. pp. 397–8.

LECOINTRE, G. 1952. Recherches sur le Néogène et le Quaternaire marins de la côte atlantique du Maroc. Vol. I Stratigraphie. Vol II Paléontologie. *Mém.Serv.Géol.Maroc.*, no. 99.

MARTIN, P. S. & GRAY, J. 1962. Pollen Analysis and the Cenozoic. *Science*, vol. 137, pp. 103–11.

MASON, R. J., BRINK, A. B. A. & KNIGHT, K. 1959. Pleistocene Climatic Significance of Calcretes and Ferricretes. *Nature, Lond.*, vol. 184, p. 568.

MIRIGLIANO, G. 1953. La macrofauna del Tirreniana di Gallipoli (Lecce). *Boll.Zool.*, vol. 20, pt. 2 (1953), pp. 115–22.

MITCHELL, G. F. 1951. Studies in Irish Quaternary Deposits: No. 7. *Proc.Roy.Irish.Acad.*, (B), vol. 53, no. 11, pp. 111–206.

— 1954. Praeger's Contribution to Irish Quaternary Geology. *Irish Nat.J.* vol. 11, no. 6, pp. 172–5.

DE MORTILLET, G. and A. 1900. *Le Prèhistorique. Origine et Antiquité de L'Homme.* 3rd edn. Paris. 709 pp.

MOVIUS, H. L. 1960. Radiocarbon dates and Upper Palaeolithic Archaeology in Central and Western Europe. *Current Anthropology*, 1, pp. 355–91.

1963. L'Age du Perigordien, de l'Aurignacien et du proto-Magdalenien en France sur la Base des datations au Carbone 14, *Bull.Soc.Meridionale de Spél. et de Préhist.*, nos. 6–9, pp. 132–42.

MÜLLER-BECK, H. 1959. Bemerkungen zur Stratigraphie des mitteleuropäischen Jungpleistozäns. *Eiszeitalter Gegenw.*, vol. 10, pp. 144–60.

NAIRN, A. E. M. (editor). 1961. *Descriptive Palaeoclimatology.* New York. 380 pp.

NAIRN, A. E. M. & THORLEY, N. 1961. The Application of Geophysics to Palaeoclimatology. In *Descriptive Palaeoclimatology* (ed. by A. E. M. Nairn). pp. 156–82. New York.

NANGERONI, G. 1950. Tre Nuovi Lembi di Morenico Günz nel Prealpi Lombarde. *Inst.Lombardo di Sci. e Lett.*, vol. 83, pp. 1–8.

NILSSON, E. 1952. Pleistocene climatic changes in E. Africa. *Proc. 1st Pan-Afr.Congr. on Prehist.* (1947). Oxford. pp. 345–55.

1960. Södra Sverige i senglacial tid. *Geol.Fören.Stockh.* Förh. vol. 82, pt. 1, pp. 134–149.

NORDMANN, V. 1928. La Position stratigraphique des Dépôts d'Eem. *Danm.Geol.Unders.* (2), no. 47, 81 pp.

OAKLEY, K. P. 1953. Dating Fossil Human Remains. In *Anthropology Today* (edited by A. L. Kroeber), pp. 43–56. Chicago.

1954. Study Tour of Early Hominid Sites in Southern Africa, 1953. *S.Afr.Arch.Bull.*, vol. 9, pp. 75–87.

1961 *Man, the Tool-Maker.* 5th edn. *Brit.Mus.(Nat.Hist.)*, London. 98 pp.

1963. Analytical Methods of Dating Bones. In *Science in Archaelogy* (edited by D. R. Brothwell & E. S. Higgs). pp. 24–34. London.

1963a. Fluorine, Uranium and Nitrogen Dating of Bone. In *The Scientist and Archaeology* (edited by E. Pyddoke). London. pp. 111–119.

1963b. Note on the Antiquity of Halling Man, in Kerney, M. P. Late Glacial Deposits on the Chalk of South East England. *Phil.Trans.*, B, vol. 246, pp. 203–254.

1964. The Problem of Man's Antiquity. *Bull.Brit.Mus.* (*Nat.Hist.*) Geol., vol. 9, no. 5, 155 pp.

OAKLEY, K. P. & HOWELLS, W. W. 1961. Age of the Skeleton

from the Lagow Sand-pit, Texas. *Amer.Antiquity*, vol. 26, no. 4, pp. 543–5.

OAKLEY, K. P. & MONTAGU, M. F. A. 1949. A reconsideration of the Galley Hill skeleton. *Bull.Brit.Mus.* (*Nat.Hist.*) Geol., vol. 1, no. 2, pp. 25–48.

PATERSON, T. 1940. The effects of frost action and solifluxion around Baffin Bay and in the Cambridge district. *Quart.J. Geol.Soc.Lond.*, vol. 96, pp. 99–130.

PEABODY, F. E. 1954. Travertines and cave deposits of the Kaap escarpment of South Africa, and the type locality of *Australopithecus africanus* Dart. *Bull.Geol.Soc.Amer.*, vol. 65, pp. 671–706.

PENCK, A. & BRÜCKNER, E. 1909. *Die Alpen im Eiszeitalter*, Leipzig. 1189 pp.

POSNANSKY, M. 1961. Iron Age in East and Central Africa – points of comparison. *S.Afr.Arch.Bull.*, vol. 16, pp. 134–6.

PRAEGER, R. LL. 1892. Report on the Estuarine Clays in the North-East of Ireland. *Proc.Roy.Irish.Acad.* (3), vol. 2, pp. 212–89.

ROSHOLT, J. N. & ANTAL, P. S. 1961. Absolute dating of deep-sea sediments by the Pa ^{231}/Th ^{230} method. *J.Geol.* vol. 62, pp. 162–85.

   1963. Evaluation of the Pa ^{231}/U-Th ^{230} U method for dating Pleistocene Carbonate rocks, *U.S.Geol.Surv.Prof.Pap.* 450–E, pp. E108–11.

RUSSELL, I. C. 1887. Quaternary history of Mono Valley, California. *U.S.Geol.Surv.8th Ann.Rep.* (1886–87), pt. 1, pp. 261–394.

SERNANDER, R. 1910. The Swedish Peat Bogs as Evidence of Post-Glacial Changes of Climate. *Int.Geol.Cong.*, XIe Sess. Stockholm. Ib *Die Veränderung des Klimas.* pp. 197–246.

SIMPSON, G. C. 1930. The Climate during the Pleistocene Period. *Proc.Roy.Soc.Edinb.*, vol. 50, pp. 262–96.

   1934. World Climate during the Quaternary Period. *Quart.J.Roy.Met.Soc.*, vol. 60, 425–78.

   1957. Further Studies in World Climate. *Quart.J.Roy. Met.Soc.*, vol. 83, pp. 459–85.

SOERGEL, W. 1928. Das geologische Alter des *Homo heidelbergensis. Palaont.Z.*, vol. 10, pp. 217–33.

SOLOMON, J. D. 1939. The Pleistocene Succession in Uganda.

In O'Brien, T. P., *The Prehistory of Uganda Protectorate*. Cambridge. pp. 15–50.

SUTCLIFFE, A. J. 1960. Joint Mitnor Cave, Buckfastleigh. *Trans.Nat.Hist.Soc.*, Torquay, vol. 13, pt.1, pp. 17–20.

1964. The Mammalian Fauna in The Swanscombe Skull (edited by C. D. Ovey). *Roy.anthrop.Inst.occ.Pap.*, no. 20, pp. 87–111.

TAUBER, H. & DE VRIES, H. 1958. Radiocarbon measurements of Würm interstadial samples from Jutland. *Eiszeitalter Gegenw.*, vol. 9, pp. 69–74.

TOBIAS, P. V. 1962. Early Members of the Genus *Homo* in Africa, *in* G. Kurth ed. *Evolution und Hominisation*, Stuttgart. pp. 191–204.

TYLOR, A. 1868. On the formation of Deltas; and on the evidence and Cause of great Changes in the Sea-level during the Glacial Period. *Geol.Mag.*, vol. 5, pp. 576–7.

UREY, H. C. 1947. The thermodynamic properties of isotopic substances. *J.Chem.Soc.*, pp. 562–81.

VAUFREY, R. 1955. See Refs to Part II.

VENZO, S. 1955. Le attuali conoscenze sul Pleistocene Lombardo con particolare riguardo al Bergamasco. *Atti.Soc.Ital. Sci.Nat.*, vol. 94, no. 2, pp. 155–200.

VIERKE, M. 1937. Die ostpommerschen Bändertone als Zeitmarken und Klimazeugen. *Abh.geol.-palaeont.Inst. Greifswald*, vol. 18, pp. 1–34.

VAN DER VLERK, I. M. 1953. The Stratigraphy of the Pleistocene of the Netherlands. *Proc. Koninckl.Nederl.Akademie van Wetenschappen*, Amsterdam. ser. B., vol. 56, no. I, pp. 34–44.

1955. The significance of Interglacials for the stratigraphy of the Pleistocene. *Quaternaria*, vol. 2, pp. 35–9.

1957. Pleistocene correlations between the Netherlands and adjacent areas: Conclusions. *Geol. en Mijnb.*, (NS), vol. 19, pp. 310–12.

1959. Problems and Principles of Tertiary and Quaternary Stratigraphy. *Quart.J.Geol.Soc.Lond.*, vol. 115, pp. 56–62.

VAN DER VLERK, I. M. & FLORSCHÜTZ, F. 1950. *Nederland in het Ijstijdvak*. Utrecht. 287 pp.

1953. The palaeontological base of the sub-division of the Pleistocene in the Netherlands. *Vern. Akad.Wet.Amst.*, (1), vol. 20, no. 2, pp. 1–58.

VAN DER VLERK, I. M. *et al.* 1957. Pleistocene correlations between the Netherlands and adjacent areas: A Symposium. *Geol.en Mijnb.*, (N.S.), vol. 19, pp. 230–312.

DE VRIES, H. 1958. Radiocarbon Dates for upper Eem and Würm-interstadial samples. *Eiszeitalter Gegenw.*, vol. 9, pp. 10–17.

DE VRIES, H. & OAKLEY, K. P. 1959. Radiocarbon Dating of the Piltdown Skull and Jaw, *Nature,Lond.*, vol. 184, pp. 224–6.

WARREN, S. H. 1948. The Crag Platform, its Geology and Archaeological Problem. *S.E.Nat&Antiq.*, vol. 53, pp. 48–52.

WAYLAND, E. J. 1929. African pluvial periods. *Nature,Lond.*, vol. 123, p. 607.

1931. Pleistocene pluvial periods in Uganda. *Rep.Brit. Assoc.*, (1930), pp. 385–6.

1934. Rifts, Rivers, Rains and Early Man in Uganda. *J.Roy.anthrop.Inst.*, vol. 64, pp. 333–52.

WELLS, L. H. 1959. A reconsideration of the Tilbury Fossil skeleton, *Proc.Univ.Bristol Spel.Soc.*, vol. 8, pp. 179–85.

WELTEN, M. 1944. Pollenanalytische, stratigraphische und geochronologische Untersuchungen aus dem Faulenseemoos bei Spiez. *Veröff.Geobot.Inst.Rübel*, vol. 21, 201 pp.

WEST, R. G. 1955. The Glaciations and Interglacials of East Anglia. *Quaternaria*, vol. 2, pp. 45–50.

1956. The Quaternary deposits at Hoxne, Suffolk, *Phil. Trans.Roy.Soc.Lond.* (B), vol. 239, pp. 265–365.

1957. Interglacial deposits at Bobbitshole, Ipswich, *Phil.Trans.Roy.Soc.,Lond.*(B), vol. 241, no. 676, pp. 1–31.

1958. The Pleistocene Epoch in East Anglia, *J.Glac.*, Cambridge, vol. 3, no. 23, pp. 211–16.

1960. The Ice Age. *The Advancement of Science*, vol. 16, no. 64, pp. 309–440.

1963. Problems of the British Quaternary, *Proc.Geol.Ass. Lond.*, vol. 74, 2, pp. 147–86.

WOLDSTEDT, P. 1950. Thomson's pollen-diagram of the Cromer Forest Bed. *Nature,Lond.*, vol. 165, p. 1002.

1954. *Das Eiszeitalter*. vol. 1, 2nd edn. Stuttgart. 374 pp.

1956. Uber die Gliederung der Würm-Eiszeit und die Stellung der Löss in ihr., *Eiszeit u.Gegenw.*, vol. 7, pp. 78–86.

1958. *Das Eiszeitalter*, vol. 2, 2nd edn. Stuttgart. 438 pp.

1960. Die Letzte Eiszeit in Nordamerika und Europa. *Eiszeit. u.Gegenw.* vol. 11, pp. 148–165.

WOOLDRIDGE, S. W. 1958. Some Aspects of the Physiography of the Thames Valley in Relation to the Ice Age and Early Man. *Proc.Prehist.Soc.* (NS), vol. 23, (1957), pp. 1–19.

WRIGHT, H. E. 1957. The Late-Glacial Chronology of Europe. *Amer.J.Sci.*, vol. 255, pp. 447–60.

WRIGHT, W. B. 1937. *The Quaternary Ice Age.* 2nd edn., London. 478 pp.

ZAGWIJN, W. H. 1957. Vegetation, Climate and Time Correlations in the Early Pleistocene of Europe. *Geol.en Mijnb.*, (NS), vol. 19, pp. 233–44.

ZAGWIJN, W. H. & ZONNEVELD, J. I. S. 1956. The Interglacial at Westerhoven. *Geol.en Mijnb.*, (NS), vol. 18, pp. 37–46.

ZEUNER, F. E. 1944. *Homo sapiens* in Australia contemporary with *Homo neanderthalensis* in Europe, *Nature,Lond.*, vol. 153, p. 622.

1946. *Dating the Past.* 1st edn., London. 444 pp.

1954. Riss or Würm? *Eiszeit u.Gegenw.*, vol. 4/5, pp. 98–105.

1959. *Dating the Past.* 4th edn. London. 516 pp.

1959a. *The Pleistocene Period.* 2nd edn., London. 447 pp.

1961. Faunal Evidence for Pleistocene Climates. *Ann. New York.Acad.Sci.*, vol. 95, pp. 502–7.

van ZINDEREN BAKKER, E. M. 1957. A Pollen Analytical Investigation of the Florisbad Deposits (South Africa). *Proc. Third Pan-Afr.Congr.Prehist.*, (1955). London. pp. 56–67.

1962. Carbon-14 Dates. *Current Anthropology*, vol. 3, p. 218.

Part Two

Archaeological Dating

Chapter 1

General

ARCHAEOLOGICAL DATING – 'the use of implements as zone fossils' – has been criticized and neglected by some students of the Pleistocene on the grounds that palaeolithic cultures have usually been relatively dated in the first place on the basis of geological (or palaeontological) evidence, and that it is therefore illogical to use cultural material in turn to date fossils or geological deposits. To the present author this seems to involve no more 'circular reasoning' than the time-honoured method of dating geological formations by their contained fossils, which was introduced by William Smith the Father of English Geology. As with fossils, so with artifacts, there are bound to be occasional discoveries proving the unexpectedly early appearance or late survival of a particular type; but by and large both have invaluable applications in the relative dating of Quaternary deposits. Indeed, at certain levels and in some regions Stone Age industries provide time-lines that would otherwise be lacking. By using the spread of palaeolithic traditions as time-lines it can be shown that there is probably no simple equivalence between the African pluvials and European glacials, and moreover that the onset and cessation of pluvial conditions were almost certainly not synchronous throughout the Continent.

Chapter 2

Palaeolithic Cultures in Europe and the Near East

THE STANDARD SUCCESSION of palaeolithic cultures was first worked out in France and bordering countries, largely as a result of researches carried out by archaeologists and stratigraphers working on river and cave deposits. The author has surveyed elsewhere the development of these studies during the second half of the last century (Oakley, 1964). In broad outline the cultural sequence in France may be set out as in the table on p. 142, which uses Breuil's terminology (with slight modification) and gives the more or less conventional correlation with the Alpine Glacial sequence.

The earliest generally accepted flint industry in France is the *Abbevillian*, found *in situ* in the 45-m terrace of the Somme at Abbeville in the Somme Valley. This is the most primitive phase of the Chelles-Acheul hand-axe tradition of African origin, in which the flaking is by free-swinging stone technique and therefore appears very coarse (Fig. 20*). The term *Chellean* has been widely[1] used for the earliest stage of the hand-axe sequence, but in fact the artifacts contemporaneous with the gravels at the type-locality (Chelles-sur-Marne) belong to the beginning of the more developed or Acheulian stage, in which the coarse stone-on-stone flaking has been followed by flatter flaking produced by the use of the cylindrical hammer[2] technique or indirect percussion on a boulder.

Where Chellean is still used for the equivalent of the Abbevillian, it may be better to qualify it (*eg* 'East African Chellean' = Abbevillian).

* Stone artifacts are all of flint or chert unless otherwise stated.

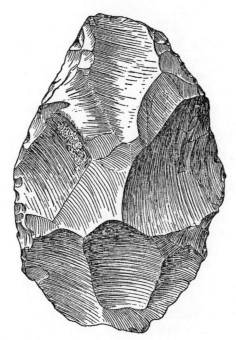

Figure 20 Abbevillian-type hand-axe from gravels at Chelles-sur-Marne. *After Breuil.* ($\frac{2}{3}$).

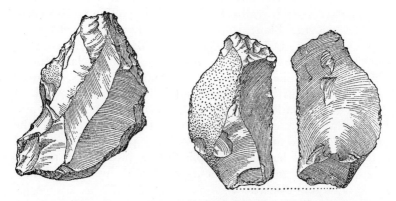

Figure 21 Clactonian flake-tools from Lower Gravels 100 ft terrace of Thames, Swanscombe, Kent (*left:* derivative; *right:* contemporaneous). *British Museum* (*Natural History*) afterwards abbreviated to *B.M.N.H.* ($\frac{1}{2}$).

The oldest artifacts in Britain are *Clactonian*[3] artifacts (Fig. 21) scratched by late Mindelian solifluxion and occurring derived (Fig. 21 left) in the Swanscombe gravels. On the basis of African studies it seems probable that the first palaeolithic tradition to reach Western Europe would have led to the fabrication of 'pebble-tools' out of the local flint-nodules. One facies of such an industry would have been 'Abbevillian' hand-axes, another facies would have been 'Clactonian' chopping- and flake-tools. Although African pebble-tool culture (Oldowan) has not been recorded in Europe, it *has* been recognized in the Near East (Stekelis *et al.*, 1960). The Buda flake-and-pebble-tool industry in Hungary is remarkably similar to the Clactonian, but whether linked to the Oldowan or to the Asiatic chopper-tool complex or was an independent development is not resolved (Kretzoi and Vértes, 1965).

The subdivision of the *Acheulian* culture (Figs. 22, 23) into seven individual stages in the Somme Valley was based partly on typology, but largely on the inferred relative ages of the deposits containing particular assemblages of artifacts. It is very doubtful if these numbered stages can be used reliably for dating outside the Somme Valley (Breuil & Koslowski 1931; Bordes, 1952, 1954), where typologically only three divisions are distinguishable: Lower, Middle and Upper Acheulian (Bowler-Kelley, 1937 p. 6). Important assemblages and sequences of Acheulian industries have been studied in the Thames Valley (Wymer, 1964); Torralba, Spain (F. C. Howell in press); Torre in Pietra, Rome (Blanc, 1954); and in the Levant (Stekelis, 1960, Neuville, 1931, Garrod *in* Garrod and Bate, 1937).

The Abbé Breuil, to whom we owe the detailed classification of the palaeolithic industries in the Somme terraces, pictured the flake-industries and hand-axe industries as the work of different populations, living respectively to the north-east and to south-west, and overlapping in Northern France, which he saw as occupied mainly by flake-industry people during glacial stages and by hand-axe people during interglacial periods. Although there may be elements of truth in this conception, it is now largely discarded.

The *Levalloisian* industries (Fig. 25) are of more complex origin. It seems that some Acheulian groups, towards the end of Mindel–Riss times (for example at Cagny during the Pre-Riss

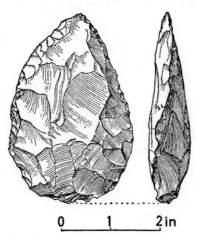

0   1   2in

Figure 22 Ovate hand-axe: Acheulian IV, *argile rouge* on 30-m terrace.
St Acheul, Somme Valley.
B.M.N.H. (½).

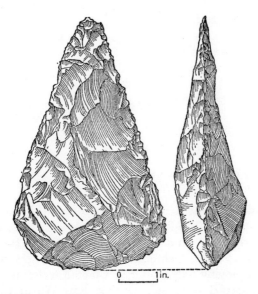

0   1in.

Figure 23 Middle Acheulian hand-axe, Skull Layer, Middle Gravels 100 ft
terrace, Swanscombe.
B.M.N.H.

PALAEOLITHIC SUCCESSION IN FRANCE AND BRITAIN

AURIGNACIAN *sensu lots*			*Probable Correlation with Alpine Sequence* *
UPPER PALAEOLITHIC		Magdalenian	Würm III Glacial
		Solutrean	Würm II/III
		Gravettian	Interstadial
		AURIGNACIAN *sensu stricto*	Würm II Glacial
		Chatelperronian replacing	Würm I/II
		Mousterian	Interstadial
		Main MOUSTERIAN, and	Würm I Glacial
		Upper LEVALLOISIAN	
MIDDLE PALAEOLITHIC		Early MOUSTERIAN, also	
		Middle LEVALLOISIAN,	Riss–Würm
		Tayacian and Micoquian (=	Interglacial
		Acheulian VI, VII)	
		ACHEULIAN V, Tayacian,	Riss II glacial
		High Lodge† Clactonian	Riss I/II
		and	Interstadial
		Lower Levallioisian	Riss I glacial
LOWER PALAEOLITHIC		ACHEULIAN III/IV and Proto-	Pre-Riss cold
		Levalloisian	phase
		ACHEULIAN III Also	⎱ Mindel–Riss
		CLACTONIAN	⎰ Interglacial
		ACHEULIAN I–II facies	
			Mindel II Glacial
		'ABBEVILLIAN' = facies of early	Mindel I/II
		CLACTONIAN?	Interstadial

* See p. 67 for north-west European terminology.
† Fig. 24. Compare Jabrudian of south-west Asia, Fig. 29.

phase), adopted the Levallois technique, which one might briefly describe as 'pre-fabricating flake-tools before detaching them from the core'. In the succeeding Riss period some Acheulian groups used this technique extensively, others did not use it at all, employing only primitive Clacton technique to obtain flakes for special purposes. During Riss–Würm times some groups, perhaps in origin 'Acheulian', ceased making hand-axes and specialized in the production of flake-blades (Levalloisian

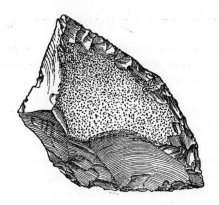

Figure 24 Acheulio-Clactonian scraper, High Lodge, Mildenhall, Suffolk. *B.M.N.H.* (½).

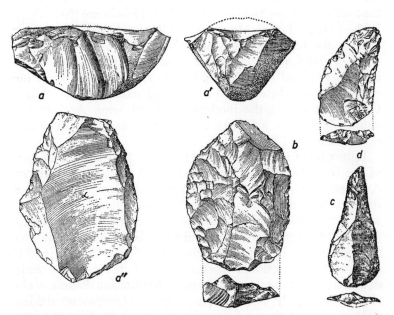

Figure 25 Levalloisian artifacts: *a, b, c,* from the Thames Valley; *d,* from the Somme Valley. *B.M.N.H.* (⅓).

a, a', a" tortoise-core (3 views), from below Coombe Rock, Northfleet, Kent; *b* flake with faceted striking platform, similar to the one struck from area *a,* on the core, from the same site; *c* pointed flake-tool from a 'floor' in the Crayford brickearths; *d* knife-like flake-tool from loess on 10-m terrace, Montières (Somme).

III–IV). The true Mousterian industries were probably made by people of different origin, who also adopted the Levallois technique. At one time archaeologists used Levalloisian and Mousterian almost synonymously, but in fact some Mousterian industries are entirely non-Levalloisian, showing exclusive use of the simpler Clacton technique of striking flakes. Acheulian and contemporaneous industries are classified as Lower Palaeolithic, and the Mousterian complex of industries as Middle Palaeolithic, but this differentiation is not clear-cut.

The recognition of regional variants in Middle and Upper Palaeolithic culture groups and their re-definition on the basis of larger assemblages excavated on a more precise strati-graphical basis has proved most important from the point of view of their use in dating.

Thus, whereas, the term Mousterian has been applied in the past on a very crude typological basis to various flake industries, ranging in age from Mindel–Riss to Post-Pleistocene (Neolithic), in the restricted sense Mousterian culture only lasted from Late Riss to the beginning of Main Würm. Again, so long as the term *Aurignacian* was used in a loose sense it included blade industries spread over a considerable range of time from the end of the Last Interglacial to the final stadium of the Würm Glaciation; but in the modern restricted sense Aurignacian culture had quite a limited time-range throughout its fairly extensive area of distribution.

Industries of the MOUSTERIAN[4] COMPLEX associated with men of the Neanderthal species and confined to Europe, Western Asia and North Africa, have been studied in recent years both statistically and according to their topographical distribution with some very interesting results.[5] Industries in this complex (Figs. 26, 30) can be most conveniently classified on the basis of three criteria: whether they include hand-axes (*bifaces*) (and if so in what proportion); whether utilized flakes were mainly struck from discoidal cores (typical Mousterian flaking technique) or mainly from prepared cores (*Levalloisian*[6] flaking technique), and on the frequency of flakes with faceted butts. Bordes and Bourgon, who used these criteria statistically in 1951, diagnosed the *Typical Mousterian* as an industry without bifaces (or with very few), with more than 45 per cent of the flakes showing faceted butts and more than 25 per cent struck in the Levalloisian technique. They differentiated the Mousterian of the La Quina type, for which they proposed the name *Charentian*,[7] classifying this as another industry without hand-axes, but in which the majority of the flakes had plain striking platforms and in which the use of Levalloisian technique was very infrequent.

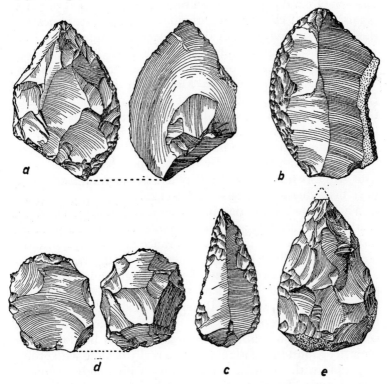

Figure 26 Mousterian flint artifacts from the type-site, Le Moustier rock shelter, Dordogne.
a, b side-scrapers (*racloirs*); *c* point; *d* disc-core; *e* biface.
B.M.N.H. ($\frac{1}{2}$).

Among the industries of the Mousterian Complex distinguished by the presence of hand-axes, these authors included the *Micoquian*,[8] which had previously been counted as a form of Late Acheulian. It is characterized by pointed plano-convex bifaces, often of superbly fine workmanship. In the palaeolithic sequence in the Somme and Seine terraces, some Micoquian industries include flakes of Levalloisian facies, but in other Micoquian industries including that of the type locality the associated flakes are of Clactonian facies.[9]

Quite distinct from the Micoquian are the so-called Mousterian industries of Acheulian tradition in which there are small triangular or heart-shaped (cordiform) bifaces. The presence or absence of hand-axes in Mousterian industries was at one time regarded as of chronological significance, but this appears to have been a survival from the nineteenth century concept of straight-line cultural evolution in which Acheulian biface-culture supposedly developed into the Mousterian flake-culture.

McBurney's study of the Mousterian industries showed (McBurney, 1950a) that the sites with hand-axes are mainly confined to the maritime lowlands of western Europe, while in the hilly and mountainous districts of the interior, where ice-age conditions must have been more severe, the industries were different in character and for the most part lacked hand-axes. This suggests that regional differences between industries may have been due to environmental factors.

Whereas the Mousterian industries found in the cave sites of south-west France are mainly non-Levalloisian, the contemporaneous industries in northern France are mainly Levalloisian. This may have reflected differences in the raw material available in the two regions, for the large nodules of good quality flint in the north lend themselves to the Levalloisian flaking technique, whereas the smaller nodules of cherty flint found in the Dordogne are more readily worked into discoid cores from which centrally-directed flakes can be removed in typically Mousterian fashion. Are we really dealing with groups of people with different traditions, or with manifestations of several types of activity carried out by groups with the same tradition but in varying circumstances? We cannot be sure. Certainly it has to be borne in mind that primitive hunting peoples travel considerable distances every year to maintain food supplies or in search of essential raw materials. It must be emphasized again that one can only establish the cultural identity of widely separated industries if the assemblages of artifacts are sufficiently large to allow detailed comparison. The occurrence of a particular technique in two industries is insufficient evidence that they were produced by people of the same tradition or culture. For example, the simple Clacton technique of flaking has been used in almost all periods from Pre-Abbevillian to Neolithic. Even the more elaborate Levalloisian technique of preparing the core in readiness for detachment of flakes or flake-blades has been used by quite unconnected peoples and at various periods. It was first used by the Acheulian hand-axe people of southern Africa. Possibly the later Mousterian populations of Europe learnt this technique through diffusion of the idea from Africa. This is difficult to prove, but if true the first use of Levalloisian technique might serve as an approximate time-line connecting the continents.

A number of archaeologists (eg, Movius, 1953, pp. 164–6) have held the view that the Levallois-type flake-blades in the Mindel–Riss, Riss and Riss–Würm deposits of Europe were not the work of Mousterian groups but of Acheulian hand-axe people, in which case they were presumably manifestations of some specialized activity related to particular environmental conditions. This is quite probably the explanation of the Proto-Levalloisian artifacts (Bordes, 1950) associated with Acheulian bifaces in the deposits dated as Pre-Riss in the Somme Valley (see p. 109, note 63), but the later occurrences can equally well be regarded as variant Mousterian industries with or without hand-axes. Bordes and Bourgon, for example, classified the Levalloisian industries in the Somme terraces as Mousterian of Levalloisian facies.

Among the variants of Mousterian discovered in recent years (Figs. 27, 28) are the *Moustérien denticulé* (Bordes & Bourgon, 1951, p. 23), which has been recognized in south-west France, Italy and North Africa; the *Micro-Mousterian*,[10] found in France, Italy, Montenegro, North Africa and Syria; and the *Pontinian*,[11] another miniature Mousterian industry in which the tools are made on small pebbles. The last is a geographical variant restricted to certain districts in Italy and undoubtedly reflecting an adaptation to the only easily available raw material. The Micro-Mousterian and the Denticulate Mousterian may be manifestations of specialized activities, varying in date from site to site, but it is equally possible that they reflect diffusions of culture, or migrations of specialized artificers, in which case they will be most valuable dating lines in connection with the chronology of the Neanderthal men.

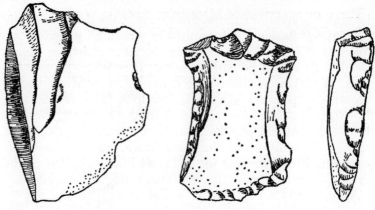

Figure 27 *Moustérien denticulé*, Grotta S. Bernardino, Italy.
l flint flake with burin facets; *r* quadrangular scraper.
After P. Leonardi. (⅔).

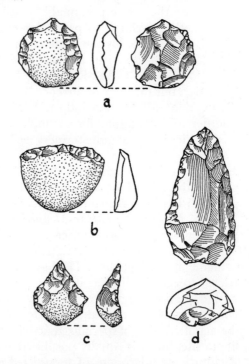

Figure 28 Pontinian artifacts from sites in Italy.
a, b from Agro Pontino, Italy; *c, d* from Grotta del Fossellone, Circeo.
After M. Taschini. (⅔).

There were survivals of Mousterian tradition in some mountainous regions, for example the so-called Alpine Palaeolithic culture in Austria and Switzerland (Tschumi, 1949).[12]

In the east of Europe from the German highlands, through Hungary, Northern Greece (Higgs, 1963) and USSR there are Mousterian industries containing a substantial proportion of bifacial leaf-shaped artifacts. This Eastern Mousterian culture appears to have contributed to the origin of the Szeletian (p. 160).

During the 1930s, excavations at Jabrud in Syria led Dr Alfred Rust (1950) to discover a number of cultural horizons below the typical Levalloiso–Mousterian: there were layers containing mainly flake tools struck in Clacton fashion, alternating with layers containing similar flakes associated with hand-axes (bifaces). He named the flake-industry *Jabrudian*, and the alternating layers with bifaces Acheulio-Jabrudian. Subsequently it became clear that the Jabrudian industry occurred at a number of sites in the Middle East, and that it always comprised numerous elaborately trimmed scrapers made on thick flakes with plain striking platform, very similar to the Charentian of France, and associated with variable numbers of small bifaces. In fact this was the industry (Fig. 29) which had previously been called Final Acheulian in the Near East (*eg* Layer E in the Mount Carmel Cave named et-Tabun).

We should note here that the *Tayacian*[13] industries (Fig. 30) have been included by Bordes and Bourgon within the Mousterian Complex. They classified them under the heading of Mousterian without hand-axes, but characterized by *non-*Levalloisian flakes mainly of the non-faceted type. It appears to be not very well known[14] that the essential feature of Levalloisian technique is preparation of the *face* of the core, and that faceting of the striking platform although common in Levalloisian industries is by no means confined to them. Moreover, a substantial percentage of typical Levalloisian flakes have plain striking-platforms (Fig. 31).

We must briefly take into account an industry known as *Emiran*[15] found at the top of the Middle Palaeolithic zone at a number of cave and rock-shelter sites in Palestine and Lebanon, and described as transitional between Mousterian and Aurignacian. The industry is predominantly Mousterian in facies

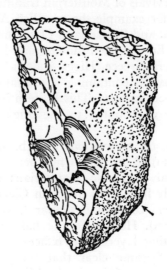

Figure 29 Jabrudian flake-scraper from Layer Ea, Tabun Cave. *After Garrod and Bate*, 1937. (⅔).

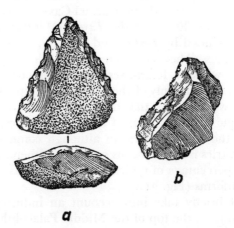

Figure 30 Tayacian flake-tools: *a* 'proto-Mousterian' point, Combe Capelle, Dordogne; *b* typical utilized Tayacian flake, La Micoque, Tayac. *B.M.N.H.* (½).

but includes an unusually high proportion of end-scrapers, nearly 50 per cent of which are on punched blades. Burins, on the other hand, are rare. The significance of the expression punched–blade and the term burin will become evident as we proceed. The implement peculiar to the Emiran industry, the type-fossil so to say, is a small point with characteristic trimming at the base on both faces, and signs of use at both ends. This Emiran point was rare, even at the type locality (Fig. 32).

Figure 31 Flake of '*le type Levallois*' from Oise Dept., France. The face of the flake was prepared on the core, yet the butt was not faceted in this case. *After G. de Mortillet.* ($\frac{1}{2}$).

For radiocarbon dating of Middle Palaeolithic cultures see Chart B.

THE UPPER PALAEOLITHIC INDUSTRIES
These industries, which in many parts of Europe and Western Asia abruptly succeeded the Middle Palaeolithic or Mousterian Complex, show considerable regional variation, but also a number of important features in common. The characteristic stone tools (mainly flint) were made on narrow parallel-sided *blades* (Fig. 33) struck from cores by a new technique, apparently involving the use of hammer and punch. The tools usually included specialized implements known as *burins* or gravers

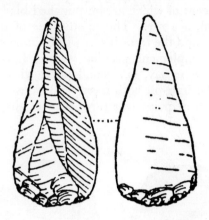

Figure 32 Emiran point from the type-site. *After Garrod.* ($\frac{1}{1}$).

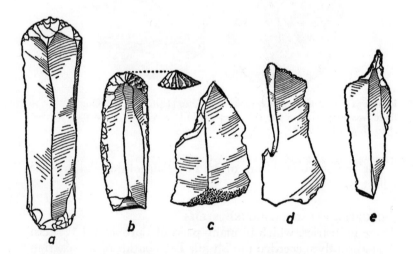

Figure 33 Upper Palaeolithic blade-tools: *c* Aurignacian; *d* Gravettian; *b* & *e* Solutrean; *a* Magdalenian; End-scrapers *a* & *b*; burins *c* & *d*; piercer *e*. *B.M.N.H.* ($\frac{2}{3}$).

which were used for working bone, antler, ivory and occasionally soft stone, and no doubt wood. A typical burin (Fig. 34) is a flint blade with margins sliced obliquely at one end so that they meet to form a narrow chisel edge. However, this is only one form, and over 25 specialized types of burin were devised by the Upper Palaeolithic peoples, who were much more inventive than their predecessors, making a wide range of tools and weapons involving several new techniques. They mastered the working of bone, antler, and ivory of which they made extensive use. They also made considerable use of red ochre, evidently for ceremonial purposes.

Owing to the terminology of palaeolithic archaeology being developed first in Europe, the divisions Lower, Middle and

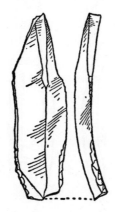

Figure 34 Typical burin from the Magdalenian type-site, La Madeleine rock-shelter.
B.M.N.H. (⅖).

Upper Palaeolithic are not easily applied in Africa and Asia (except on the fringes of Europe), and it is therefore important to remember that the term Upper Palaeolithic almost invariably implies a blade-and-burin culture. The contemporaneous industries in the greater part of Asia and Africa are called Late Palaeolithic to avoid confusion.

Interstratified with the Jabrudian at the type-locality in Syria, Rust (1950) discovered two horizons containing a blade-industry of Upper Palaeolithic type. This *Pre-Aurignacian* (now known as Amudian) is the oldest known manifestation

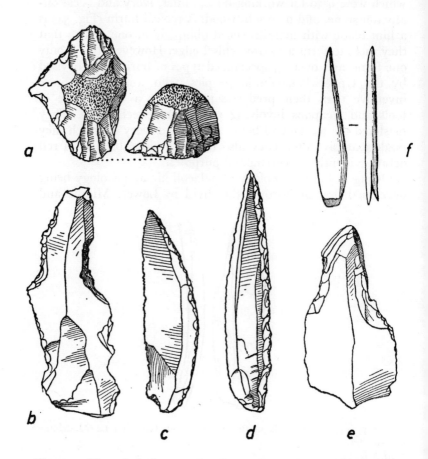

Figure 35 The principal types of artifact which distinguish the sub-divisions of the Aurignacian *sl* into Chatelperronian, Aurignacian *ss*, and Gravettian. From Western European cave-sites. *a* Nosed scraper, Aurignacian, Dordogne; *b* strangulated blade-scraper, Aurignacian, Dordogne; *c* Chatelperronian point from the type-site, Chatelperron, Allier; *d* Gravettian point, Dordogne; *e burin busqué*, Aurignacian-type, Vale of Clwyd; *f* split-base bone point, Aurignacian, Dordogne. *B.M.N.H.* ($\frac{3}{4}$).

of the culture-complex which in its full development at a considerably later date replaced the Mousterian: it has also been detected in the Jabrudian zone at et-Tabun and at Adlun between Sidon and Tyre where it was contemporaneous with the Late Monastirian sea-level (Garrod & Kirkbride, 1961, pp. 7–43). There is good evidence suggesting that the earliest blade-tool people continued for a time to live side by side with the Jabrudian, towards the end of the Riss–Würm Interglacial, but that both were temporarily replaced in the Levant by the last of the Mousterians during the Early Würm stage. The Emiran industry indicates that the two traditions hybridized in Palestine and Lebanon before the blade tradition finally superseded the Mousterian. A blade-tool tradition with Emiran traits spread into North Africa (cf Dabba culture, p. 206).

According to the straightforward concept of the Upper Palaeolithic which held the field until the third decade of the present century, the Mousterian was succeeded by Aurignacian, Solutrean and Magdalenian cultures. The 'Aurignacian' was subdivided (Fig. 35) by the Abbé Breuil (1912) on the basis of the leading tool-types as follows:

Upper Aurignacian: straight pointed blades with blunted back margin essentially like the blade of a pen-knife: called Gravette Points (Fig. 35d); tanged-blades, shouldered points of the type named after the site at Font Robert, in the uppermost level (Fig. 36).

Middle Aurignacian: steep keeled and nosed scrapers made from small cores, having a characteristic fluted appearance (Fig. 35a); notched blades or strangulated scrapers (Fig. 35b), beaked burins or burins busqués (Fig. 35e) and split-base bone points (Fig. 35f).

Lower Aurignacian: curved pointed blades, with blunted back margin: called Chatelperron Points (Fig. 35c).

At a time when the only blade industries known in North Africa were the Capsian and Oranian, which somewhat resemble the Lower and Upper Aurignacian, the view was held that these represented waves of migration from across the Mediterranean, whereas the 'Middle' Aurignacian was indigenous and developed in Europe during an interval when communication with North Africa was cut. Later work showed that the North African blade industries were in fact very late (in part Post-Pleistocene),[16] and that there was really no acceptable evidence that the Upper Palaeolithic cultures of the Aurignacian family in Europe were of African origin.[17]

Further researches made it clear (Garrod, 1938) that the 'Aurignacian' represented a diversity of cultural strains grouped under one name. Three main traditions have now been recognized in this complex.

The tradition represented by the 'Lower Aurignacian' in the discarded nomenclature has been called *Chatelperronian* (Garrod, 1938, p. 19) by many authors or *Lower Perigordian* by others

Figure 36 Gravettian (Upper Perigordian) shouldered point of the Font-Robert type, Dordogne. *After Watson.*($\frac{1}{1}$).

(p. 159). This culture, characterized by curved blade points, was foreshadowed in Palestine during Jabrudian times by the 'Pre-Aurignacian', which has now been renamed *Amudian* (Fig. 37).[18] The true Chatelperronian tradition appears to have been developed in Western Europe by the earliest representatives of the newly emerged *Homo sapiens sapiens* (*eg* Combe Capelle man) during an early interstadial of the Würm Glaciation. One of the still unsolved problems of prehistory is the extent to which Chatelperronian culture was coexistant with Late Mousterian in Western Europe.

The second European Upper Palaeolithic tradition, *Aurignacian sensu stricto* (Garrod, 1938, p. 20) or Middle Aurignacian in the older nomenclature, probably had an eastern origin, but it did not stem from the Western Asiatic 'Aurignacian' as known in Palestine. Indeed the whole of the long 'Aurignacian' sequence in the Levant, now termed *Antelian* (Waechter, 1962, p. 498 & Ewing, 1947), appears to have been essentially local and unproductive of any far-travelling new tool traditions. A comparable local development of an Aurignacian-like culture occurred in Iraq and has been described under the name *Baradostian*.[19] The Aurignacian *ss* and the autochthonous eastern cultures Antelian and Baradostian probably evolved

Figure 37 Amudian blunted-back knife (*left*) and retouched blade (*right*) from Abri Zumoffen, Lebanon. *After Garrod and Kirkbride.* ($\frac{1}{1}$).

independently, although in origin they were contemporaneous. Elements of Aurignacian *ss* culture can be traced across Europe from the Middle East. Dr Garrod suggested that its origin might have been on the Iranian plateau 'or even further east'.

Carleton Coon's discovery of numerous fluted steep scrapers typical of true Aurignacian culture at a level dated as more than 34,000 years old in the Kara Kamar cave in Afghanistan (Coon, 1957, pp. 232–6) goes some way to support this idea. In the west, the oldest known Aurignacian industries are about 34,000 years old.

The third tradition, named *Gravettian*[20] (Upper Aurignacian of the older nomenclature), was evidently evolved from a Chatelperronian prototype. Since the oldest Upper Palaeolithic culture in South Russia is of this tradition, it has generally been assumed that the Gravettian originated in that part of the world. It is almost unrepresented in the Near East although the root-culture (Chatelperronian) shows some Gravettian traits. In Western Europe on the other hand, Gravettian culture abruptly superseded the Aurignacian *ss*, evidently as a result of a fresh wave of immigrants from the east.

Figure 38 Venus of Willendorf carved in limestone. *del R. Powers.* ($\frac{2}{3}$).

The Upper Gravettian is distinguished by shouldered points (Fig. 36) and by the occurrence of carved female statuettes of which the Venus of Willendorf is the best known example (Fig. 38). The fact that these statuettes are most abundant in South Russia, while occurring sporadically in the west (Garrod, 1938, p. 23), is some indication of the main direction from which the Gravettian people or their tradition spread. Some authorities stress the relative independence of the *Eastern Gravettian* or *Pavlovian* culture. In the Near East the Antelian culture evolved into the *Atlitian*.

As a result of his excavations in the Dordogne, Monsieur D. Peyrony came to the conclusion that the Chatelperronian and

Gravettian were phases of a single tradition which he named *Perigordian*,[21] and which he considered had evolved in France where it for the most part coexisted with the Aurignacian. This view has been systematized by Mme. de Sonneville-Bordes (1959) and followed by most workers in France, including Professor Movius. As all the blade-cultures have such an immensely wide distribution it seems more likely that, as Professor Garrod suggested, the French sequence is the result of successive migrations from the east superimposed on local developments.

Elements of the Perigordian and Aurignacian traditions can be recognized in the Far East; the Late Palaeolithic industries of North China include a certain proportion of blade-tools amongst pebble-tools and flake artifacts of a much more archaic and typically indigenous facies.[22]

According to the classic scheme evolved by French archaeologists in the last century the 'Aurignacian' was followed by the Solutrean and that in turn by the Magdalenian culture. *Solutrean* industries are distinguished by extensive and skilful use of pressure-flaking or indirect percussion in the trimming of blade-tools, and in the production of elegant flint weapon-heads, the best known being the bifacial *feuilles de laurier* (laurel-leaf spearheads) and the willow-leaf points (Fig. 39). As the Solutrean culture manifestly did not evolve from the preceding 'Aurignacian' (nor did it evolve into the overlying Magdalenian) it was presumed to represent yet another wave of immigrants from the east who occupied extensive areas of Western Europe for a while and then departed.

It has generally been supposed that the Solutrean culture originated in Hungary, and that its bearers spread westwards, gaining success as hunters through use of their newly invented projectile head, the pressure-flaked bifacial spearpoint. In many western areas Solutrean industries overlie the Gravettian. Their distribution is patchy: there is practically no evidence of Solutrean cultures east of the Dneister, or in Italy. There is certainly evidence suggesting that the technique which distinguishes it had very early roots in Central Europe, particularly in Hungary, where bifacial leaf-shaped points (Fig. 40) reminiscent of Solutrean forms have been discovered in Late Acheulian and Mousterian contexts. However, the view now generally held (Movius, 1953) is that these finds represent the beginnings of an independent tradition known as *Pre-Solutrean* or *Szeletian,* which arose in Central Europe and attained its

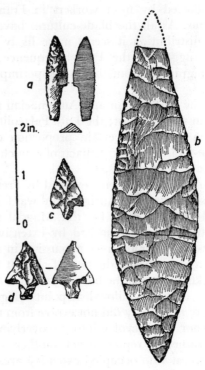

Figure 39 Solutrean (and Aterian) artifacts: *a* shouldered willow-leaf point, Solutrean, Dordogne; *b* Solutrean laurel-leaf blade from the type-site; *c* Solutrean arrow-head from Parpallō, Spain; *d* Aterian arrow-head from Morocco for comparison with *c*.
B.M.N.H. (½).

maximum development contemporaneously with the Chatelperronian and Aurignacian.

The discovery of the Szeletian, which at a number of sites in Czechoslovakia *underlies* the Gravettian, was primarily due to Lothar Zotz.[23] It is still not clear whether it has any direct connection with the much later classic Solutrean of the west (or even with the Proto-Solutrean which preceded the latter).

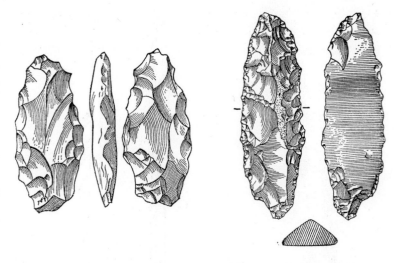

Figure 40 Szeletian and related blade industries: *a* bifacial leaf-shaped point, Szeleta, Hungary; *b* Jerzmanowice point from Ojcow Cave Poland. *a After Freund, b B.M.N.H. E. 202. (½).*

Other possibilities have had to be considered since Professor Pericot Garcia (1942) discovered in the cave of Parpalló in the Valencia province of Eastern Spain a Solutrean industry containing tanged projectile points (Fig. 39c) almost indistinguishable from the arrowheads of the *Aterian* culture in North Africa (see p. 204). The similarity of many Aterian artifacts to Solutrean forms is remarkable and it may be that there were occasional cultural connections in Late Pleistocene times between Morocco and Spain. However, the 'Solutrean' should probably no longer be viewed as a single invading culture, but rather as the manifestation of specialized ideas (Movius, 1953, p. 174) on the preparation of projectile points by pressure-flaking, which diffused widely and were taken up by several groups of Late Palaeolithic hunters having similar requirements (Smith, 1962). Thus, while Solutrean assemblages are useful for local or R.2 dating, they cannot be relied upon for distant correlation unless they are large enough to be identified on the basis of very extensive and detailed comparison.

During the final phases of the Upper Palaeolithic Age, there were very marked regional developments of culture in Western

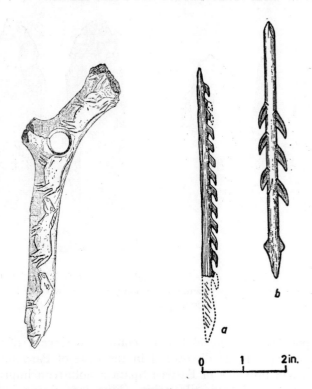

Magdalenian artifacts of reindeer antler:
Figure 41 (*left*) Engraved *bâton de commandement* from La Madeleine rock shelter, Dordogne. *B.M.N.H.* (⅓)
Figure 42 (*right*) barbed points, (a) from Bruniquel; (b) from La Madeleine. *B.M.N.H.*

Europe. The *Magdalenian*[24] is the best known of the later cultures, largely because of its outstanding artistic achievements in cave art and in the decoration of reindeer-antler artifacts (Fig. 41). The Magdalenians made extensive use of burins in their 'groove and splinter' technique devised mainly for making barbed points (Fig. 42). This culture was centred on France, but spread over Northern Spain, Belgium, Switzerland, South Germany and Western Czechoslovakia. That it probably originated as a branch of the Perigordian (Gravettian) culture which developed contemporaneously with the Solutrean in France is indicated by the presence of a *Proto-Magdalenian* industry immediately below the Solutrean at some sites in the

Dordogne. Other Epi-Gravettian cultures developed contemporaneously in various parts of Europe, notably the *Creswellian*[25] in Britain, the *Romanellian* and '*Grimaldian*'[26] in Italy, the *Hamburgian*[27] (and its successor the *Ahrensburgian*[28]) in north-west Germany. At about the same time a degenerate industry of Gravettian tradition was being fabricated in South Russia during the hunting of the last mammoths.[29] Shouldered and tanged points (Fig. 43) were very common in the Hamburgian and Ahrensburgian industries, and provide a link between them and the other blade-cultures of Central and Eastern Europe.

The local and regional sequences of Upper Palaeolithic cultures in Europe and the Near East have been established and correlated mainly through stratigraphical studies of cave deposits, loesses, glacial, periglacial, alluvial and colluvial formations, and raised beaches. Radiocarbon dating has recently thrown much new light on the chronology of these cultures (Movius, 1960). Their probable stratigraphical positions and chronometric ages are summarized in Chart C.

CAVE DEPOSITS AND OPEN SITES

As so many of the Middle and Upper Palaeolithic sequences have been established on the basis of the excavation of cave deposits, these perhaps call for a few explanatory comments. The deposits formed on the floors of caves or in rock-shelters (the shallow caves known in France as *abris*) generally include cave-earth, an ungraded deposit mainly consisting of clayey or silty matter washed or blown in and mixed or interstratified with waterlaid sand or coarser material; talus cones and rubble due to roof-falls, which may be loose or consolidated by carbonate of lime into hard breccia; and layers of travertine or stalagmite formed by the evaporation of hard water rising as a spring and flooding the floor or dripping from the roof. Any of these deposits may contain the bones of animals that frequented the cave or whose remains have been washed or carried in. In caves which have been occupied from time to time by prehistoric man, the natural deposits alternate or interdigitate with 'occupation layers' consisting usually of the ashes of fires (hearths), broken animal bones and artifacts. These are usually

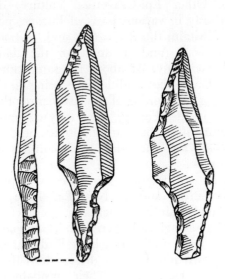

Figure 43 *a* Ahrensburgian tanged-point ($\frac{5}{8}$), *b* Hamburgian shouldered point ($\frac{1}{1}$) from Meiendorf. *After J. G. D. Clark.*

concentrated near the mouths of caves. Systematic excavation of such cave deposits, layer by layer, reveals the changes and substitutions of culture which have taken place in course of time (Fig. 44). By comparing the sequences in a series of different caves, it is possible to establish the general succession of cultures in a region. The standard Middle and Upper Palaeolithic successions were established through excavations in the caves and rock-shelters in the limestone hills of Southern France.

It should be emphasized that although cave occupation sites have supplied a great deal of information about the Palaeolithic succession, stratified deposits on open occupation sites have provided almost as much, if not quite as much, in some areas; for example the camp-sites of the Perigordian horse-hunters at Solutré (Fig. 45), of the Pavlovian (Eastern Gravettian) mammoth-hunters at Věstonice and of the reindeer hunters of Meiendorf.

It has been suggested that the development of Palaeo–Indian lithic cultures in North America owed something to the spread from north-eastern Asia of a Solutrean tradition of making bifacial foliates, but until the earliest occurrences of these in Siberia (Wormington, 1962, Smith, 1962) have been dated by radiocarbon, speculation on this is useless.

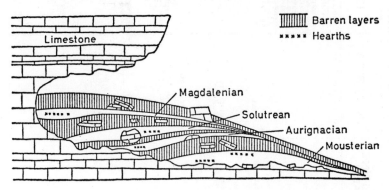

Figure 44 Diagrammatic section of ideal rock-shelter (or *abri*) *eg.* in S.W. France.
B.M.N.H.

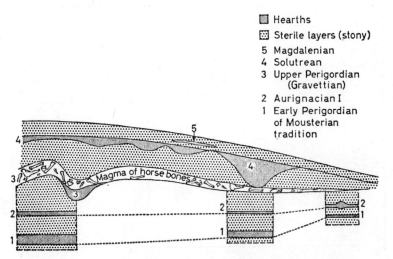

Figure 45 Camp-site of Gravettian horse-hunters at Solutré. Section in Crot du Charnier.
After Breuil and Arcelin, with revision based on Combier.

CHART B

RADIOCARBON DATING CHART OF
MIDDLE PALAEOLITHIC CULTURES AND MIDDLE/UPPER TRANSITION

YEARS B.C. (based on C-14 dates)	IRAQ AND AFGHANISTAN	SYRIA AND LEBANON	PALESTINE (ISRAEL)	N. AFRICA	EUROPE
30,000	SHANIDAR C, Baradostian, GRN 2016—33,390±600; KARA KAMAR (Afghanistan) "Aurignacian" W224—34,000±3,000		KEBAREH F, Final Levalloiso-Mousterian (cf. Emiran), GRN 2551—33,350±500; *el WAD G-E*, *Emiran*; *‡SKHUL? Levalloiso-Mousterian*; TABUN B, Upper Levalloiso-Mousterian, GRN 2534—37,750±800; *‡SKHUL? Levalloiso-Mousterian*	HAUA FTEAH XX, Dabba culture, GRN 2550—31,150±400	ARCY sur CURE, Chatelperronian, GRN 1742—31,910±250; SALZOFENHÖHLE, Alpine Palaeolithic, GRN 761—32,550±3200; LA QUINA, Final Mousterian, GRN 2526—33,300±530; NIETOPERZOWA, Mousterian/cf. Szeletian, GRN 2151—36,550±250
40,000		KSAR'AKIL (3B), Levalloiso-Mousterian, GRN 2579—41,800±1,500; JERF AJLA (Syria), Mousterian, NZ.76—42,050±2,000	TABUN C, Levalloiso-Mousterian, GRN 2729—38,950±1,000; KEBAREH, Levalloiso-Mousterian, GRN 2561—39,050±1,000; *TABUN D, Levalloiso-Mousterian*	*ED-DABBA (Type site Dabba culture)*, GRN 3260—38,550±1,600; HAUA FTEAH XXVIII, Levalloiso-Mousterian, GRN 2564—41,450±1,300; HAUA FTEAH XXXIII, Levalloiso-Mousterian, GRN 2023—45,050+3,200 -2,300	*KRAPINA? Mousterian*; LA COTTE de ST. BRELADE, Levalloiso-Mousterian, GRN 2649—45,050±1,500; GIBRALTAR (Gorham's Cave i?) Mousterian, GRN 1473—45,750±1,500
	SHANIDAR D-TOP, Levalloiso-Mousterian, GRN 2527—44,950±1,500				
50,000	SHANIDAR D, Levalloiso-Mousterian, GRN 1495—48,650±3,000	RAS el KELB, Levalloiso-Mousterian, GRN 2556—>52,000			LEBENSTEDT, Mousterian, GRN 2083—53,290±1,010; MUSSOLINI CANAL 2, Pontinian, GRN 2572—55,950±500
60,000					*WEIMAR-EHRINGSDORF, Mousterian Pre-Würm*

Radiocarbon-dated sites in roman type

Sites where C-14 dates not available, position inferred, in italic type

Vertical arrows: earlier and/or later than level of name

‡ Alternative positions of SKHUL II

CHART 'C'

STRATIGRAPHICAL FRAMEWORK AND RADIOCARBON DATING OF UPPER PALAEOLITHIC CULTURES

YEARS B.C. (based on C-14 dates): 5,000 — 10,000 — 15,000 — 20,000 — 25,000 — 30,000 — 35,000 — 40,000 — 45,000 — 50,000

WESTERN EUROPE

MESOLITHIC CULTURES

AHRENSBURGIAN
HAMBURGIAN

MAGDALENIAN — VIb, VIa, Vb, Va, IV, III, II, I

Proto-Magdalenian — ?

SOLUTREAN — Upper, Middle, Lower, Proto

AURIGNACIAN — V, IV, III, II, I, O

PERIGORDIAN — (Gravettian) VI, V, IV A, III, (Chatelperronian) II, I

SURVIVING MOUSTERIAN TRADITIONS

CENTRAL/EASTERN EUROPE

MESOLITHIC CULTURES

MAGDALENIAN

EASTERN GRAVETTIAN (Pavlovian)

AURIGNACIAN

SZELETIAN and comparable industries

ALPINE PALAEOLITHIC

MOUSTERIAN CULTURES

RADIOCARBON-DATED SITES (YEARS B.C.)

La Vache: Final Magdalenian GRN (mean of 2 dates) 10,740

Angles sur l'Anglin: Magdalenian III GRN 1913—12,310±80

Altamira: Magdalenian III M 829—13,540±700

Evidence from early Magdalenian & Middle Solutrean levels in Dordogne caves.

Abri Pataud: Proto-Magdalenian GRN (mean of several dates) 18,500–19,000
Laugerie Haute: Lower Solutrean GRN 1888–18,940±250
Laugerie Haute: Proto-Magdalenian GRN 1875–20,030±250

Abri Pataud: Perigordian IV GRN (mean of 2 dates) 18,050
W (mean of 2 dates) 21,850

Pavlov: Eastern Gravettian GRN 1325–22,970±160
Dolni Vestonice: Eastern Gravettian GRN 1286–23,820±180

Arcy sur Cure VII: Aurignacian II GRN 1717–28,850±250
La Quina: Aurignacian I. GRN 1493–29,450±350
Willendorf II: Aurignacian GRN & H (mean of 3 dates) 29,700

Arcy sur Cure VIII: Chatelperronian GRN (mean of 2 dates) 31,840
Salzofenhohle: Alpine Palaeolithic GRN 761–33,000±520
La Quina: Late Mousterian GRN 2526–33,300±530

Nietoperzowa: Mousterian/cf. Szeletian GRN 2181–36,550±1260

Gorham's Cave G: Mousterian GRN 1473–45,740±1,500

Stratigraphy / Stages (bottom)

POST-GLACIAL — III

LATE GLACIAL — Ia, Ib, Ic, II, III

MILDER PHASE

WURM III — YOUNGER LOESS III

PAUDORF SOIL

WURM II — YOUNGER LOESS II

GOTTWEIG SOILS

WURM I — YOUNGER LOESS I

YEARS B.C. (based on C-14 dates): 5,000 — 10,000 — 15,000 — 20,000 — 25,000 — 30,000 — 35,000 — 40,000 — 45,000 — 50,000

Epi-Palaeolithic or Mesolithic Cultures in Europe and the Near East

AT ONE TIME it was widely believed that at the end of the Ice Age the Magdalenian hunters had followed the reindeer herds migrating northwards and that there had been an interval during which Western Europe was vacant until it was inhabited by the immigrant Neolithic farming people. The alleged break between the Palaeolithic and Neolithic periods was referred to as the Ancient Hiatus (Mortillet, 1900, p. 238). However, in the last two decades of the nineteenth century, assemblages of artifacts were discovered at various localities which clearly filled this gap: they were termed Epi-Palaeolithic, Early Neolithic or *Mesolithic*. The last term, proposed in 1892 by an English archaeologist, J. Allen Brown (1892, pp. 66–98), eventually prevailed; but we should remember that it was Edouard Piette's publication (1889, p. 203) of his discovery in the cave at Mas d'Azil (Ariège) of a cultural zone between the Magdalenian and the Neolithic which really eliminated the so-called Hiatus.

The Mesolithic stage of culture may be defined as the continuation of the hunting, fishing and food-gathering economy into Post-Pleistocene (Holocene) times; it was terminated by the beginning of the farming economy which constituted the Neolithic Revolution. Thus the duration of the Mesolithic 'period' varies widely from region to region. In the Near East, where the Neolithic Revolution took place within a few centuries of the arbitrary termination of the Pleistocene period

(8000 BC) the Mesolithic phase was extremely short: but in some parts of Britain it lasted for 6,000 years (from 8000 to 2000 BC), while in Australia the aborigines continued to live at an essentially Mesolithic level of culture from the end of the Ice Age until the present day. In geological terms, the Mesolithic cultures of Europe extend through three stages (Clark, 1936):

Mesolithic III Atlantic
" II Boreal
" I Pre-Boreal

Mesolithic industries are recognizable mainly by the presence of stone bladelets of regular, often geometrical, form known as *microliths* (Fig. 46), at one time misleadingly called pygmy flints. Prototypes were already present in some Upper Palaeolithic

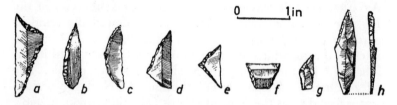

0 _____ 1 in

Figure 46 Microliths: *a* Capsian; *b* Azilian; *c* & *d* Kenya Capsian; *e* Bandarawelian (Ceylon); *f* & *g* Tardenoisian; *h* Maglemosian.

industries. Microliths were evidently set in a shaft or handle, forming composite tools and weapons such as barbed arrows and spears. The 'micro-burin' (Fig. 47), at one time regarded as a miniature tool, and as the type fossil of one of the main Mesolithic industries, is now recognized as a by-product of the manufacture of microliths.[30]

Many Mesolithic peoples lived by fowling, fishing and gathering shellfish or snails – as witness the shell-mounds or *kjökenmöddinger* of Denmark and the Capsian *escargotières* of North Africa. There were several partly contemporaneous cultures at this stage in Western Europe: the *Sauveterrian*[31] and its derivative the *Tardenoisian*[32] were largely confined to sandy country or heathland; the *Maglemosian*[33] and *Azilian*[34] to forest environments; the *Kongemose*[35] and its derivative the *Ertebølle*[36] or Kitchen-midden culture, the *Obanian*,[37] *Larnian*[38] and *Asturian*[39] to shore-lines. In addition to food-gathering and fishing, these peoples were hunters: the commonest game in Europe at that time was red deer (*Cervus elaphus*), although aurochs (*Bos primigenius*) were also common. A leading item of equipment of the Mesolithic hunter-fishers, particularly of the Maglemosian, Azilian and Obanian cultures, was a barbed point cut out of red-deer antlers. It had a flattened cross section. Some of these antler barbed points were holed in the manner of harpoons, but it is possible that many were mounted as leister prongs for spearing fish, and others as projectile points for killing game (Fig. 48). Dogs were domesticated at this stage, both in north-west Europe and the Near East, and were no doubt used as an aid in hunting.

The cultures of Mesolithic peoples were essentially based on Upper Palaeolithic traditions but adapted to new and rapidly changing environments. In north-west Europe as conditions

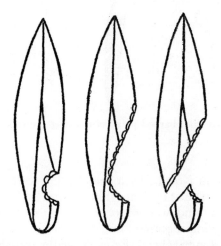

Figure 47 Diagram to illustrate how in the production of a microlith by notching a blade, there is a basal reject, the so-called microburin. *After W. F. Rankine.*

became milder following the recession of the ice sheets, there were considerable alterations in shore-lines (see pp. 74–5), and a spreading of forests. There were extensive changes in the game animals: mammoth, woolly rhinoceros and cave bear became extinct, while reindeer as they migrated northwards were replaced by red deer. All these changes reacted on culture. In the

Figure 48 Maglemosian barbed point of red deer antler from Star Carr, Yorkshire.
B.M.N.H. (½).

Near East and in North Africa the changes were different but related: as the zone of cyclones shifted northwards, areas which had been fertile and wooded changed to desert, water levels shrank, and springs became more precious.

The hafted stone axehead (for example the tranchet-axe) was invented by Mesolithic people in the newly forested regions for felling trees and the working of wood. In maritime provinces, including the newly flooded parts of Europe, now free from ice, hunting was extended into the sea, with the invention of equipment for taking whales, seals and deep-sea fish (J. G. D. Clark, 1952, pp. 59, 74, 84). The introduction of skin-boats and dug-out canoes at this time (J. G. D. Clark, 1952, p. 283) led to the opening of new channels of migration and communication. It was apparently during this stage of culture that man first reached Ireland;[40] and there was also some community of tradition between North Africa and Mediterranean Europe (Smith, 1952, p. 19).

In the Near East a basic change in man's way of life occurred during the Mesolithic stage, probably again in response to ecological conditions. A long succession of cultures[41] developed from the Near Eastern blade-culture complex and led to the production of microlithic industries which included flint sickle-blades with 'corngloss', indicating that in this region people at the Mesolithic stage of culture had invented equipment to reap cereal grasses, leading to Neolithic culture. This important microlithic culture has been named *Natufian* (Garrod, 1932). The Natufians lived mainly in rock shelters and on the adjoining hill-side terraces. They were still living to a large extent by fishing and hunting (gazelle was the predominant game in this dry environment); but they had begun to reap, presumably, the wild emmer wheat which is common in Palestine. There is every reason to believe that before very long they had learnt to cultivate it, thus beginning the Neolithic Revolution which led to civilization. It is now regarded as questionable whether the final stage of the Natufian (Garrod, 1957, p. 226) can really be separated from the earliest or Pre-Pottery phase of the Neolithic, when the first permanent settlement was established by the spring at Jericho (*c* 7500 BC).

Chapter 4

Palaeolithic Cultures in Africa

PALAEOLITHIC ARTIFACTS RANGING in age from the end of the Lower Pleistocene onwards are widespread in Africa, and in several regions they occur in much greater abundance than in Europe. Some of the earlier industries are almost identical with those found in Europe and Asia, while others are entirely local.

In various parts of Africa, mainly south of the Sahara, high-level river gravels have been found to contain large numbers of chipped pebbles, mostly in quartzite, which have been accepted by some authorities as pebble-tools, but which in fact may have been produced by natural agencies. These problematical specimens consist of rounded pebbles or small slabs of stone with one or more edges flaked in a *single direction*. They were first recognized in Uganda by the geologist E. J. Wayland in 1920,[42] who later referred them to a hypothetical culture which he named *Kafuan* on the basis of their occurrence in terraces of the Kafu River.[43] J. D. Clark (1958) has now demonstrated that the Kafuan type of flaking can be produced naturally, for instance when stones fall from the sides of gorges and strike other stones or rock surfaces out of water. It cannot be denied that some undoubted palaeolithic industries[44] include a proportion of pebble-tools of the simple Kafuan type, but it is no longer possible to accept this type of flaking as the sole proof of the existence of 'man the tool-maker' at a particular horizon where there is any room for doubt.

The oldest undoubted artifacts in the world are the *Oldowan* pebble-tools which occur in Late Villafranchian deposits in South Africa, East Africa and North Africa. As there are indications at several localities of association with *Australopithecus sensu lato* it is believed that they were made by these ape-like hominids, who probably began making sharp-edged stone tools to aid carnivorous habits, developed perhaps in response to drought (Oakley, 1951).

The *Oldowan*[45] culture was first recognized by Dr L. S. B. Leakey in the basal bed (Bed I) of the series of lacustrine sediments exposed in the sides of the Oldoway (Olduvai) Gorge in Northern Tanzania (Fig. 49). The associated fauna was at one time regarded as of early Middle Pleistocene Age, but further studies have shown that it can be equated with that of

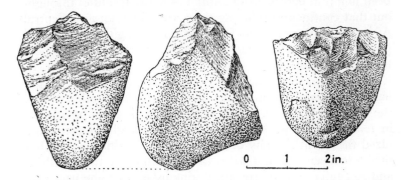

Figure 49 Oldowan pebble-tools of lava from Bed I, Olduvai Gorge. *B.M.N.H.*

the Omo Beds in Abyssinia and should in fact be placed in the upper part of the Lower Pleistocene (Leakey, 1959, p. 493). The Oldowan industry consists of pebbles of lava and quartz flaked by percussion to form crude chopping and cutting tools varying in size from about the dimensions of a ping-pong ball to that of a croquet ball (Leakey, 1951, p. 34). A strong but sharp cutting edge was made by striking off flakes in *two directions* at one end or along one side of the pebble or lump of rock so that the flake–scars intersected at a sub-acute angle.

Oldowan tools (or equivalent types) have been found at Kanam in Kenya, in the Transvaal, in the Cape Province (Vaal Valley), in the Omo Valley, Abyssinia, in Morocco, and at Ain Hanech in Algeria (Map 1). There is little doubt that the earliest tool-makers spread over the open savannah and bushy grasslands of almost the whole continent of Africa within a comparatively short time. At some localities, for example at Ain Hanech (Arambourg, 1950), a high percentage of the pebble-tools are multi-faceted (*ie* polyhedral); possibly these were used as missile stones for killing game rather than for cutting and chopping up the carcases.

The 'Great Hand-axe Culture' (Lowe, 1952*a*), already familiar to European archaeologists through the discoveries of flint hand-axes (*bifaces*) at Hoxne, Grays Inn Lane (London) and St Acheul (Somme), was eventually traced to Africa, which was clearly its 'heart-land' (Fig. 71). Stone bifaces have been found in enormous quantities at many localities throughout that continent, excluding some areas in West and Central Africa which were densely forested even during the interpluvial phases. (For more detailed distribution map of Chelles-Acheul hand-axe industries see Howell & Clark, 1963, p. 462.) In Europe the earliest phase of the biface or hand-axe culture has been named Abbevillian (Chellean of some authors), and the succeeding phases, which showed a marked improvement in technique, Acheulian. In Africa archaeologists have recognized the essential unity of the hand-axe tradition which has therefore been called *Chelles-Acheul*,[46] although the Chellean and Acheulian phases are still distinguished by some workers.

When stone artifacts were collected layer by layer in the sediments exposed in the Olduvai Gorge it was found that whereas in Bed I the end-product of the industry was a simple pebble-tool with fairly short cutting edge made by the removal in two directions of a few flakes at one end or along one side, in Bed II (Leakey, 1951, p. 41) a percentage of the tools was more advanced. These had been worked in the same general way but more extensively. Numerous flakes had been removed by percussion, first in one direction and then in the other, mainly struck from around the periphery of the pebble, so that it became a biface (two-faced lump), either roughly pointed and pear-shaped or oval in outline, with a wavy or zig-zag margin formed by the intersection of the scars of the stone-struck trimming flakes (Fig. 50). Some were beak-shaped,[47] with one face flat and the other with central ridge running from the centre of the thick butt to the point. At first none of these various forms of hand-axe was made very frequently, but their appearance marked the dawn of the Chelles-Acheul culture. The hominids responsible for this earliest hand-axe industry in Africa were early representatives of *Pithecanthropus*,[48] for example the so-called 'Chellean skull', on an horizon dated recently as 490,000 years old in association with giant Middle Pleistocene fauna.[49]

The gradual evolution of the Chelles-Acheul industries in East Africa has been traced by systematic collecting of artifacts from the successive lake-shore deposits exposed in the Olduvai Gorge.[50] The assemblages at each level include several different

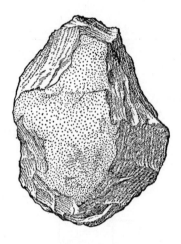

Figure 50 Chellean hand-axe of lava from Bed II, Olduvai Gorge. *B.M.N.H.* ($\frac{1}{2}$).

forms of finished artifact in addition to hand-axes, pebble-tools (in declining numbers), flake-tools and waste flakes. It should not be forgotten that in all palaeolithic industries where the dominant end-product was a core-tool (*ie* a trimmed-down lump of stone such as a pebble-tool or biface) there were always some simple flake-tools, struck from cores. Where the raw material consisted of large boulders or outcrops of rock the bifaces were frequently made out of thick flakes, but these would not count as flake-tools in the strict sense, for in being extensively trimmed down, a flake is serving as a secondary core.

In the Olduvai Gorge sequence, Dr Leakey has distinguished eleven stages of Chelles-Acheul culture. Some of the differences between the successive assemblages are only of local significance, but others undoubtedly reflect a trend in the evolution of Chelles-Acheul culture occurring through the greater part of Africa. The same general sequence has been established independently by collecting from the stratigraphically dated series of terrace deposits in the Vaal Valley of South Africa. However, the Olduvai sequence is almost unbroken and may well be regarded as the most convenient standard.

Olduvai Sequence

Cultural Stages			Bed Nos.	Geological Stage	Divisions	
E. African Acheulian	vi	Chelles–Acheul of East Africa 11	IV	'Kanjeran'	UPPER	PLEISTOCENE
	v	10				
	iv	9				
	iii	8				
	ii	7	III			
	i	6				
E. African Chellean	Transit-ional	(5)	II	'Kamasian'	MIDDLE	
		(4)				
		3				
		2				
		1				
Oldowan (Pre-Chelles–Acheul)			I	'Kageran'	LOWER	

Chellean hand-axes were made out of blocks of stone (sometimes boulders) by means of the simple stone technique, that is to say they were flaked either by a hammerstone, or the block itself was repeatedly struck on to an anvil stone. In consequence of the deep-biting flake-scars produced by this stone or block-on-block technique, Chellean hand-axes are very coarsely flaked, with wavy or sinuous edges. They grade into pebble-tools. Indeed, nearly 50 per cent of the finished tools in Bed II, although constituting part of Chellean assemblage, are indistinguishable from Oldowan types. This illustrates two points in the archaeological dating of a deposit: that it is essential to have a large assemblage – single finds being particularly misleading; and that one should be guided by the most advanced or new tool-type in an assemblage rather than by the perhaps much more numerous primitive types which may represent cultural survivals.

The artifacts in the upper part of Bed II include several types in addition to pebble-tools and crude hand-axes: discs (cores), polyhedral stones and thick flakes, and many small ones and chunks with simply trimmed edges. In the Chellean industries, flakes and flake tools are more frequent in regions of higher rainfall (J. D. Clark, 1959, p. 121).

The first hand-axe industry found *in situ* in South Africa is now recognized to be Chellean. It occurs in gravel at Stellenbosch,[51] and for many years the Chelles-Acheul culture was consequently known in that part of the world as the Stellenbosch culture. Chellean artifacts also occur in the Older Gravels of the Vaal River, ranging from 200 ft to 45 ft above the present river.[52] They have been recorded from river-gravels in almost all the drier regions of Africa. There is a general consensus of geological opinion that during the time when Chellean culture prevailed the conditions were on the whole somewhat wetter than at present, and that all the deposits containing Chellean industries *in situ* (*ie* not derived) are approximately referable to the Second Pluvial period (of which the Kamasian deposits in East Africa have generally been regarded as the typical representative).

From the point of view of intercontinental correlation one of the most important occurrences of Chellean industries is in Layer M of the 60-m or Sicilian II Beach at Sidi Abderrahman, near Casablanca in Morocco, which[53] can be correlated broadly with some phases in the Mindel or Second Glacial cycle in Europe.

The Acheulian phase is distinguished from the Chellean by

the introduction of a new flaking technique, and by the appearance of new forms of biface. In the Olduvai sequence stages 4 and 5 mark the transition between Chellean and Acheulian (Leakey, 1951, p. 73). In the succeeding true Acheulian assemblages the beaked hand-axe is rare or absent. The majority of the hand-axes are pointed or oval, symmetrical bifaces, with relatively straight margins and with surfaces formed by numerous shallow flake-scars (Fig. 51). If a suitable slab of stone is struck on the edge by a long-bone or wooden

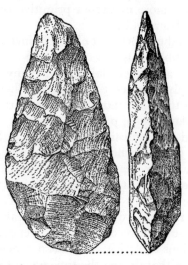

Figure 51 Acheulian iv biface of phonolite lava from occupation site at Olorgesailie, Kenya.
B.M.N.H. (⅓).

bar, the flakes which come off are thin and have diffused bulbs of percussion, in sharp contradistinction to the thick, bulbous flakes produced by the hammerstone or block-on-block method of flaking. Acheulian hand-axes were evidently largely made or at least finished by the cylindrical hammer (or bar) technique[54] or by use of indirect percussion on an anvil.[55]

As flint (or chert) was, with few exceptions, practically the only material used for stone implements by palaeolithic man in Europe, the term flint was at one time used almost synonymously with stone implement in the vocabulary of collectors;[56]

but this changed with the extension of archaeological researches into Africa, particularly south of the Sahara, where lavas, quartz and quartzites were the stones mainly used by early man. Both in Oldowan and Chelles-Acheul industries men used a wide range of rocks, but there is evidence that individual groups covered considerable distances to obtain what they considered ideal material. In the early stages of culture, ease of working may have been the main consideration, but in the Acheulian stages man had acquired such good mastery over stone that the form of the biface is indistinguishable whether it be made in lava, dolerite, ironstone, or quartzite. Even the fineness of craftsmanship was scarcely affected by the type of rock.[57] Consequently the range of material used by the Acheulian tool-makers was much wider than in the Oldowan and Chellean stages, and there is some indication that man's choice of material was now sometimes determined by aesthetic considerations.

The use of large flakes as the 'blanks' of hand-axes seems to have led to the invention of a new form of tool which in the African Chelles-Acheul industries became almost as common as the hand-axe itself: namely the *cleaver*. Typically this is a biface with a straight cutting edge at one end at right angles to the long axis. If the normal process of trimming down a large squarish end-struck flake into a hand-axe is stopped at the stage before the thin wedge-shaped end is removed the result is a cleaver (Fig. 52). There were several ways of making cleavers. Some were made on side-blow flakes, some are unifacially trimmed rectangular flakes, but the majority are wedge-shaped bifacial tools and experiments have demonstrated that they are very effective implements for skinning and dividing animal carcasses. Hand-axes, on the other hand, were essentially general-purpose tools. Cleavers make their first appearance in stage 6 of the Chelles-Acheul sequence at Olduvai, that is to say in the first typical Acheulian stage (Leakey, 1951, p. 97). They are common in all Acheulian industries throughout the greater part of Africa with the exception of the Nile Valley and the Horn, where they become much rarer.[58]

From the point of view of European comparison it is interesting to find that ovate hand-axes with S-twist made their first appearance in the East African Acheulian iii industry

(Olduvai Chelles-Achuel 8). This industry seems to mark an intrusive wave of culture at Olduvai, for the succeeding industry (stage 9) represents a development of the cultural tradition of stage 7 rather than of stage 8 (Cole, 1963, p. 146). In regard to Trans-African and Afro-Asian correlation it is worth noting that cleavers with parallelogramic cross-section made their African appearance in the same stage at Olduvai (*ie* 8 = Acheulian iii).

The most important finds of Lower Palaeolithic artifacts are

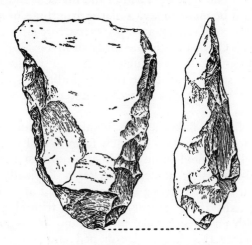

Figure 52 Acheulian iii cleaver of fine-grained lava from Bed IV, Olduvai Gorge.
After Leakey. ($\frac{1}{3}$).

those at sites which were occupied by their makers either repeatedly or for an appreciable time. These are known as occupation sites: or rather more precisely as camp-sites or *living-sites* (Leakey, 1951, pp. 140–1, 1958, 1959) if there is evidence of a variety of activities; as butchering-sites, if the only activity indicated is the dismembering of carcases of one or more forms of game; or as workshop-floors (or just 'floors'), if the only activity indicated is the manufacture of tools. In the Olduvai sequence a dozen important living-sites have been discovered and four of these have yielded fossil hominid remains.* At some

*See Fossil Hominid Dating Tables I and II.

Oldowan cultural levels the known skeletal remains may re-present killings at 'walk-about' sites rather than living-sites, as there were not always any associated 'floors' or concentration of food debris (*eg* at MK. I.). On the other hand, structures of basalt blocks on the lowest Oldowan[59] occupation levels suggest that the early hominids *may* have constructed rough shelters.

PALAEOLITHIC LIVING-SITES IN OLDUVAI BEDS

Bed IV	Acheulian	v	living-site	HK.IV.
		iv	living-site	JK.IV2.
		iii	living-site	TK.IV.
		ii	living-site	HEB.IV.
Bed III	Hope Fountain		living-site	JK.2.III East.
Bed II	Chellean	iv	living-site	MK.II.
		iii	living-sites	LLK.II and FLK.II.
		ii	living-site	SHK.II.
		i	living-site	BK.II.
	Late Oldowan		living-site	MNK.II.
Bed I	Late Oldowan		living-site below desertic surface. FLK.N.I.	
	Oldowan		living-site FLK.I.	
			living-site FLK. NN.I.	
			shelter-site (?) DK.I.	

A number of Acheulian iv occupation sites have been found at Olorgesailie in Kenya and at Isimila in Tanzania. The superb craftsmanship of these industries (Fig. 51) indicates that they represent the acme of the Chelles-Acheul cultural tradition so far as East Africa was concerned. Occupation sites of this stage have also been found at Lewa, on a plateau below the northern slopes of Mount Kenya; also at Kariandusi, between Gilgil and Nakuru in the Rift Valley, where many of the hand-axes and cleavers were made in obsidian (black volcanic glass). At Lewa the products of Acheulian culture lie exposed on the present surface, but at Kariandusi and at Olorgesailie they are embedded in the deposits of freshwater lakes which existed on the floor of the Rift Valley during the 'Kanjeran' stage.

At Olorgesailie 14 distinct *land-surfaces*, many of them carrying traces of paleolithic occupation, occur in the thick series of lacustrine clays, marls and diatomites, and are in course of being exposed by erosion at this remarkable site (Cole, 1963, pp. 150–57). Apart from two or three levels of crude artifacts, mainly flakes of Hope Fountain facies (Posnansky, 1961), the industries on these land surfaces belong to the stages of highly evolved Acheulian culture represented in Bed IV at Olduvai. On several of the surfaces living-sites have been found, for example on land-surfaces 6, 7 and 10 where E. African Acheulian iv is well represented (Cole, 1963). Remains of the animals which the Olorgesailie people hunted for food are abundant – long bones broken for marrow, and skulls smashed to extract the brain. The predominant game in the area evidently varied from time to time: on land-surface 7 the giant baboon *Simopithecus* was the animal mainly hunted; on 8 the extinct horse *Equus olduvaiensis*; on 10 the giant pig *Notochoerus*, and so on. As no traces of fire were found on any of these living sites it is presumed that the Acheulian hunters at this stage ate their meat raw – or perhaps sometimes sun-dried like *biltong*.

Stone balls (mostly polyhedral although a few are spherical) are moderately common on all Acheulian levels in East Africa. At Olorgesailie, Leakey reported twelve sets of stone balls in groups of three in levels 6, 7 and 10, as well as many isolated occurrences. He suggested that they were originally held in bags of skin tied together with twisted thongs and used as a three-ball *bolas* in hunting game (Cole, 1963, pp. 155–6); but the apparent groupings in three were probably fortuitous.

In the Vaal Valley, five stages of Chelles-Acheul culture have been distinguished (Lowe, 1937, 1952a, pp. 167–77, 1952b), but they cannot be equated precisely with the stages recognized in East Africa. Stage I is clearly Chellean; the remainder of Acheulian facies. In view of the regional differences between the stages of Chelles-Acheul culture it has been suggested that appropriate prefixes should be used in referring to them, for example French Chellean (= Abbevillian) (Lowe, 1952a, p. 176), Kenya Chellean and so on.

The first stage of the Vaal Acheulian is only represented by rolled hand-axes redeposited in the earliest Younger Gravels. The available evidence suggests that the beginnings of Acheulian culture in the Vaal coincided with exceptionally dry conditions (J. D. Clark, 1959, p. 123), as it did apparently in Rhodesia and possibly also in East Africa.

In the second stage (Vaal Chelles-Acheul III), hand-axes and cleavers were more varied in form and made in a wider range of rocks. Perhaps because the old river terraces containing abundant supplies of quartzite cobbles were now largely blanketed by wind-blown sands, the Acheulian tool-makers in the Vaal turned at this stage to large boulders of diabase and andesite as raw material for tools. In the Karroo Desert they used boulders of dolerite. Probably as a consequence of utilizing boulders (J. D. Clark, 1959, p. 125) they adopted or invented a new method of making implements. First they roughly trimmed the boulder as though they were making a large hand-axe with one face flatter than the other. Then they made a striking platform along one side by detaching a series of flakes at right angles to the upper prepared face. With a skilfully directed blow on the faceted striking-platform they detached a large thick flake, one face of which was already prepared (Fig. 53), and then they proceeded to trim it into a biface or cleaver. This is known as the *Victoria West technique* (Lowe, 1945 and Goodwin,

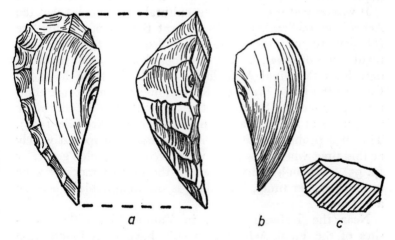

Figure 53 Victoria West Technique: *a* two views of the prepared core from which a large flake (*b*) has been struck ready to trim into a biface or cleaver; *c* diagram of Victoria West core showing position of flake. *del R.P.* (⅓).

1933), which is an African counterpart of the Proto-Leval-loisian technique developed in Europe by some Acheulian groups during the Pre-Riss cold phase (p. 69, note 63). As the two techniques were broadly contemporaneous, it has been suggested that the idea of the prepared core diffused from one continent to the other, but this is difficult to substantiate. The Vaal Chelles-Acheul III is found in the second aggradation of the Younger Gravels.

In the third stage of the Vaal Acheulian (Chelles-Acheul IV), ovate hand-axes were commoner, while conical (horse-hoof) cores were made which yielded flakes with faceted striking-platforms reminiscent of Early Levalloisian flakes in Europe (J. D. Clark, 1959, p. 127). This stage is represented in the upper half of the Younger Gravels of the Vaal, and has been correlated with the well-known E. African Acheulian iv.

The final stage (Vaal Chelles-Acheul V) corresponded with the onset of dry interpluvial conditions generally correlated with the end of the 'Kanjeran' stage. New forms of flake-tool and burin-like blades made their appearance, indicating that equipment was now being devised for more specialized uses (J. D. Clark, 1959, p. 127). Many of the implements, including bifaces, were made in indurated shale.

It was only at the end of their cultural development that the Acheulians of Southern Africa learnt the art of making fire (Oakley, 1956). This evidently enabled them to make more regular use of caves, for the first rock-shelter homes in Africa date from the Final Acheulian stage, for example Montagu Cave in the Cape Province. Regular use of fire became common practice in South-West Asia with almost dramatic suddenness at the same archaeological horizon (Neuville, 1931). Thus it is probable that a firemaking tradition spread widely at this time when conditions were becoming cooler generally (p. 95). Although fire was used in the north temperate zone in much earlier times, firemaking is known as liable to become a lost art.

Near the Kalambo Falls, in Zambia, lake-side living-sites of the Final Acheulian people have been found, and here too there is evidence of regular use of fire (J. D. Clark, 1959, p. 130). Because the containing deposits have been more or less permanently waterlogged since Pleistocene times, wooden artifacts such as digging-sticks have been preserved alongside the usual stone bifaces, cleavers, flake-tools and factory waste. Wood from these deposits has been dated at Groningen by the radiocarbon method (57,000 B.P.).

Another Final Acheulian occupation site has been found close to the kopje at Broken Hill which yielded the skull of Rhodesian Man. Small rather crude flake-tools and core-choppers were found here in an underlying layer, and proved to be similar to the assemblages occurring at *Hope Fountain* in Southern Rhodesia (Jones, 1949, pp. 68–72) which have been compared with Tayacian and Clactonian industries in Europe. At one time it was thought that industries of the Hope Fountain type (Fig. 54) were the work of a separate group of people living contemporaneously with the Acheulians. The evidence now available is against this view and suggests that more probably they represent some special, perhaps seasonal,

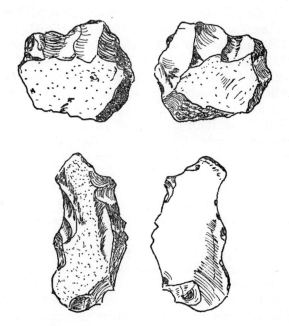

Figure 54 Core-chopper above, and rough flake-tool below, from a Hope Fountain assemblage. Zambia.
After J. D. Clark. ($\frac{1}{1}$).

activity of the biface-makers (J. D. Clark, 1959, p. 128, and 1959a).

The Stone Age of Southern Africa was at first divided by archaeologists into an Earlier Stone Age and a Later Stone Age, but as researches proceeded further it became necessary to recognize a *Middle Stone Age* (Goodwin, 1928, 1929; Malan, 1957) covering the period when specialized flake techniques were developed but before the introduction of microliths. The Middle Stone Age of Africa has much in common as regards typology with the Middle Palaeolithic of North Africa and Europe, although chronologically it corresponds with the Upper or Late Palaeolithic. It must not be confused of course with the Mesolithic which, although literally meaning middle stone age, is a term restricted to Post-Palaeolithic cultures.

In the classification now used in Southern Africa two intermediate periods are recognized (J. D. Clark, 1959, pp. 37–40): the *First Intermediate* covers the period of transition between typical Earlier Stone Age and typical Middle Stone Age, and the *Second Intermediate* that between the Middle Stone Age and the full development of the Microlithic Revolution in the Later Stone Age.

During the Earlier Stone Age (ESA), when the Oldowan and Chelles-Acheul cultures prevailed (in the Late Kageran, Kamasian and early Kanjeran stages), palaeolithic industries were relatively uniform throughout Africa, and largely confined to open country or savannah. The First Intermediate cultures which followed were more specialized in relation to environment, and consequently showed some regional diversification. The two main cultures were the *Fauresmith*[60] and the *Sangoan*.[61] The Fauresmith was confined largely to dry open country, to the grasslands and high plateaux of southern and eastern Africa, whereas the Sangoan was a culture of the more forested regions, and occurred mainly in the lower–lying lake and river basins of Central Africa.

The Fauresmith was essentially a continuation of the Chelles-Acheul tradition, so that the distinction from Final Acheulian is not always clear, particularly where the material used for making tools was mainly quartzite or sandstone. For example, in the Cave of Hearths at Makapansgat, the industry for long described as Late Acheulian was shown on more detailed analysis to be terminal Acheulian of Fauresmith facies (Mason, 1959). The widespread use of indurated shale by the Fauresmith tool-makers gave the lithic industries of this culture their main characteristics. Indurated shale is hard and can be flaked almost as easily as flint, but the production of strong cutting edges required a new kind of marginal retouch known as step-flaking. This was done by means of a hammer-stone (or by tapping the implement on an anvil-stone) and consisted of removing small flakes in such a way that they broke off short leaving a step on the surface of the tool (Fig. 55).

Figure 55 Fauresmith biface of silcrete from Brakfontein, Orange Free State. *After Burkitt.* ($\frac{2}{3}$).

Hand-axes were still extensively used by the Fauresmith people, but on an average were much smaller than in Acheulian industries, and most of them were either almond-shaped or heart-shaped. Cleavers were rougher and even in the shale areas were often made of some other rock. Discoidal cores were prepared either for the removal of one broad flake (Levalloisian type) or for the removal of a number of small flakes (Mousterian type). Long flake-blades and polyhedral stone balls were also parts of the Fauresmith equipment.[62]

An industry including long flake-blades and hand-axes of Fauresmith type has been found near East London, Cape Province, in association with a 20-ft (6–8 m) raised beach (J. D. Clark, 1959, p. 164) which may possibly be equated with the Late Monastirian stage of the Mediterranean (see p. 50).

In the Vaal Valley the Fauresmith occurs in the Youngest Gravels. Among the most characteristic tools here are almond-shaped hand-axes made of indurated shale. They are so abundant and conspicuous in the ground at some localities that farmers and diamond-prospectors have for many years noticed them and referred to them as *amandel klippe* (almond-stones) without realizing their actual nature (J. D. Clark, 1959, p. 146)

In the Southern Mountains region of the Cape Province, the Fauresmith people (*eg* the fossil Saldanha Man) made tools of Table Mountain Sandstone. In the sequence preserved in Montagu Cave the change from pear-shaped bifaces to mainly almond-shaped forms is taken to mark the division between Final Acheulian and Lower Fauresmith (J. D. Clark, 1959, p. 48).

The contemporaneous *Sangoan* culture was very widespread in Central Africa, with the Congo Basin as its focus (Fig. 56). It evidently arose out of the need for the Chelles-Acheul peoples in that region to adapt their equipment to life in wooded country. Typical Sangoan tools include heavy picks (Fig. 57), crudely finished hand-axes, circular high-back 'cores' with a flat base (probably used like the *arapia* blocks of the Australian aborigines, for planing wood),[63] tea-cosy scrapers, many utilized flakes and rounded stone balls. In the Western Congo and in Angola long but thick bifaced points and parallel-sided core-tools (*ciseaux*) are characteristic of the Sangoan (J. D. Clark, 1959, p. 151). Quartzites and fine-grained silicified sandstone (silcrete) were the rocks used most extensively.

There were several regional variants, for example in the Zambezi Sangoan (J. D. Clark, 1950, p. 186), finely pointed

Figure 56 Distributon of Sangoan-Lupemban-Tshitolian industries. *After Cole.*

hand-axes reminiscent of the Micoquian were frequently made. In the Bembezi variant,[64] found in Northern Bechuanaland and parts of Southern Rhodesia, picks are rare but rough hand-axes and flakes trimmed into denticulate and various other forms of scraper are common. This variant was probably adapted to more open bush country.

One of the interesting features of the Sangoan is that much of its lithic equipment appears to have been devised for working wood or cutting trees, and yet it clearly spread most widely

during an arid interpluvial phase of climate. Professor
Desmond Clark (J. D. Clark, 1959, p. 151) has offered an
ingenious explanation of this anomaly. During an interpluvial,
in the low-lying savannah country, open forests would have
been replaced by thicket-scrub rather than by desert, and
this terrain, where honey (the only source of sugar available to
early man) is most plentiful, is very difficult to penetrate

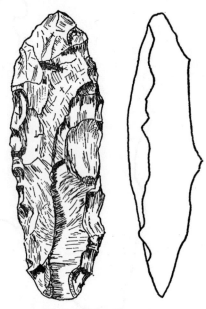

Figure 57 Sangoan *ciseau-pic* of silcrete, Congo Basin.
After Mortelmans. ($\frac{1}{2}$).

except along tracks cut by man or beast. Many of the Sangoan
tools, he suggests, may have been used in cutting a way
through thickets.

The radiocarbon dating of the Zambian Sangoan (*c* 43,000–
c 40,000 B.P. at Kalambo Falls) indicates that this culture was
contemporaneous in part at least with the Mousterian of Europe
(Charts B and D).

The *Middle Stone Age* coincided to a remarkable extent with
the Gamblian pluvial, and consequently its industries have
considerable value for relative dating. At one time the 'MSA'

was thought to be much later in the south than in the north, but in the light of the evidence now available this view is untenable. The main phases of the Middle Stone Age culture-complex show a constant relationship to a climatic sequence that was essentially identical throughout its vast area of distribution (J. D. Clark, 1959, p. 153). A typical section in a Late Pleistocene flood-plain terrace in Southern Africa shows a basal gravel with Sangoan artifacts, marking the erosion which accompanied the change from interpluvial to pluvial conditions, followed by alluvial silts of the Gamblian period, which was terminated by a phase of widespread aridity. Middle Stone Age assemblages occur on surfaces within the Gamblian alluvium, whereas deposits of the succeeding dry phase are almost invariably associated with Second Intermediate or earliest microlithic industries.

The Middle Stone Age industries are characterized by triangular points struck from cores with prepared faces and faceted striking-platforms, *ie* essentially Levalloisoid, *but* they show a wide range of regional variation. At this time, man – aided perhaps by the onset of pluvial conditions – was spreading into areas of Southern and Central Africa which were previously uninhabitable, and his equipment was necessarily becoming more specialized and adaptive (J. D. Clark, 1959, p. 154).

The two main variants in the open woodlands and grasslands were the Stillbay and Pietersburg cultures. The *Stillbay*[65] culture was very widespread, from the Cape to the Horn. In the Rhodesias, its precursor the *Proto-Stillbay*,[66] dating from early Gamblian times, has been found at a number of sites. This takes the form of an industry of unspecialized chopping tools together with triangular flakes with faceted butts, occasional thick bifaced points, notched scrapers and stone balls. The material used was mainly quartz. There is evidence for associating Rhodesian (Broken Hill) Man with an industry (Fig. 58) transitional between Late Sangoan and Proto-Stillbay. In the fully developed Stillbay industries dating from the second half of the Gamblian, the implements were finished with much greater care, and included leaf-shaped points either bifaced or unifaced, many of them with butt-ends reduced for hafting and mostly with surfaces finished by controlled flat

CHART D

CHRONOLOGY OF STONE-AGE CULTURES IN AFRICA
DURING THE LAST SIXTY THOUSAND YEARS

AFRICA SOUTH OF THE SAHARA

STRATI-GRAPHICAL DIVISION	NORTHERN AFRICA	CLIMATIC STAGE IN EAST AFRICA	CULTURAL DIVISION		CULTURE	RADIOCARBON-DATED SITE	DATE IN YEARS B.C.	LABORATORY NUMBER
HOLOCENE	BEDOUIN MICROLITHIC		Iron Age					
	NEOLITHIC SHAHEINAB 3,300 B.C.	Nakuru wet phase	Later Stone Age		LATE WILTON NEOLITHIC	Lusu, Rhodesia / Njoro R. Cave	189±150 / 970±80	–C.030 / –Y.91
	CAPSIAN c. 5,000—9,000 B.C.	Drier			NACHIKUFU I	Chifubwa	4,360±250	–C.663
		Makalian wet phase			LATE MAGOSIAN	Kalambo	7,600±210	–L.359D
	ORANIAN (Ibero-Maurusian)	Drier oscillation	2nd Intermediate		LUPEMBO-TSHITOLIAN	Mufo, Angola	9,239±490	–C.580
UPPER PLEISTOCENE	Late ATERIAN c. 15,000?B.C.	Main Gambian Stage	MIDDLE STONE AGE	Upper	FINAL LUPEMBAN / LATE PIETERSBURG (cf. STILLBAY)	Mufo, Angola / Cave of Hearths, Transvaal	12,553±560 / 13,150±730	–C.581 / –C.925
	Early ATERIAN c. 35,000?B.C.			Middle	LUPEMBAN / HAGENSTADT VARIANT	Kalambo / Florisbad	28,550±2,000 / 33,000±	–L.399I / –L.271B
	LEVALLOISO-MOUSTERIAN			Lower	SANGOAN	Kalambo	41,050±3,300	–L.399C
	LATE ACHEULIAN	Drier oscillation	1st Intermediate		FINAL ACHEULIAN	Kalambo	55,550±700	–GRN.2644
		Early Gambian	Earlier Stone Age					

c. 38,000 ? DABRA 12,000 B.C.

MAP I

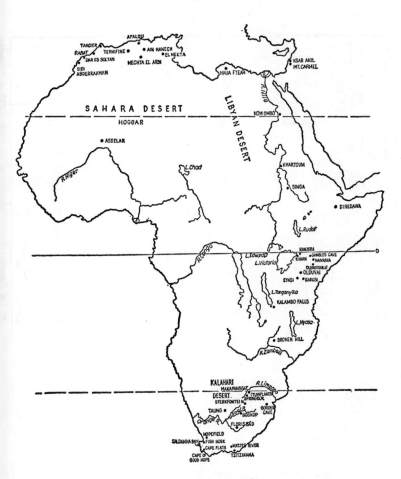

Fossil Hominid sites in Africa

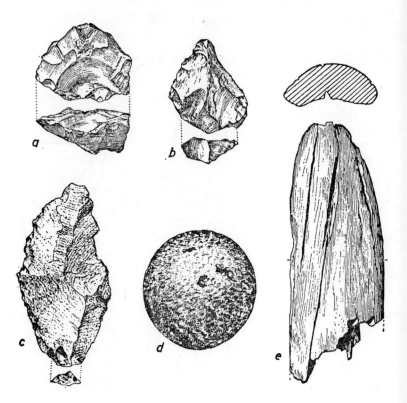

Figure 58 Artifacts found in the Bone Cave at Broken Hill, Zambia, probably to be associated with Broken Hill Man.
a Disc-core of chert; *b* & *c* quartz-flakes with faceted striking-platforms; *d* spherical 'bolas stone' of granite; *e* gouge of bone.
After J. D. Clark. (½).

flaking and later by pressure (Fig. 59). In the Rhodesias the Stillbay hunters made effective use of quartz as a raw material, but in many parts of South Africa the fine-grained silcrete (silicified sand) was the material most favoured by them.

The people of the *Pietersburg*[67] culture lived mainly in bushveld country. In the earliest phase large numbers of simple flake-blades were produced, most commonly in quartzite. In the middle and upper phases the Pietersburg tool-makers selected better material, using in preference felsite, silcrete, chert or indurated shale (lydianite). Their triangular points

Figure 59 Stillbay point of silcrete from Cape Province.
B.M.N.H. (⅔).

show an increasing use of convergent flaking in dressing the face of the core, and of pressure-flaking in finishing the surface of the implement. A climatic break indicated between the cave-earth with Proto-Stillbay and the cave-earth with Stillbay at several Rhodesian sites is paralleled by a break between the Lower and Middle Pietersburg levels in the Transvaal (J. D. Clark, 1959, p. 159).

In the grasslands of the Orange Free State, contemporaries of the Pietersburg and Stillbay peoples made extensive use of indurated shale in variants of this culture-complex, and these have a bearing on the antiquity of Florisbad Man.

In the forested country of the Congo, Angola, parts of Zambia and East Africa, the Middle Stone Age was represented by the *Lupemban*[68] culture (see Chart D). Its industries, which possessed many features of Sangoan origin, included picks, occasional hand-axes, many small ciseaux, gouges, wedge-shaped tools and many forms of scraper. The most finely finished artifacts in Lupemban assemblages are lance-like points worked on both faces (Fig. 60).

The *Magosian*[69] culture, belonging to the Second Inter-mediate group, began towards the end of the Gamblian pluvial,

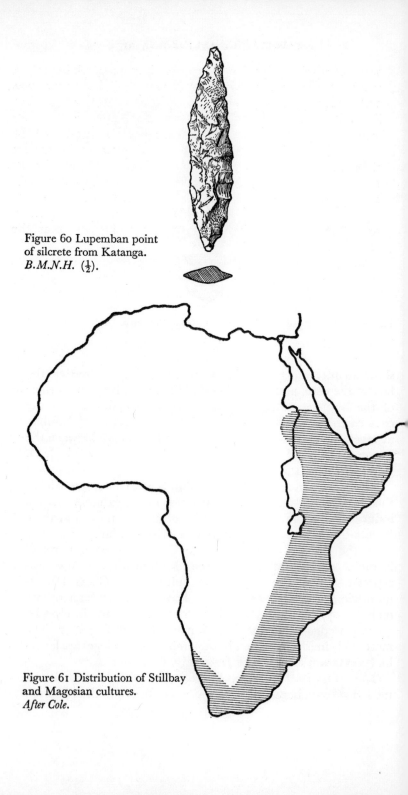

Figure 60 Lupemban point
of silcrete from Katanga.
B.M.N.H. ($\frac{1}{2}$).

Figure 61 Distribution of Stillbay
and Magosian cultures.
After Cole.

and extended through the very dry succeeding phase which marked the beginning of Post-Pleistocene time. The culture was first recognized in Uganda by E. J. Wayland, but it was first found stratified between the Stillbay and Wilton (microlithic) industries at Apis Rock[70] in Tanzania. It combines the continued use of the Levalloisoid prepared-core technique for the production of points, with the use of new techniques for the production of blades and microliths. Its distribution is much the same as that of the Stillbay from which it is derived (Fig. 61). Some authorities view the Magosian as entirely indigenous, as a natural developmental stage, but others see it as the termination of the Middle Stone Age culture-complex brought about by the influence of an outside tradition spreading from the north. Certainly the increasingly dry conditions following the Gamblian pluvial must have led to extensive movements of people, so that groups were brought into contact that were formerly isolated: and there is no doubt that the blade tradition was becoming manifest in North Africa at about this time. The introduction of microliths constituted a revolution (J. D. Clark, 1959, p. 166), for it was a realization of the superiority of composite tools and weapons, made by hafting small, specially designed pieces of stone in wood or bone.

Magosian assemblages (Fig. 62) generally include small leaf-shaped and triangular points carefully thinned and surfaced by pressure-flaking, together with backed blades, angle burins (used no doubt for grooving and slotting bone and wood), utilized blades with finely scaled edges, and microliths which included lunate (half-moon shaped) forms, probably used as the barbs of spears or arrows. Blades were struck from small cores by indirect percussion (Fig. 77): the core was evidently rested on an anvil-stone and tapped sharply, with the result that a blade was detached either from above by the primary blow or from below by the recoil – or sometimes from both ends (bipolar flaking J. D. Clark, 1959, p. 173). As a by-product of this technique, Magosian industries include 'dimple-scarred' anvil-stones. Colouring matter was being extensively used for the first time in Africa during this transition from Palaeolithic to Mesolithic, and ochre crayons have been found at a number of Magosian living-sites.

A forest variant of the Magosian has been identified in the

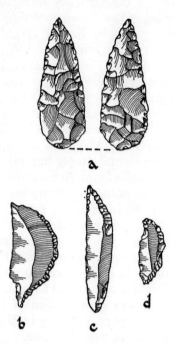

Figure 62 Magosian artifacts: *a* leaf-shaped point; *b, c, d* large lunate microliths. Somaliland.
After J. D. Clark. (⅔).

Congo Basin, and named *Lupembo-Tshitolian*.[71] This has already been reported from Zambia (Kalambo Falls) and Uganda.

Among the stone age cultures south of the Sahara which have been counted as Palaeolithic is the rather anomalous *Kenya Capsian*.[72] At first called 'Kenya Aurignacian' (Leakey, 1931, pp. 70–109), this has generally been regarded as a far-flung offshoot of the blade and burin tradition which spread from Eurasia into North Africa during the later phases of the Würm glaciation. Confined to Kenya and Tanzania, it appears to have had an existence independent of the contemporaraneous Epi-Levalloisian cultures (Stillbay and Magosian). The earliest phase evidently commenced during the Gamblian pluvial but later phases continued at least until the Makalian wet phase.

As we shall see (p. 213), the true Capsianculture was much later in origin and confined to the high plains of Tunisia and Eastern Algeria. Whether the Kenya Capsian represents an early wave of the blade tradition that was remotely ancestral to the Capsian, or whether it had an entirely independent, autochthonous, origin is still uncertain. It has been suggested by Leakey (Cole, 1963, p. 256) that through the fall in sea-level during the Würm Glaciation, a land connection was briefly established between Arabia and Somaliland, and that the blade tradition was brought into East Africa at that time by wandering groups of hunters of Asiatic origin. The distances involved are great, but it should be remembered that groups of Zulus are known to have moved from Natal to Lake Victoria (2,000 miles) and half way back again in less than a century (J. D. Clark, 1959, p. 168).

This culture has been divided into two stages. The Lower Kenya Capsian occurs *in situ* in the Melawa Gorge[73] in deposits containing a typical Gamblian fauna. The Upper Kenya Capsian is found in occupation layers of the rock-shelter known as Gamble's Cave II, near Elementeita, which is the type locality (Leakey, 1931, p. 116–19). Although the Lower Kenya Capsian dates from Gamblian times, and is therefore Late Pleistocene, there is still uncertainty about the age of the Upper Kenya Capsian, which is probably Post-Pleistocene. The presence of pottery and the abundance of ostrich-shell beads in the Upper Kenya Capsian layers (Leakey, 1931, pp. 103–4; Cole, 1963, p. 264) are consistent with a Mesolithic phase of culture. Moreover, two barbed bone points of Ishangian type (Fig. 63) have recently been reported (Oakley, 1961) from these levels, strongly suggesting that they are not older than Makalian. Until radiocarbon dating of the Upper Kenya Capsian is available, little more can be said.

It has been suggested (Cole, 1963, p. 256) that to avoid confusion the original name 'Kenya Aurignacian' might be retained for the Lower stage, and Kenya Capsian restricted to the Upper. The Upper Kenya Capsian is interesting from the viewpoint of race since it is associated with human skeletal remains of Mediterranean Caucasoid type ('Proto-Hamitic').

The Kenya Capsian industries include large numbers of backed-blades of Chatelperron-type, angle-burins, end-scrapers and lunates, all in shiny black obsidian, which is known to have been mined at this time in the Njorowa Gorge and on Eburru mountain in the Kenya Rift Valley (Cole, 1963, p. 262). On two occasions excavations revealed lunates in positions indicating that they had been hafted as arrow barbs (Cole, 1963, p. 261).

Turning to consider the Palaeolithic cultures in NORTHERN AFRICA, one is reminded that the Sahara must at times have been a considerable barrier to the movement of early populations, for the cultural sequence in the north is in many ways more similar to that in Western Europe and south-west Asia than to the sequence south of the Sahara, for which the terminology Earlier, Middle and Later Stone Ages was devised.

The occurrence of *Oldowan* tools in Late Villafranchian deposits in Algeria (see p. 173) and the geological dating of the

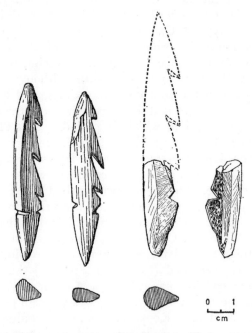

Figure 63 *right* Butt-end of bone harpoon from Upper Kenya Capsian, layer 13, Gamble's Cave II; *left* uniserial bone harpoons from Makalian Lake Beds, Ishango.
After de Heinzelin; Oakley 1961a.

Chellean culture in Morocco (Fig. 64) have already been noted (p. 177). The evolution of the succeeding *Acheulian* culture occurred mainly during the 30-m or Tyrrhenian transgression and terminated with the recession preceding the 18-m or Monastirian I beach. The deposits and faunas associated with Acheulian industries in Algeria, Tunisia and in the Sahara indicate quite clearly that pluvial conditions existed in North Africa as they did in East Africa during the development of this culture. The correlations of the Early Acheulian industries of Lake Karar and Ternifine (Palikao), and of the Upper Acheulian of Sidi Abderrahman, have an important bearing on the dating of the oldest fossil remains of man in North Africa. [74]

The fact that pebble-tools of primitive appearance occurred amidst the advanced Acheulian (Micoquian) assemblage at Sidi Zin (Alimen, 1957, p. 39) in Tunisia may be noted as a warning against placing much reliance on one or two isolated artifacts as evidence of the age of the containing deposit.

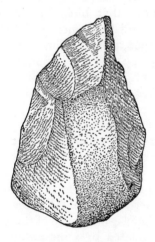

Figure 64 Chellean biface of quartzite pebble, Layer M, Sidi Abderrahman, Morocco.
After Neuville & Ruhlman. ($\frac{1}{2}$).

In many parts of North Africa, the Acheulian industries are succeeded by assemblages in which the main components are products of *Levalloisian* technique. There are indications in a number of areas that this transition from Lower to Middle Palaeolithic began during an interpluvial, but was completed under pluvial conditions.

Doubts have often been expressed about the separate existence of a 'Levalloisian' culture, and many authorities now regard industries which employed the prepared-core technique as either a facies of the essentially African Acheulian culture and its specialized off-shoots (Caton-Thompson, 1946), or as a facies of the distinct *Mousterian* tradition, generally regarded as of Eurasiatic origin. It is true to say that in general the term Levalloisian is now mainly used in North Africa for industries representing a culture of African (Acheulian) origin. Many industries which at one time were called Mousterian (for example in Egypt) are now recognized as of Acheulio-Levalloisian origin and are called Levalloisian in this sense. At the same time there were contemporaneous outliers of culture, for example in Cyrenaica, which can be matched almost exactly with the *Levalloiso-Mousterian* culture in Palestine. There are in fact faunal indications that biological interchange occurred between the Levant and Cyrenaica during Upper Pleistocene times (McBurney, 1960, p. 171). These true Mousterian industries (McBurney, 1960, p. 168) are in flint, and are distinguished by large numbers of beautifully finished side-scrapers and points made on flakes with faceted striking platforms, and by small oval tortoise-cores accompanied by miniature discoid cores.

The earliest traces of *Acheulio-Levalloisian* industry in Upper Egypt occur in the 9-m terrace of the Nile (McBurney, 1960, pp. 135–9; Butzer 1959), which is most reasonably to be correlated with the fall in sea-level to the 18-m or Monasterian I beach of the Mediterranean. A fully developed Levalloisian industry occurs in the 3–4-m terrace of the Upper Nile, Egypt, which has been correlated by some authors with the 7-m or Monasterian II beach; but the view that it is related to some phase of the Last Pluvial is widely favoured.

Farther south-west, in the spring-deposits of the Kharga Oasis in the Libyan Desert, the evolution of Levalloisian culture in relation to stages of the Last Pluvial (p. 92), have been studied in detail by Miss Caton-Thompson (1952, pp. 26–32). The Levalloisian industries here are devoid of hand-axes, but the culture was evidently a direct descendant of the Acheulio-Levalloisian which preceded it stratigraphically. The industries show a concentration on the production of flake-tools, including flake-blades, by means of the prepared core technique. In the Lower Levalloisian the 'tortoise' cores are oval, and in an unstruck condition are not unlike Acheulian bifaces. As cultural evolution proceeded into the Upper Levallosian stage, cores became rounder or discoidal, and the flake-tools smaller, showing increased use of retouch to adapt them for specialized purposes.

In connection with the preservation of human remains, it is notable that in North Africa, as in Europe and Western Asia, men began using caves and rock-shelters extensively at the time when their industries were acquiring a Mousterioid (or Levalloisoid) form.

In the Maghreb, the Levalloiso-Mousterian is succeeded by industries of a type peculiar to North Africa: they are distinguished by the presence of tanged or stemmed implements, and have been named *Aterian* after the alluvial site at Bir-el-Ater in southern Tunisia.[75] The homeland of this remarkable culture, which is the high-water mark of the Levalloisian tradition, was evidently the Atlas massif. Aterian peoples not only occupied the shores of the Western Mediterranean and the Atlantic coast of Morocco, but ranged south to the Sahara's equatorial limits and to the borders of the Nile Valley. During the development of this culture conditions were for the most part wetter than at present, which would largely account for Aterian industries being widespread in the Sahara, and extending into the Libyan Sand Sea. However, at one Aterian site (in south Tunisia) the associated flora indicates very dry conditions (Alimen, 1957, p. 64), so it is possible that these people were able to live in deserts.

There is radiocarbon evidence that the Aterian was contemporaneous with Late Mousterian and Upper Palaeolithic cultures in Europe and Asia. One of the most important sites from the point of view of dating is the cave of Dar-es-Soltan[76] in the coast of Morocco, where two levels of Aterian industry occur in a red loam containing the last traces of the 'archaic' *Rhinoceros merckii* fauna and overlying the Ouljian beach. Charcoal from the lower level is > 30,000 years B.P. At the eastern extremity of its range, the Aterian culture appears to have survived until the declining phases of the Last Pluvial. Aterian at Fachi (Tibesti) is dated c 20,000 B.P.

In Aterian industries there was much more selection of material than in the preceding Mousterian. Thus in the rock-shelter at Taforalt,[77] the Mousterian industry in the lower layers of the sequence is in basalt, whereas the three overlying Aterian industries are in flint. Many sites show a decreasing use of quartzite and an increasing use of flint.

As regards technique the Aterian industries are predominantly Levalloisian. Thus, 70–100 per cent of the cores on Aterian sites are tortoise-cores (Caton-Thompson, 1947, p. 90), mostly very small. There are no true blades in these industries, but numerous parallel-sided flakes struck from prepared cores and known as *flake-blades* (Caton-Thompson, 1946, p. 61). These were often trimmed into end-scrapers and points. Side-scrapers of the type found in Mousterian industries occur, but in declining numbers. The outstanding innovation was the making of *tanged* missile points (McBurney, 1960, p. 159) and end-scrapers. The stem or tang was made by chipping two deep concavities in either side of the centre of the striking-platform of the flake-blade. The chipping was usually extended on to both sides, so that the stem acquired a diamond-shaped cross section. The Aterian tang (Fig. 65) was clearly devised for the purpose of attaching the flake-blade to a handle or shaft. Some of these artifacts were evidently spear- or arrowheads, but others were too thick and heavy to be used in that way and were more probably intended as scrapers. In the most evolved phase, the tanged points are bifacially trimmed by pressure flaking. These *pointes marocaines* (Caton-Thompson, 1947, p. 115) are scarcely distinguishable from the tanged arrowheads found in the Solutrean industries of Levels III and IV at Parpallo in Spain (p. 160, Fig. 39c).

Aterian industries also include miniature hand-axes (sometimes known as *petits coup-de-poings* – Caton-Thompson, 1947, p. 97) and thin bifaces reminiscent of Solutrean 'foliates', or leaf-shaped spearheads (Fig. 66). A surface assemblage found near the fort of 'Sbaikia in Algeria, comprising bifacial implements ranging from thin hand-axes to small 'foliates', was termed the *'Sbaikian* industry (Caton-Thompson, 1947, p. 114;

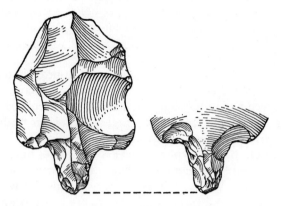

Figure 65 Aterian tanged artifact of silcrete, Cyrenaica. *After Watson.* ($\frac{1}{2}$).

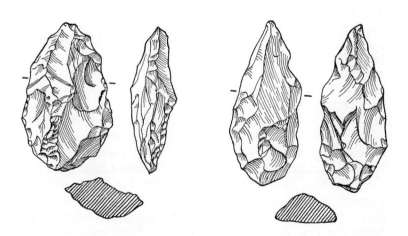

Figure 66 Artifacts of Aterian-type *a petit coup-de-poing* of silica-glass *b* bifaced foliate of silica-glass, Libyan Desert. *After Oakley* ($\frac{7}{8}$).

Alimen, 1957, p. 48), but the idea that all the artifacts were contemporaneous and that they represented a distinct culture has now been abandoned. Excavations at Taforalt have established that Solutrean-like foliates occur in normal Aterian assemblages (Fig. 39d).

The resemblance of the Aterian to the approximately contemporaneous Stillbay culture has often been remarked upon, and has given rise to the suggestion that the two cultures represent twin derivatives from a parental Levalloisian tradition in Central Africa (Caton-Thompson, 1947, p. 115).

At Kom Ombo in Egypt a remarkable series of flint artifacts have been referred to the final phase of silt formation in that part of the Nile Valley.[78] These *Sebilian* industries were considered by their discoverer, Vignard (1923), to show an evolutionary transition from an increasingly small Levalloisian flake industry to a blade industry. As it is now known that this was geologically at a time long after the appearance of blade culture in adjoining regions the cultural significance of the Sebilian is no longer rated very high. Indeed, like the mainly contemporaneous *Khargan*,[79] it is best regarded as one of the many diminutive Epi-Levalloisian industries produced in North Africa during the declining phases of the Last Pluvial. The occurrence of 'micro-burins' in some of the Sebilian assemblages has suggested that these may be Mesolithic rather than Palaeolithic, but as we shall shortly see this is not a reliable criterion.

A large number of sites along the coast of the Maghreb have yielded evidence that the Mousterian and Aterian industries were succeeded by a true blade culture, distinguished by an overwhelming abundance of backed blades struck from small flat rectangular cores (McBurney, 1960, p. 212). These industries are most conveniently termed *Oranian*[80] but the authors of this name later reverted to the earlier name *Ibero-Maurusian* invented in 1909 by Pallary.[81] As these industries include a proportion of geometric microliths and micro-burins (Fig. 67), their affinities have been widely regarded as being with the Capsian (p. 213), but recent researches have established that they are partly of Late Pleistocene antiquity, whereas the latter are Post-Pleistocene. One of the most important sites from the point of view of dating the Oranian stratigraphically, is Sidi Mannsour, near Gafsa in Tunisia.[82] Here a prolonged

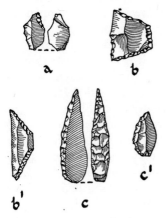

Figure 67 Oranian (= Ibero-Maurusian) artifacts: *a* 'micro-burin'; *b*, *b'* geometric microliths; *c*, *c'* backed blades (*lamelles à dos rabattu*). From Tunisia.
After Vaufrey. (⅔).

aggradation, following a phase of catastrophic earth-movement, began with the accumulation of coarse sediments containing traces of Mousterian culture, and these were followed conformably by fine sediments containing Oranian industries. The cycle of aggradation was terminated by erosion which dissected these sediments, leaving ridges which were then occupied by people of the Typical Capsian culture.

Although Oranian culture is found mainly in the western half of North Africa (the Maghreb), industries of this group have been reported from as far east as Cyrenaica. In the excavation of the cave known as Haua Fteah, Dr C. B. M. McBurney (1960, pp. 213–16) found in upward sequence that the percentage of backed blades suddenly jumped, while burins at the same time almost vanished, in the zone 11½ ft–9 ft below the surface. He interpreted this as indicating that the bearers of the Oranian culture moved in from an outside area. According to the available radiocarbon evidence their arrival here took place in the tenth millennium BC.

Early parallels of the Oranian are known in the Levant, but the culture is so uniform from Haua Fteah westwards that a largely indigenous origin is more probable. One can say that it corresponds approximately with one of the Epi-Gravettian variants which followed or overlapped the Magdalenian in Spain (McBurney, 1960, p. 221).

Largely through McBurney's researches in Cyrenaica (McBurney, 1950), it is now known that the Oranian was not the earliest blade culture to reach North Africa. In the hills of the Gebel region a site called Hagfet ed Dabba, or Cave of the Hyena, has yielded two blade industries representing successive phases of what he has termed the *Dabba* culture (McBurney, 1960, p. 224). These differ from Oranian industries chiefly in that burins are very abundant, and tools made from backed blades are more varied in form and size. The earliest phase of the Dabba culture is distinguished by a peculiar type of transverse burin which occurs also in the Emiran industry at the beginning of the Upper Palaeolithic phase of culture in the Levant.[84] The Dabba culture may well represent a group of Emiran hunters who wandered from south-west Asia and formed a colony in Cyrenaica shortly before 30,000 BC.

Both phases of the Dabba culture are represented in the Haua Fteah cave (in the 18½ to 11½-ft zone) (McBurney, 1960, p. 202). It is of considerable interest from the point of view of archaeological-climatic correlation that there was a marked change in the local climate during the time that this culture flourished. Whereas the cave-earths containing the Mousterian and very earliest Dabba industries were sandy and full of stalagmitic incrustations, probably through formation under mild wet conditions, the deposits containing most of the Dabba and all of the Oranian industries are gravelly and full of thermo-clastic material indicating formation under a dry climate with sharp frosts in winter (McBurney, 1960, pp. 199–202). The chronology of Stone Age cultures in Africa can at present only be sketched in bare outline as in Chart D.

For distribution of Palaeolithic industries in Africa see forthcoming publication co-ordinated by J. D. Clark, *The Atlas of African Prehistory* (1966).

Chapter 5

Mesolithic Cultures in Africa

ALTHOUGH ELEMENTS OF Neolithic culture such as ground stone axes occasionally reached some parts of Southern Africa during the second half of the *Later Stone Age,* which lasted from about 6500 BC until the coming of iron in the Christian era, this age is generally counted throughout the sub-continent as equivalent to the Mesolithic, because its industries were essentially the work of hunters and food-gatherers. A few of the later groups herded cattle but there is no certain evidence of cultivation of plants in any part of southern Africa before the Iron Age.

The cultures of the Later Stone Age[85] appear to have superseded the Second Intermediate or Magosian group during the Makalian wet phase. They are predominantly microlithic and distinguished by some important innovations: the bow-and-arrow had evidently become the chief hunting weapon, largely replacing the spear; bodily adornment had now become more important, as evidenced by the widespread use of shell ornaments; while extensive use was made of new techniques for grinding and piercing stone and bone. There were four major Mesolithic culture groups in Southern Africa: Nachikufan, Wilton, Smithfield, and on the north-west border, Tshitolian.

The *Nachikufan*[86] is found on open sites as well as in caves or rock-shelters in Zambia and in the adjoining parts of Central Africa. This was a culture adapted to open woodlands or savannah. The microliths produced in the earliest phase are non-geometric, but geometric types appear in phase two, including large trapezes which were almost certainly used as transverse arrowheads, of special value for hunting in wooden country where the visibility is limited. Bored stones were made by the Nachikufan people, and probably had a variety of uses, for example as the weights of digging-sticks and as the heads of throwing-sticks. Nachikufan assemblages also include bone points, small bipolar cores, dimple-scarred anvil stones, mortars, grindstones and pestles. Some of the grinding equipment was evidently used for pigment, but some was no doubt used in the preparation of vegetable food. Although radiocarbon dating has confirmed the great antiquity of the earliest phase, the association of the final phase with pottery of Iron Age type indicates that it lasted until the Christian era. The oldest known paintings (they are schematic) in Southern Africa are attributed to a late phase of the Nachikufan culture.

The *Wilton* and *Smithfield* were both specialized hunting cultures adapted to open country. The Wilton is the more widespread for it is known in East Africa as well as throughout the greater part of South Africa. It developed out of the Magosian[87] either in the Rhodesias, or possibly further north. In South Africa it arrived late, long after the establishment of the Smithfield which developed in isolation in the central plateau region, mainly where this is incised by the Vaal and Upper Orange Rivers.

The Wilton culture is essentially microlithic, whereas the Smithfield (excluding 'Smithfield C', which shows Wilton influence) is characterized by various special forms of scraper of macrolithic proportions. In both cultures are found bone awls and other bone tools, bored stones, ostrich-shell beads and very occasionally polished stone axeheads.

The Wilton folk occupied rock-shelters as well as open sites. The 'Type Wilton'[88] comes from the eastern half of the Cape Province. Industries of this culture include many lunates, micro-drills or borers and tiny quadrangular end-scrapers called thumb-nail scrapers, which are known to have been mounted in handles with mastic or resin (Fig. 68). Among the materials used for these artifacts were quartz – including semi-precious rock-crystal – chalcedony, jasper, and in Kenya, the black volcanic glass obsidian. The Wilton people made much use of pigment, mainly red ochre. Even in the south the earliest phase dates back just over three millennia,[89] but the latest phase is found with Hottentot pottery.

The Smithfield[90] culture was closely linked with the distribution of indurated shale in South Africa, and its industries reflect the fact that this material is not very suitable for making microliths, but good for making large blades and flakes. Three forms of the culture are known: A and B mostly on open sites, C mostly in rock-shelters. Smithfield A is characterized by large circular scrapers, end-scrapers on broad splayed blades of 'duck-bill' form, and concavo-convex side-scrapers (Fig. 69).

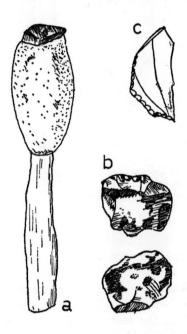

Figure 68 *a* Reconstruction of Wilton thumb-nail scraper mounted on handle with mastic or resin; *b* Wilton thumb-nail scraper of chalcedony showing traces of original mastic. Eastern Cape Province; *c* Wilton lunate ('crescent') of clear quartz from Zambia. *After J. D. Clark a & b, Gabel c.* ($\frac{3}{2}$).

Bored stones are very common in this phase. Smithfield B is associated with rock-engravings, and judging from the occurrence of some artifacts in bottle-glass it persisted into modern times. Smithfield C is more microlithic, and has been found associated with naturalistic paintings in rock-shelters.

From the point of view of archaeologically dated remains of

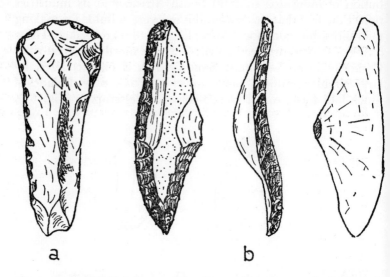

Figure 69 Smithfield industry of the Orange Free State: *a* duck-bill end-scraper on blade (slightly enlarged); *b* concavo-convex side-scraper on side-blow flake ($\frac{1}{2}$). Both of indurated shale.
After J. D. Clark.

man (see Hominid Dating Table XII), the sites of the Later Stone Age are of special interest. The living sites of these peoples (*strandloopers*), whose culture was mainly either Wilton or Smithfield in its affinities, have been found both in the open and in caves along the coasts of South Africa, and are usually associated with shell-middens.

The late *Tshitolian*[91] industries in the moderately forested parts of the Congo Basin include leaf-shaped and tanged projectile points, some of them with denticulate margins, and transverse arrowheads, generally associated with a wide range of wood-working tools. In some areas the latest of these industries show obvious links with the Saharan Neolithic.

Continuing a survey of African Mesolithic cultures northwards, we next encounter the *Ishangian*[92] (see p. 197 and Fig. 63), which has been recognized and defined on the basis of discoveries by Dr J. de Heinzelin on the west shores of Lake Albert (Map I). At the type site, Ishango, industries representing three stages of this culture occur in a series of stratified, fossiliferous lake beds which are referable to the Makalian wet phase. The assemblages include chunky scrapers and utilized, but rather unstandardized, flakes in quartz; Mousterioid cores, and some showing evidence of bipolar flaking, 'dimple-scarred' anvil stones, stone rubbers, and most important of all, quantities of biserially-barbed bone harpoons. These latter, which have been found in all stages of manufacture, were evidently used mainly for killing fishes in the lake.

The distribution of prehistoric bone harpoons in Africa suggests that they represent a fishing tradition which spread quite rapidly (but in which direction is unknown) along a north–south zone stretching from the Central African lakes to the mouth of the Nile and beyond, and along an east–west zone bounded on the north by the Sahara, from the headwaters of the Nile to the headwaters of the Niger. The bone harpoon tradition appears to have originated in, or reached Africa at the close of the Gamblian and to have persisted in some areas through Neolithic times.

In East Africa two main groups of local Mesolithic cultures developed out of earlier palaeolithic traditions.

(1) The blade-and-burin tradition, which took root there during the Gamblian pluvial, gave rise to the *Hargeisan*[93] culture on the Somali plateau, during the Epi-Gamblian dry phase, and during a later humid phase to the *Elmenteitan*[94] culture, which was confined to the Kenya Rift Valley. The Elmenteitan is anthropologically important for it is associated with a number of fossil human remains, of the Caucasoid race. Archaeologically it is notable for pottery[95] of quite varied form together with an obsidian industry which includes long sharp two-edged blades with butts reduced for hafting, squarish fabricators, and numerous lunates. Burins occur only as rarities. It is probable that at least in its late phase, the Upper Kenya Capsian also was Post-Pleistocene, and should be counted as Mesolithic (p. 197).

(2) The other palaeolithic tradition, of the 'Levalloisian'-Stillbay-Magosian lineage, gave rise to the *Wilton* culture. Fully microlithic and retaining few traces of its Magosian origins in South Central Africa, it was also represented in many parts of East Africa during post–Makalian and Nakuran times. Three

phases of East African Wilton[96] are known: the earliest, Wilton A, began during Makalian times; Wilton B, which is found mainly in rock-shelters, occurred through Nakuran times; while Wilton C, associated with shell-mounds on the shores of Lake Victoria and the Indian Ocean, survived until the coming of iron about AD 1000 or even later.

In South Somaliland, the Stillbay-Magosian tradition gave rise to the *Doian*[97] culture. This emerged during the dry phase following the Makalian and reached its maximum development in the Nakuran wet phase. The Doian shows a declining use of the prepared-core technique, and an increasing use of the blade-technique. Its industries include small finely made bifacial points, unifaced *limaces*[98]; short crescentic blades with the so-called Heluan retouch (see p. 213), and triangular hollow-based arrow-heads probably reflecting a Neolithic tradition in Egypt.

The Elmenteitan, Doian and Wilton people are classed as 'Mesolithic' because although they had some pottery, they had no means of food-production – that is to say, they had no domesticated animals, and cultivated no plants. On the other hand, a few human groups living in settlements in East Africa at about the same time are believed, by some, to have cultivated root or cereal crops, for example the people of the Hyrax Hill and variants of the *Stone Bowl Cultures* of Kenya,[99] possibly dating from late Makalian through Nakuran times, although some at least were Iron Age (Cole, 1963, pp. 306–15).

While the Kenya Capsian culture was developing into the Elmenteitan in the Kenya Rift Valley, the same culture appears to have given rise to other Mesolithic variants farther north, for example the *Khartoum Mesolithic* (Arkell, 1949; Cole, 1963, pp. 251–5), represented at the name-site by an assemblage that includes quartz lunates as the main microlithic component, together with narrow backed–blades, disc-shaped ochre-grinders, barbed bone harpoons and pottery decorated with impressions made by a cord or the barbed spine of a catfish.

In North Africa, as in East Africa, the Mesolithic phase was represented by a large number of cultures, some of which were Epi-Levalloisian, some in the blade tradition, others of hybrid facies, but all showing a microlithic tendency, and generally with a few traits emanating from the Neolithic world, whose nucleus was in the Near East, but which was spreading into North Africa in the fifth millennium BC.

The extensive flint industry found at Heluan, south of Cairo, is generally classified as Mesolithic for it shows clear affinities with the Natufian of Palestine. The *Heluan industry*[100] includes 'crescents', that is to say, narrow lunates, with backs blunted by retouch from both sides (Heluan retouch), together with other microliths, and small blades which appear to have been hafted for use as sickles, and tanged arrowheads with characteristically notched bases.

Between the end of Pleistocene times and the arrival of Neolithic farming communities, the western half of North Africa, generally known as the Maghreb, was occupied by peoples with cultures in the blade tradition, who became established there towards the close of the Palaeolithic stage and largely replaced the Aterians with Mousterioid tradition. There were two main groups: the people of *Oranian* culture, already briefly described as being in part Upper Palaeolithic, who had a mainly coastal distribution; and the people of the true Capsian culture, who were mainly confined to the high plains. Since the latter culture attained its typical development in Post-Pleistocene times it is now classed as Mesolithic.

The *Capsian*[101] was first described by J. de Morgan at El Mekta, near Gafsa, in Tunisia, where it is associated with a shell-mound, very characteristic of the culture, occurring on a hillside and covering an area of over 1,400 sq yds. The shell-mound is about 3 ft thick, and careful excavation has revealed that it contains three successive industries: Early Capsian, Typical Capsian and Evolved or Upper Capsian. All three phases include geometric microliths and 'micro-burins' associated, especially in the typical industry, with many large flint tools, pyramidal and barrel-shaped blade cores, large blunted-back points of Chatelperron-type and angle-burins. Scalene triangles and lunates were made in increasing numbers, while trapezes became common in the final phase. These industries (Fig. 70) also include stone mullers, bone awls and ostrich-shell beads.

Capsian shell-mounds contain large numbers of calcined flints ('pot-boilers'), shells of four species of land-snail, which were consumed in great quantities, and remains of small

H

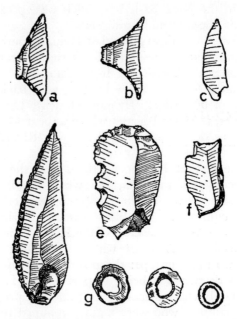

Figure 70 Upper Capsian artifacts, Tunisia: *a, b* geometric microliths; *c* 'micro–burin'; *d* point of Chatelperron-type; *e* broad end-scraper; *f* angle-burin; *g* ostrich-shell beads.
After Vaufrey. (⅔).

animals such as jerboas and lizards. Bones of large mammals are scarce. At some localities the final phase of the Capsian was contemporaneous with Neolithic culture, and its assemblages include pierced marine shells such as those of *Nassa* (Alimen, 1957, p. 58). The typical Capsian culture was confined to Tunisia and eastern Algeria, although the late phase was more widespread. Radiocarbon dating indicates that the typical phase was contemporaneous with the Makalian wet phase of the East African sequence (Chart D). The unweathered condition of the majority of the Capsian shell mounds is probably largely due to the fact that very dry conditions have prevailed on the high plains of the Maghreb since the mounds accumulated.

For distribution of Later Stone Age industries in Africa, reference should be made to the forthcoming publication, co-ordinated by J. D. Clark, *The Atlas of African Prehistory* (1966).

Chapter 6

Palaeolithic Cultures in Asia

IN THE YEAR that Lyell published his *Geological Evidence of the Antiquity of Man* (1863), Bruce Foote (1914; Piggott, 1950, p.15) of the Geological Survey of India discovered a palaeolithic implement near Madras and recognized it as essentially similar to those found by Boucher de Perthes in the ancient gravels of the Somme which had established the existence of man in Europe during the Pleistocene period. Foote's discovery was the first of many showing that palaeolithic cultures with a certain basic uniformity extended far beyond the confines of Europe throughout the greater part of Africa and much of Asia.

Researches during the present century have shown that although the early palaeolithic industries of westernmost Asia (the Near East) and central and southern India were based on the bifacial hand-axe tradition, and closely parallelled those of Europe and Africa, there were contemporaneous industries in north-western India, Burma, China and south-eastern Asia (including Java) which had different characteristics as though resulting from an independent tradition.[102] The distinctive implements in these latter industries are forms that have been termed 'choppers' and 'chopping-tools', made for the most part on pebbles or roughly tabular blocks. Most prehistorians now consider that during Middle Pleistocene times and to some extent later, the hunting and food-gathering populations of Asia were under the influence of two tool-making traditions: the *bifacial hand-axe tradition* of African origin spreading from the west into Peninsular India, and the more conservative, perhaps indigenous, *chopper/chopping-tool tradition* which dominated early cultures in the Far East. In northern India the two traditions appear to have overlapped and blended.

The palaeolithic industries of south-east Asia seem to have owed much to the long persistence there of the basic tool-making tradition of man, with its limited range of stone artifacts based on pebbles, blocks of stone and simple flakes. The chopper/chopping-tool industries should be seen as characterized, not so much by the presence of these old fundamental types of stone tool, as by the *absence* of two technological innovations which evidently spread from the west having originated probably in Africa: namely the development of the Acheulian type of bifacial hand-axe and of the prepared-core or Levalloisian technique of flake-production (Movius, 1953, p. 182). The pebble-tool tradition (and associated 'Clactonian' primary flaking) appears to have persisted in some parts of Asia with little modification until the end of the Stone Age. Where palaeolithic industries in the remoter regions (for example the Patjitanian in Java) include implements approximating to bifacial hand-axes, and flakes to some extent prepared, it is by no means easy to be sure that such artifacts represent the ultimate spread of the western traditions, for allowance must be made for autochthonous developments at primitive levels of technology – that is to say for parallel evolution of culture, given similar requirements and raw materials. However, as we shall see, the similarity between certain African and Asiatic palaeolithic industries is so detailed that some continuity of tradition is beyond question.

If the industries of the hand-axe and chopper/chopping-tool provinces of Asia (Fig. 71) represent separately developed traditions, as Professor Movius and most western prehistorians now believe, the interesting question arises as to whether these traditions originated with two different genera or species of mankind. The data bearing on this are still very scanty, but it seems worthwhile reviewing the palaeolithic cultures of southern and eastern Asia in some detail, region by region (Map 2), with this question in mind. At least we shall then have a background on which to set the existing finds of fossil man and any new ones in Asia that may be announced in the next few years.

In the INDIAN SUB-CONTINENT the oldest deposits claimed to contain evidence of tool-making man date from the end of the Second Himalayan Glaciation (Mindel). South-west of

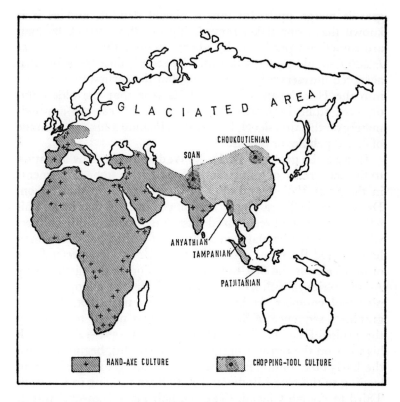

Figure 71 Distributon of hand-axe and chopper/chopping-tool cultures in the Old World during Late Middle Pleistocene times. *After Movius.*

Rawalpindi in the Soan Valley of the Northern Punjab (Pakistan) fan-gravels in the upper part of the Boulder Conglomerate, which merges into the ground-moraine of the second glaciation, have yielded large, high-angled flakes in quartzite, with strongly marked but rather flat bulbs of percussion (de Terra & Paterson, 1939, pp. 285–304). All these flakes are in a highly battered condition. They have been compared with the very dubious 'Cromerian industry' in Britain. None of the blocks or boulders from which the flakes were struck has been found. The rolled condition of the flakes has been interpreted as evidence of 'manufacture while the Boulder Conglomerate was in process of formation' (Movius, 1949, pp. 376–7). As the containing gravels merge upstream into a glacial deposit, and as it is known that stone flakes remarkably like those struck by man are sometimes produced by glacial action, this *'Punjab Flake Industry'* should perhaps be critically re-examined[103] before it is accepted unreservedly as evidence that the earliest men ranged into the Himalayan ice-fields. It is true that the oldest un-doubted stone industries in Asia, as in Africa, are approxi-mately on this time-level, but they all include a high percentage of flaked pebbles or blocks.[104]

In 1928 the geologist Dr D. N. Wadia (1928) drew attention to the occurrence of unquestionable primitive stone implements in the Soan Valley, and after further research in that region, Dr Helmut de Terra (1936) announced in 1936 that he and his fellow workers had recognized there a new palaeolithic culture, which could not be matched in Europe or Africa, and for which he proposed the name *Soan.* The Soan (or as some prefer *Sohan* or *Soanian*) was the first to gain recognition in the distinctively Asiatic series of cultures which constitute the chopper/chop-ping-tool complex, as Movius eventually termed it. A strati-graphical sequence of Soan industries was pieced together by the geologist Dr T. T. Paterson (1939, pp. 301–12), through his work on the terraces of the Soan and Indus, beginning with the Early Soan dating from the Second Interglacial period, and leading to the true Middle and Late Soan ranging in age from Third to Fourth Glacial. (The 'Punjab Flake Industry' was at one time called *Pre-Soan,* but this was only in the chronological sense for even assuming its human origin there was no sugges-tion that it represented a 'culture' related to the Soan.)

The characteristic tools of Soan industries (Fig. 72)[105] have been made on flat or rounded river-pebbles, usually boldly flaked along one margin and evidently intended for chopping, cutting and scraping. Some of these pebble-tools are almost hemispherical, with a working edge produced by steep flaking from a flat base, either a natural fracture plane or formed by breaking the pebble in two. These so-called *'choppers'* are similar to many Oldowan pebble-tools (p. 173). Others, made on flatter pebbles, are flaked alternately from both sides, either along one edge to produce a semicircular *'chopping-tool'*, or around the whole periphery forming a 'proto-handaxe' or 'discoidal core'.

The Early Soan industries comprise more massive and coarsely flaked artifacts than the Middle and Upper or Late Soan (now often referred to as Indian Middle Stone Age). That is to say, there was a general trend in development towards smaller and more finely worked tools, with an increasing use of flakes. In the 'Late Soan' industries small pebble chopping-tools occur, but flakes and flake-blades predominate, and they were struck from cores prepared in the Levalloisian fashion. On a workshop site at the base of the Potwar Silt (a loessic deposit of probably Early Würm glacial age) nearly 50 per cent of the flakes had faceted butts (Paterson, 1939, p. 312).

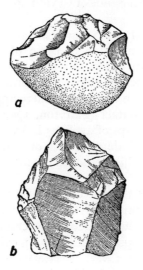

Figure 72 Early Soan tools from north-west India: *a* chopper made of basaltic trap-rock; *b* quartzite flake-tool.
B.M.N.H. (⅓).

Apart from their higher content of pebble-tools relative to flake tools, Early Soan assemblages are remarkably similar to Early Clactonian flint industries in Europe (Paterson, 1939, p. 307); and even the difference noted could be due to the fact that flint nodules are more readily broken down into flakes than pebbles of quartzite or lava. In the type area the Soan artifacts are made on pebbles which are either of a fine-grained lava (Pinjal basaltic trap, with greenish-grey patina) or of a brownish quartzite. The chief features of the Soan industries in the Northern Punjab were obviously largely determined by the form of the pebbles which were most easily available for making stone implements in that region. However, the Soan culture was certainly not merely a local development, for sites with an identical industry have been found as far away as 350 miles south-east of Rawalpindi[106]; while farther south, indeed wherever they occur in the Indian sub-continent (Fig. 73), the contemporaneous hand-axe industries seem to show the influence of an underlying Soan tradition. The rather amorphous artifacts of the *Ratnapura* culture reported by Deraniyagala from the Gem Sands of Ceylon appear to reflect crudely both traditions.[107]

In the Northern Punjab, some bifacial hand-axe industries are represented in addition to those of the Soan chopper/chopping-tool group. From this it has been inferred that the two cultures coexisted in that region and developed independently until Late Soan times when there appears to be evidence that they were in contact (Paterson, 1939, p. 312). However, even the earliest groups of artifacts in the gravels of the Indus and Soan rivers include examples of both cultures so that it cannot be decided which reached the area first (Movius, 1949, pp. 385–6).

It is possible that the question implicit in the last statement is based on a false premise. It should not be assumed without very good proof that any two so-called cultures which appear to have existed contemporaneously in a particular region during early palaeolithic times were necessarily produced by different human groups. Both the 'cultures' may represent the seasonal or localized activities of a single nomadic group. The Australian aborigines supply many parallels. Just as the quite distinctive Hope Fountain industries in Africa were simply a facies of Chelles-Acheul culture, so the Clactonian in Europe and the Soan industries in Asia may have been produced by the people who in some circumstances made bifacial hand-axes. If this proved to be the case it would not invalidate the view favoured in this book that the chopper/chopping-tool tradition was basic, and that the bifacial hand-axe tradition of African origin only became strongly imprinted in the western and southern parts of Asia.

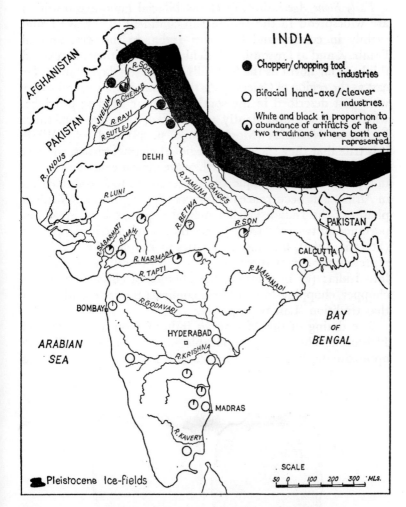

Figure 73 Map of India showing the distribution of chopper/chopping-tool industries and of bifacial hand-axe/cleaver industries.
After Lal.

Early Stone Age industries of the bifacial hand-axe tradition are widespread in the Indian sub-continent. They are found mainly in central and Southern India, in the west around Bombay, and as far south as Trichinopoly, but they also extend thinly as far north as the foot-hills of the Himalayas and as far east as the region of Calcutta. As the Indian hand-axe industries were first described in the south-eastern or Madras province, where they are abundantly represented, they are sometimes known as *Madrasian* (Movius, 1949, p. 381 and ref.). While it is true that they show a few regional characteristics, the fact should not be overlooked that they are almost exactly the same in typology, tool technique and succession as their counterparts in Africa. The occurrence of cleavers (Fig. 74) in the Acheulian phases of the Indian Chelles-Acheul sequence is of great importance for two reasons: (1) since they occur also in the Levant (Stekelis, 1960), but only as rarities in Europe, they evidently represent the direct spread of Acheulian tradition from Africa into India; (2) in contrast, the absence of cleavers from the chopper/chopping-tool cultures confirms the independence of that tradition (Lal, 1956, p. 91).

The dating of the Madrasian industries on any scheme of Pleistocene chronology applicable outside India is still only approximate, but the occurrence of a few unrolled hand-axes

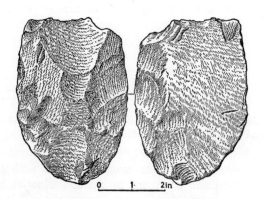

Figure 74 Madrasian cleaver of quartzite from 'laterite', Madras. *B.M.N.H.*

of Middle Acheulian type in the terraces of the Indus and Soan rivers (Pakistan) has made it possible to date the main stages of that industry in terms of the Himalayan glacial sequence as Second Interglacial (Middle Pleistocene). In central and southern India, the glacial/interglacial regimen of the north was replaced by a mainly pluvial/interpluvial climatic sequence, registered as alternate aggradation and down-cutting by the main rivers.

The most prolific sites of Madrasian artifacts are in detrital laterites[108] and fluviatile sands and silts preserved in river terraces a few miles outside Madras. The majority of the implements are in a pale brown sedimentary quartzite which has been patinated to a dark brown. In sections at Vadamaduri (Paterson, 1939, p. 328 and Movius, 1953, p. 184) north-west of the city a river-laid boulder conglomerate, passing laterally into grits and sands, has yielded a large series of deeply patinated (and mostly heavily rolled) artifacts, which include hand-axes of both Abbevillian and Early Acheulian types. In the overlying brick-red detrital laterite there are Middle Acheulian bifaces of pear-shaped and oval forms, associated with unfaceted but well-dressed flakes, some of which show marginal retouch. At another site, Attirampakkam (Paterson, 1939, p. 328 and Movius, 1953, p. 185) a large number of very fresh Upper Acheulian artifacts have been obtained from the basal lateritic gravel in the 20-ft terrace of the Kortalayar river, a deposit representing a pluvial phase of climate generally regarded as equivalent to the Third Glaciation in the Himalayas. This was the period when palaeolithic occupation of the coastal plain seems to have been most widespread. The Madras Upper Acheulian industry is of considerable interest from the point of view of distant correlation, for it includes not only Levalloisoid flakes with faceted butts, and plano-convex hand-axes of Micoquian form, but two specialized types of artifact which made their first appearance at Chelles-Acheul stage 8 in the Kanjeran deposits at Olduvai, Tanzania (p. 180): namely, ovate hand-axes with S-twist and cleavers made on flakes with parallelogrammic cross-section produced by the side-blow technique.

The fact that 'Lower, Middle and Upper Acheul' hand-axes in the Madras region are almost invariably associated to some extent with artifacts of 'Lower, Middle and Upper Soan' types has been regarded as evidence of contact between two cultures undergoing parallel evolution, but taking another viewpoint it really seems to argue in favour of 'Acheul' and 'Soan' artifacts in this area being simply two aspects of a single culture.

One of the most important occurrences of hand-axe industries is in the Narbada Valley of Central India, which occupies an intermediate position between the periglacial zone in the north and the tropical belt to the south. In this valley (Paterson, 1939, pp. 313–30) there is an association between Acheulian (Madrasian) industries and a typically Middle Pleistocene fauna including *Elephas* (*Palaeoloxodon*) *namadicus* and the hippopotamus *Hexaprotodon namadicus*. The Quaternary sequence here comprises four stages, including two major aggradations:

4 Cotton-soil (Regur-clay), forming a low terrace, with a Late Stone Age industry, of Holocene age.

3 Upper Narbaba Group of sediments (the 'Second Aggradation'): gravel and sand followed by silty clay; separated from the Lower Group by an erosional disconformity, it contains a similar fauna but the only contemporaneous artifacts are Upper Soan.

2 Lower Narbada Group of sediments (the 'First Aggradation'): coarse cemented conglomerate with a rich *namadicus* fauna associated with Middle Acheulian or Madrasian hand-axes and cleavers; overlain by sands capped by reddish silt with limy concretions.

1 Laterite with heavily eroded surface on which the alluvial beds (2, 3) were laid down. Formed by weathering of the local volcanic rock (Deccan trap) under a tropical climate with high annual rainfall but hot dry seasons.

It has been suggested that the entry of Madrasian hunters into this valley may have been connected with the change in climate from wetter to progressively drier conditions, for the Lower Narbada bone beds probably mark a period of seasonal desiccation.

It is worth noting that the Narbada sediments include seams packed with the shells of land and freshwater molluscs. Those in the upper group may well prove to be datable by the radiocarbon method.

In 1881 W. Theobald[109] who worked for the Geological

Survey recorded that a human skull (which he listed under *Homo sapiens*) had been found in a 'conglomerate bone bed' in the Narbada Valley. Whether this skull was fossil and contemporaneous with the *namadicus* fauna or whether it represented a later burial is a question that could have been answered by the relative dating techniques available today, but unfortunately after being preserved for a time in the museum of the Asiatic Society of Bengal it was lost.

Before proceeding to consider the palaeolithic cultures of Asia eastward of India, we should note that while the early (Middle Pleistocene) industries in this sub-continent reflect traditions that were very widespread, subsequent ones such as the 'Late Soan' were more specialized and probably developed in comparative isolation. These Upper Pleistocene industries are now usually grouped under *Indian Middle Stone Age*,[110] for they provide a close parallel with the Middle Stone Age industries of Africa. Small choppers and chopping-tools form an integral part of the Indian industries, but the predominant implements are *scrapers* made on Levalloisian flakes and flake-blades, or on pieces of raw material (core scrapers), whereas points are notably absent. From their character and distribution it has been inferred that these industries were primarily developed in adaptation to wooded country, although some regional variants can be distinguished. Contrary to the popular conception, 'scrapers' were mainly tools for woodwork, not for dressing skins.

The 'Late Soan' assemblages dating from the time of the Second Aggradation in the Narbada Valley represent the earliest manifestation of Indian Middle Stone Age culture. The slightly later Mousterioid Soan industries in the Northern Punjab may conceivably have owed something to the European Levalloiso-Mousterian tradition which certainly extended up the Oxus valley to the borders of Afghanistan (Allchin, 1953), only separated from Pakistan by comparatively short routes through mountain passes.

There is no evidence of the Upper Palaeolithic blade and burin tradition penetrating India before *Late Stone Age* (Post-Palaeolithic) times. Blade industries with so-called burins have been reported from the Kurnool district of Madras and from a site near Bombay, but it is now certain that these date from early Post-Glacial times and therefore count as Mesolithic (Cammiade and Burkitt, 1930, but *cf.* Movius, 1953, p. 185). The late variants of the Indian Middle Stone Age culture found for instance in Southern India show occasional attempts to produce parallel-sided blades, but these were a development of Levalloisian flake-blade tradition rather than an innovation.

Archaeological interest in Burma began in 1894 when Dr F. Noetling, a member of the Geological Survey of India, reported that he had found stone implements *in situ* in Upper Miocene or Lower Pliocene strata near Yenangyaung.[111] This naturally led to controversy. While none doubted that the specimens were artifacts, there was much uncertainty about their date. In 1935, Dr T. O. Morris (1935), then in an oil and mining company, published some new data showing that the implements in question, probably Late Stone Age, had been derived from a surface site and redeposited with Pliocene fossils (Movius, 1943).

At about the same time true palaeolithic artifacts were discovered by Morris in the ancient gravels of the Irrawaddy, and subsequent research in this great valley by H. L. Movius and H. de Terra working with the American Southeast Asian Expedition in 1937 and 1938 led to the recognition of a new Lower Palaeolithic culture, entirely devoid of hand-axes and clearly a representative of the chopper/chopping-tool complex. As this new culture was first recognized in Upper Burma, Movius (1943, p. 341) named it *Anyathian*, after *ān-ya-thā =* Upper Burma.

The Pleistocene river terraces in the Upper Irrawaddy, of which five have been recognized (T.1 to T.5), provide a convenient basis for the geological dating of the Anyathian industries (Movius, 1943, p. 345). The earliest examples of this culture occur in the 'Lateritic Gravel' and in the T.1 gravels which according to de Terra (1943) were laid down during a major pluvial phase following the Second Himalayan Glaciation. The culture appears to have persisted practically unchanged until the end of the Pleistocene period and even later, although the industries in T.1 and T.2 (Middle Pleistocene) are classed as Early Anyathian, and those in T.3 and T.4 (Upper Pleistocene) as Late Anyathian.

Anyathian industries were made almost entirely on pebbles of two kinds of rock: *silicified tuff* (a rock consisting mainly of consolidated volcanic ash) and *fossil wood* (Fig. 75). There is an almost inexhaustible supply of fossil wood in the Tertiary formations of Burma, which outcrop all the way from the Upper Chindwin in the north to the Gulf of Martaban in the south. Whereas silicified tuff can be chipped in any plane, most of the fossil wood in Burma consists of silicified stems of dicotyledonous trees with a longitudinal grain and therefore only flakes easily in one plane. The influence of this last material on the shape of

Figure 75 Anyathian hand-adze of fossil-wood, Upper Burma. *B.M.N.H.* ($\frac{2}{5}$).

many Anyathian implements is very evident. Thus industries largely in fossil wood include a high proportion of artifacts where the end of the pebble or block has been shaped into the cutting edge. Even so, the typology of the Burmese palaeolithic industries was not entirely determined by the qualities of the raw material: many of the Anyathian artifacts in silicified tuff (flaking as easily as chert) are identical in form with those in fossil wood.

Four fundamental categories of stone implement occur in the Anyathian industries. Although first defined by Movius (1943) on the basis of the Burmese material, the same categories can be recognized in greater or lesser proportion in all industries of the chopper/chopping-tool complex, irrespective of the raw material employed, and the terminology is thus quite widely applicable. The categories are:

Chopper (*sensu stricto*): a large *unifacial* tool, made on a pebble or angular chunk, with one[112] curved or straight cutting edge, and secondary work confined to the upper face. The only essential difference from a scraper is one of gross size. Many thick 'side-scrapers' could equally well be termed 'small choppers' in Movius's sense.

Chopping-tool: a core implement, either made on a pebble or angular chunk of rock, differing from a chopper[113] in being essentially *bifacial*, in the sense that the cutting edge has been flaked from both faces. The working edge is usually sinuous (wavy), since it has been formed by the intersection of flake-scars due to blows struck alternately from the two sides.

Hand-adze: a tabular block with single-bevel cutting edge (straight or curved) at right angles to the long axis at one or both ends. More than half of the fossil-wood artifacts in the Early Anyathian industries are single-ended hand-adzes (Fig. 75).

Proto-handaxes: roughly pointed plano-convex pebble-tools (or thick flakes), worked on the upper surface only. The butt end usually retains much of the original crust or cortex of the pebble. Implements in this category might equally well be described as 'pointed hand-adzes'.

Implements falling into these categories can of course also be found in early palaeolithic industries outside the chopper/chopping-tool province, for example in the pebble-tool and hand-axe industries of Africa and Europe. This is only to be expected if the categories represent fundamental forms of stone tool,[114] but the point worth emphasizing again is the conspicuous absence of true bifacial hand-axes from the chopper/chopping-tool industries of Asia.

Almost the only appreciable difference between Early and Late Anyathian industries is the lower frequency but the more refined workmanship of hand-adzes in the latter (Movius, 1943, p. 374). It looks as though the basic tool-making tradition of man persisted in Burma with a minimum of change (and none due to outside influences) throughout Middle and Upper Pleistocene times. The blade-tool tradition failed to reach

Burma (as it did to reach India) until well after the end of Pleistocene times. Indeed, Anyathian types of artifact (particularly in fossil wood) were still being manufactured in Burma after part of the population had become familiar with Neolithic ways of life (Movius, 1943, pp. 378–80).

The double question of when man first spread into the Irrawaddy Valley and from which direction is still unanswerable. Judging from groups of unifacial pebble-tools reported from localities in the Kwae Noi Valley, Thailand (Heider, 1960), the chopper/chopping-tool tradition extended through that country, but at what geological stage has not yet been determined. Man probably first appeared in south-east Asia *after* the Siva-Malayan (Villafranchian) fauna (Colbert, 1943, p. 426) had begun migrating through Burma and Malayasia into Java, but *before* the dispersal of the Sino-Malayan (Middle Pleistocene) fauna (Movius, 1943, p. 377) of which remains are found in Northern Burma, South China and Java. Traces of the Siva-Malayan fauna have been found in the Upper Irrawaddy Beds (Colbert, 1943, p. 398), but not in association with contemporaneous artifacts. Fossil remains of the later Sino-Malayan fauna have been discovered in fissures on the plateau of the Northern Shan States (at Mogok – see Colbert, 1943, p. 417), but so far no trace has been found of associated human culture. Yet at Chou-kou-tien in the Peking region (Map 2), separated from the Shan States by little more than 1,500 miles of reasonably transversable country, the oldest known remains of man on the mainland of Asia occur in direct association with a branch of the Sino-Malayan fauna and a typical chopper/chopping-tool culture.

The discovery of this *Choukoutienian* culture (Fig. 76) is usually attributed to Dr Pei Wen-Chung, who in April 1931 recognized undoubted stone artifacts in the fossiliferous deposit at Choukoutien Locality I (Black, *et al.*, 1933, p. 110), which had already yielded teeth and bones of Peking Man (*'Sinanthropus'*). It is, however, of historic interest that as early as the summer of 1921, the Swedish geologist Dr J. G. Andersson was a member of a small party examining loose material which had fallen from the face of the quarry exposing a fossiliferous fissure in the limestone at this locality, and he noticed in it some fragments of white quartz, a mineral normally absent from the deposits

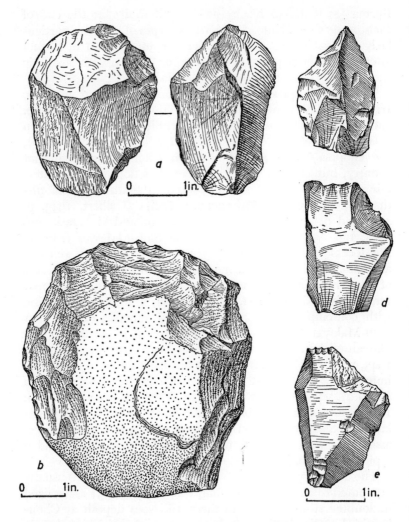

Figure 76 Choukoutienian artifacts: the industry of Peking Man. *a* chopping-tool of quartz; *b* chopping-tool of greenstone; *c* pointed flake of quartz; *d* bipolar flake of quartz; *e* bipyramidal crystal of quartz used as tool. All from Locality I, Choukoutien.
After Pei and Black.

there. The significance of the occurrence was immediately obvious to him, for he turned to his companions and exclaimed dramatically, 'Here is primitive man, now all we have to do is to find him' (Black, *et al.*, 1933, p. 6). One of his companions was Dr O. Zdansky, who in fact discovered the first fossil human tooth at this same site in 1923.

The Abbé Breuil (1935) was the first to point out that the implements found with the remains of '*Sinanthropus*' cannot be compared directly with European Palaeolithic types and should be regarded as representing a separate cultural development for which he proposed the name Choukoutienian. Eventually it was recognized as falling into line with other industries in the chopper/chopping-tool complex.

Artifacts of this culture[115] have been found at four localities in the Choukoutien region, which lies about 26 miles south-west of Peking. The most important assemblages are at Locality 1, where they occur in the stratified occupation debris of a former cave, in direct association with the ashes of artificial fires, remains of '*Sinanthropus*', and the broken-up animal bones[116] representing the Sino-Malayan fauna which these early men hunted during Mindel II Glacial times.

In comparison with the quantities of chips and waste lumps the number of deliberately shaped stone implements recovered from the Choukoutien cave deposits is relatively small. Many of the artifacts are so lacking in form that they had been found isolated, say in a Pleistocene gravel unconnected with a cave or obvious living site, they would not have been recognized as of human origin. Indeed Andersson's flash of perception seems to have been unheeded, for fossil bones, both human and animal were extracted by palaeontologists from these deposits over a period of seven years before any stone artifacts were recognized in them!

The raw material of the industry comprised mainly pebbles of sandstone and quartz collected from the bed of a local stream, and blocks of vein quartz obtained from outcrops in the nearby granite hills. Occasionally artifacts were made in transparent rock-crystal which Peking Man probably had more difficulty in obtaining.

As in the Early Soan and Early Anyathian, core implements in the sense of flaked pebble-tools formed an important element in the typical or Early Choukoutienian industry, including both choppers and chopping-tools, which were mostly large and heavy. In fact the oldest known example of the industry is a chopping-tool in chert which was found with several pieces of foreign stone and burnt bone in the fossiliferous gully-deposit known as Locality 13.

Flake-tools are actually far more numerous than core-tools in the Choukoutien industries, but the impression gained from examining a total assemblage is that the early Peking tool-makers simply made considerable use of the waste chips which resulted from the flaking of boulders or pebbles into choppers or chopping-tools. The industry is probably not far removed from that of the basic tool-making tradition of man, with pebble core-tools as the primary artifacts and elementary flake tools as by-products that were used as occasion demanded.

Rather formless small chips, the waste of the industry, were found in abundance throughout the occupation layers at Locality 1. Thick flakes with plain striking-platforms, classifiable as Clactonoid, also occurred with moderate frequency. These had been mainly produced by ordinary 'free flaking' of the cores by hammerstones, several of which were found on the site. In flaking the smaller lumps of stone, Peking Man frequently used the 'bipolar' technique, in which the piece to be flaked is held resting on an anvil-stone while its free end is struck with a hammerstone (Fig. 77). (The method is reminiscent of cracking a nut with a pebble.) Some of the the resulting flakes (and the corresponding flake-beds on the parent lump or core) show a bulb of percussion at both ends on account of the rebound from the anvil.

Only a small percentage of the Early Choukoutienian flakes show any secondary work or marginal retouch, although signs of use are not uncommon. The majority of the trimmed flakes (scrapers) at Locality 1 are in quartz. Side-scrapers are the commonest forms, and may have been used for working wood as well as for removing flesh from bones. Flake-tools of roughly beaked form and a few crude points also occur.

As regards evidence of cultural evolution, pebble-tools were rather commoner in the lower occupation layers at Locality 1, while flake tools were more abundant in the upper layers; and no doubt related to this trend was the increasing use made of

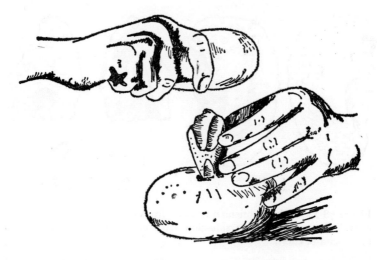

Figure 77 Bipolar technique: This was used by Peking Man but developed to a fine art in the Late Stone Age.
After Lowe.

chert relative to quartz in the sequence of assemblages. However, the amount of difference between the industry in the lower and in the upper layers at Locality 1 is extraordinarily small in view of the deposits being about 50 m thick. In contrast the cultural layers in the Castillo Cave in Spain are less than half as thick yet they range from Lower Mousterian to Mesolithic. The stability of the culture of Peking Man appears to have matched the stability of the fauna in the region (Pei in Black, *et al.*, 1933, p. 130), and both may reflect the lack of any immigration into the region over a long stretch of time.

Hearths are an important feature at Locality 1. First regular use of fire may have spread during Mindel I/II interstadial; The Buda hearths at Vértesszöllös, Hungary (Kretzoi & Vértes, 1965) are of that age.

At Locality 15 (Pei, 1939; Movius, 1949) there is a cemented fissure deposit, accumulated in a former cave, which has yielded stone artifacts and animal bones (but no human remains). This industry (Fig. 78) is basically like that of Locality 1 but technologically more advanced and classed as

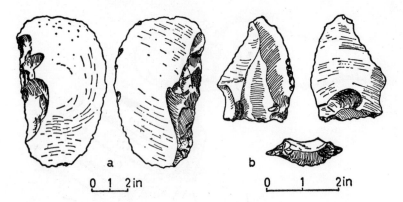

Figure 78 Late Choukoutienian artifacts from Locality 15, Choukoutien: *a* oval cleaver made from side-blow flake of fine-grained sandstone; *b* flake-point of chert.
After Pei.

Late Choukoutienian. Whereas most of the flake artifacts in Locality 1 appear to be accidental shapes, a high percentage of those in Locality 15 are deliberately shaped implements; and they were made in a wider range of rocks. The industry includes the usual types of unifacial choppers and small bifacial chopping tools, but also some polyhedral cores (bolas stones?), some pick-like forms, several distinctive kinds of flake-tool and small semi-bifacial points.

Among the relatively wide range of well-defined tools in the Late Choukoutienian there are several which invite comparison with items in the palaeolithic industries in other regions. The pick-like artifacts and some of the flakes recall the industries of the Fenho complex in the early Upper Pleistocene deposits of Shansi and Honan (p. 236). A few massive side-blow flakes from the site vaguely recall African cleavers of that form; they were struck from unprepared oval boulders, and show careful chipping of the bulbar edge as though to facilitate holding. Most remarkable of all from the point of view of correlation are the semi-bifacial points, reminiscent of Proto-Stillbay points in Africa, and triangular flakes struck from prepared cores. These latter can only be described as Levalloisoid, but we do not know whether they represent an independent invention of the prepared core technique, or the spread of that tradition from the west.

That the food remains in the occupation layers at Locality 15 and at Locality 1 include in addition to burnt bones the seeds of hackberry (*Celtis*) suggests some continuation of the cultural tradition of Peking Man, but whether there was any change in the human population or whether it remained stable during the period represented we do not yet know. It is a curious fact that whereas the bipolar technique of flaking was used so frequently in the Early Choukoutienian industry, it has not been observed in the Late Choukoutienian. The cultural innovations evident in the latter would seem to fall best into line with its dating from Third Glacial times,[117] when human migration was probably taking place widely, yet the associated mammals provide little support for placing it later than the end of the Middle Pleistocene (Kurtén, 1960).

Palaeolithic artifacts are known from over a hundred and seventy localities in Northern China (Chia *et al.*, 1960), mainly in the basin of the Yellow River or Huangho, in the provinces of Honan, Shansi and Shensi. At more than sixty of the sites the artifacts have been found *in situ* in stratified deposits, and from a study of all this material the sequence and stratigraphic dating of the Palaeolithic cultures in this part of China is gradually emerging. There are four main groups of industries here in the following stratigraphical order, beginning with the oldest:

(1) – Industries of the *Lower Reddish Clays*, in which the predominant artifacts are simple flakes with large striking-platforms at an obtuse angle to the plane of fracture (*ie* Clactonoid). These flakes were often struck directly from the core with a hammerstone, but sometimes after one flake had been removed the core was worked on an anvil-stone (bipolar technique). There are also some accompanying core-tools which are unifacial (*ie* true choppers in Movius's sense), and there is a clear case for grouping these industries with the *Early Choukoutienian*.

(2) – Industries in the *Upper Reddish Clays* and intercalated fluvio-lacustrine deposits in the same area. These are characterized by more complex tool-types than the preceding

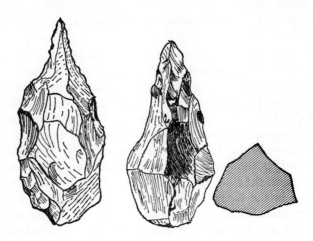

Figure 79 Thick pointed flakes of hornfels: Tingtsun culture.
After Pei. ($\frac{1}{3}$).

Choukoutienian; they included large trihedral points (Fig. 79),
some of which resemble the 'proto-handaxes' of the Patjitanian
culture in Java; bifacial chopping-tools; and at some sites
abundant 'bolas-stones', usually of limestone. As one of the
best-known industries of this group occurs in the lowest terrace
of the Fen river at Ting-Ts'un they have been referred to the
Tingtsun culture.[118] Since there was considerable variation in
these industries, which occur at a number of nearly contemporaneous sites in the valley of the Fen river and adjacent parts
of the main Huangho Valley, they are better grouped under the
term *Fenho Complex* (Chang, 1960).

At Ting-Ts'un the artifacts are in black cherty rock (hornfels). Some of the flakes are gigantic (weighing over 4 lbs[119]),
and since they commonly show twin bulbs of percussion it is
probable that they were detached by repeatedly dashing or
hurling the core against an anvil-stone.

The habitat of the Tingtsun people was largely forested, and
the climate slightly warmer and more humid than at present.
The associated fauna (Movius, 1956, pp. 16–7) includes
Rhinoceros merckii and *Elephas namadicus*, typical of the Middle
Pleistocene, but the presence of some new arrivals in China

regarded generally as more characteristic of the Upper Pleistocene, suggests that the Fenho Complex may date in part at least from Third Interglacial times. The Late Choukoutienian at Location 15 is probably slightly earlier (Chang, 1960, p. 55), but it has a number of features in common with the Tingtsun industry, for example, both industries lack the bipolar technique that characterized the Early Choukoutienian.

Tingtsun Man (Movius, 1956, pp. 22–3) is known only by three teeth, but may well belong to the same group of hominids as the Ma-pa Man whose cranium was discovered in the Kwangtung Province in 1959 (Chang, 1960, p. 58). They were approximately contemporaneous (Late Middle Pleistocene) and both show traits in advance of the typical Pithecanthropines, *ie* they were probably primitive Chinese neanderthaloids.

(3) – Industries from the *Basal Gravel* (Chia *et al.*, 1960, pp. 28–9, and S.S. Chang, 1959) of the Malan Loess in Shansi have recently been recognized as distinct both from the typical industries of the Fenho Complex and from those in the Loess itself. For example the implements from the Basal Gravels of the Loess at Hou Kou TaFeng are mainly medium to small points and scrapers with very fine retouch. The large and crudely flaked types found in the Tingtsun industry are entirely lacking in this sub-Loess industry, which probably dates from a phase of erosion following the period of the Reddish Clays.

(4) – The industries associated with the Malan Loess and its marginal deposits of Fourth Glacial Age in the Ordos, Shansi and Shensi provinces are known as *Ordosian*. Two occupation sites were discovered in the Ordos region of Inner Mongolia in the 1920s by Father Teilhard de Chardin and Licent (de Chardin and Licent, 1924). The associated fauna indicates that the sites were occupied under cold-steppe conditions. The richest cultural assemblage was found at Shitungkou: it included flake artifacts of Levalloiso-Mousterian types (points and scrapers) in association with pebble-tools (unifacial choppers) and well-developed blade-tools. The latter were mainly points and scrapers, but simple burins also occurred and some bifacial leaf-shaped points recalling those found at Locality 15. The Ordosian made extensive use of nondescript flakes and chips, probably because raw material was scarce and had to be used with great economy. At the second site,

Sjara-Osso-Gol, famous for a rich fauna and the Ordos Tooth (*Homo* cf *neanderthalensis*), almost all the artifacts were *minuscule*, made from very small flakes or chips of quartzite, jasper or limestone, with little or no retouch.

The surface finds in Mongolia indicate that the Ordosian tradition was widespread. Originally classified as Moustero-Aurignacian, these industries (Movius, 1955, pp. 277–280) comprise three components: the archaic chopper/chopping-tool element, possibly with Choukoutienian roots (and in any case basic); Mousterian-like scrapers and points made on flakes; and true blade-tools, indicating the spread of the true Upper Palaeolithic tradition into northernmost China. There is clearly a link between the Ordosian and the Late Palaeolithic industries found in East Siberia in the Yenisei Valley and Transbaikalia, which show the same three components (Okladnikov, 1961).

From the point of view of this book one of the most important archaeological assemblages in China is that found in the loamy filling of a small cave on the top of the Choukoutien Hill. Five thin occupation layers were found in this Upper Cave (Pei, 1939), from which the excavators unearthed a few dozen bone and stone artifacts, four human skulls (*Homo sapiens* of different types), and remains of 49 species of vertebrates, including the extinct cave-bear *Ursus spelaeus*.

The *Upper Cave industry* (Movius, 1955, pp. 280–2) is for the most part Upper Palaeolithic (or Mesolithic) in facies, for it includes a bone needle with a drilled eye, numerous perforated marine shells and carnivore-teeth, limestone beads made by grinding and drilling (Fig. 80) and evidence of the extensive use of red ochre. On the other hand the stone artifacts include two choppers and one chopping-tool, and a series of quartz flakes showing use of the bipolar technique – an indication of the local survival of some elements of the Choukoutienian tradition. The associated fauna is judged to be a phase later than that associated with the Ordosian, but whether it dates from the last stage of the Pleistocene or the beginning of Holo-cene time will probably not be settled before radiocarbon dating is applied to the shells, bones and ash layers of this site.

During the final phase of the Malan Loess and early Post-Loessic period the prevailing culture in Northern China was

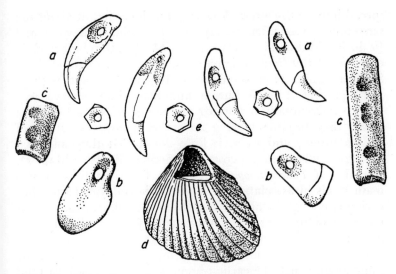

Figure 80 Upper Cave culture: perforated canine teeth *a* carnivore, *b* red deer; *c* incised bird bones; *d* perforated marine shell (*Arca*); *e* stone beads. *After Pei.* ($\frac{1}{1}$).

characterized by micro-artifacts together with a proportion of pointed Mousterian-like flake-tools. These industries link the Northern Woodland microlithic tradition with the flake industries of the Loess. Typical assemblages have been described from the sand-dune region in Eastern Shensi known as *Sha-yuan*, after which the culture has been named.

While on the subject of the Late Palaeolithic cultures of Northern China, a brief reference should be made to the related question of whether any of the early *Non-Ceramic Cultures of Japan* can be counted as Palaeolithic. For long this matter has been controversial, but now it is widely agreed that a variety of Blade Culture was introduced into Hokkaido[120] during a phase of the Last Glaciation. The entry of scattered bands of hunters into Japan appears to have taken place along with mammoths[121] when an Upper Pleistocene lowering of sea-level temporarily connected these islands with the main-land. Indeed Fossil Man is now admitted as on record from Japan (Suzuki, 1962).

As we have already noted, the earliest palaeolithic traditions spread into south-eastern Asia very much earlier, at about the same time or soon after the dispersal of the Sino-Malayan fauna (*ie* during Middle Pleistocene times). Many of the characteristic elements of this fauna originated in or at least migrated from Southern China (von Koenigswald, 1939 and Colbert, 1943, p. 427), passing through Burma and Siam into Malaya (see Map 2). Eventually a number of these species reached Java where they began replacing an earlier Pleistocene fauna of Indian origin, and there is little doubt that they migrated through Malaya and across the Sunda Shelf[122] (Map 2). Remains of *Pithecanthropus* have been found in Java at two main levels in association with the Sino-Malayan fauna, but curiously enough without traces of human culture: the earliest recorded culture there is represented by the Patjitanian industry (see below) which occurs at a higher horizon.

It is hoped that some clues bearing on the problem of the route along which the earliest hominids spread into Java (and at what date) will emerge from the researches now being undertaken in Siam (Thailand). The pioneer work on the Stone Age of Siam was carried out by F. and P. Sarasin but the material which they obtained, from excavations in caves, was probably all Mesolithic. A few of the tools recovered by H. R. van Heekeren from gravels of the River Kwai during the Second World War are undoubtedly elements of a palaeolithic culture in the chopper/chopping-tool tradition, for which the name *Fingnoian* has been proposed (van Heekeren, 1948). Many unifacial pebble-tools were later discovered by Karl Heider (1960) in a low terrace of the River Kwai, and have been described as proto-handaxes. In 1961 excavations[123] in the Sai Yok Caves in the same valley exposed Early Palaeolithic material evidently of considerable promise.

A large number of primitive palaeolithic artifacts in quartzite were discovered by H. D. Collings in 1938 in the Tin Gravels of the Perak Valley in Northern Malaya (Collings, 1938). As the main find-spot was a trench on the rubber estate of Khota Tampan[124] Collings named the industry *Tampanian*, and it was soon recognized as another typical representative of the chopper/chopping-tool complex of cultures, closely comparable with the Patjitanian of Java (Movius, 1949, pp. 403-4).

The Tampanian industry occurs in the gravel of a terrace which has been tentatively correlated with an early stage of the Second Glaciation,[125] or even a phase earlier on the evidence of its height above sea-level. However, in the absence of any associated fossils its dating is necessarily very insecure. Similar Tin Gravels somewhat farther south in Perak have yielded a tooth of *Elephas namadicus*, which is at least an indication that these deposits are Middle Pleistocene (Andrews, 1905).

The majority of the Tampanian tools from the gravel at the type-site have been made from rounded river pebbles of quartzite, but quartz was also used. Although all the types of 'core-tool' characteristic of a chopper/chopping-tool assemblage are represented, *flakes* form an integral part of the industry.

MAP 2

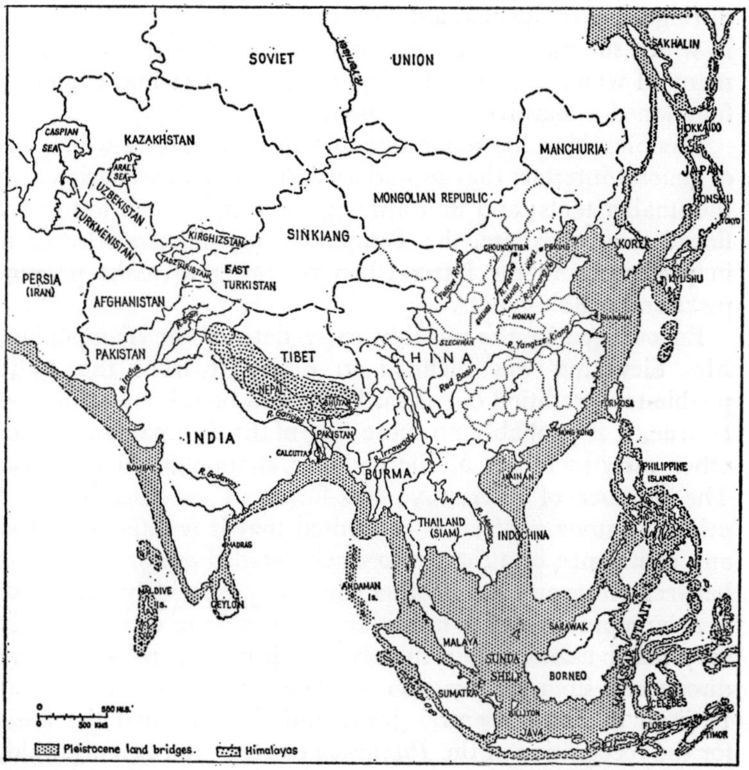

Central Asia and the Far East: distribution of land and sea during Pleistocene times

In a re-survey of the Tampanian, Mrs Ann Sieveking (Walker and Sieveking, 1962) has attempted to break away from the system of classification used by Movius, and has established categories based on the general appearance and probable function of the tools, regardless of whether made on cores or flakes. She considers that the artifacts which she terms pebble-picks are the most primitive tools in the industry, and closely resemble some Oldowan pebble-tools. The tools which occur in greatest abundance in the Tampanian are those which she terms points, divisible into large points (= proto-handaxes of Movius), and small points made either on pebbles or on flakes. She argues that cleavers form a definitive tool-type in this as in other chopper/chopping-tool industries, and she divides them into bifacially-trimmed forms (= chopping-tools of Movius) and unifacial forms (=true choppers of Movius). She also distinguishes scrapers as a definitive but rather broad category, in which she includes, for example, the hand-adzes of Movius, many of which are in fact made on thick flakes and evidently functioned as massive end-scrapers.

Mrs Sieveking has made two further observations which are of general interest: that secondary work is mainly restricted to the smaller tools; and that although quartz is much less easily flaked than quartzite, the Tampanian tool-makers selected it in preference to the latter when requiring to make pebble-picks and pebble-points.

Encouraged by the possibly early date of the Tampanian, Mrs Sieveking was inclined to derive it from the basic pebble-tool tradition of Africa. While in a broad sense this may be true, it is probably no more true of the Tampanian than of other early members of the chopper/chopping-tool complex. The number of alternative tool-forms in an assemblage of primitive stone artifacts is so limited that it is difficult to feel any confidence in attempts to trace detailed cultural affinities between one group and another when they are widely separated.

A large number of palaeolithic artifacts (over 2,000), mostly very massive and only a minority with regular retouch, were discovered in 1936 by von Koenigswald and Tweedie at Patjitan in South Central Java, and these formed the basis for the recognition of the *Patjitanian* culture (von Koenigswald, 1936). At first the industry was described as Chellean, as the bluntly pointed chopping-tools forming about 6 per cent of the implements at the type-site resemble Chellean hand-axes. On closer examination they proved to differ fundamentally from Chellean or Abbevillian hand-axes, for the flaking on both faces of the Javanese core-tools is mainly longitudinal instead of criss-cross: there is little doubt that they were developed independently of their Eur-African equivalents, even if perhaps they served a similar function.

The vast majority of the Patjitanian artifacts (Movius, 1949) are in silicified tuff (Fig. 81), although a fair number are in silicified limestone and a few in fossil wood. They are for the most part deeply patinated in ochreous hues. The raw material of this industry consisted of large boulders. The style of flaking is unusually coarse, and in many of the tools large areas of the cortex of the boulder have been left. As a preliminary to flaking the large boulders the Patjitanian tool-makers appear to have shattered them by dropping other stones on to them. The resulting 'shatter-blocks' rarely show definite bulbs of percussion.

It is difficult to classify the Patjitanian industry in terms of core- and flake-tools. In fact the majority are *flakes*, but varying widely in form and size from unretouched 'shatter-flakes' on the scale of gigantoliths (*eg* over 30 cms long, and some 7 lbs in weight), to quite small scrapers and points with some evident secondary trimming. Among those flakes with clear bulbs of percussion, Clactonoid forms are commonest. A few show faceted butts (Fig. 82), although much of this faceting is either secondary or fortuitous. There was sometimes a crude preparation of the blocks from which flakes were struck, but no truly Levalloisian or 'tortoise-cores' occur. Flake-scrapers, including straight-edged, concave and discoidal forms, are common in the industry, suggesting that the Patjitanian culture included a considerable amount of wood-working.

In spite of the overall preponderance of flakes in this industry, unquestionably the most characteristic Patjitanian implements are massive core-tools, particularly the plano-convex choppers with good resolved flaking on the upper surface, and the oval or bluntly pointed chopping-tools (Fig. 81) which were first mistaken for Chellean hand-axes. Hand-*adzes* are also important components in the Patjitanian industry (as they are in the Anyathian and Tampanian), but these would really be

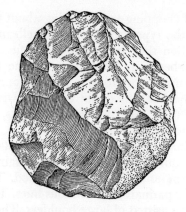

Figure 81 Patjitanian chopping-tool of silicified tuff from the type-site. *After Movius*. ($\frac{1}{3}$).

Figure 82 Patjitanian flake-tool of silicified tuff from the type-site. *After Movius*. ($\frac{1}{2}$).

better regarded as coroid-tools than as core-tools in the strict sense, for most of them were fabricated out of thick flakes secondarily treated as cores. The secondary flaking on the hand-adzes is mainly on the domed upper surface, but the 'cleaver-end' was commonly sharpened by bifacial retouch.

The precise stratigraphical dating of the Patjitanian is uncertain because the majority of the known examples are from the type site where they occurred in a recent spread of gravel of the Basoka River, and were presumably the residue of some older formation. A few rolled and obviously derived but typical pieces were found in the basal gravel of the 30-ft terrace of the Basoka, which is of Upper Pleistocene age; so it has been argued that the Patjitanian industry originated on an earlier horizon, either late Middle Pleistocene or very early Upper Pleistocene, but probably the former (*ie* the Upper Trinil Beds) according to de Terra (1949, p. 468). It is not unlikely that they were derived from a limestone cave,[126] which was destroyed by erosion: but much more field research is necessary in this region before the problem of the dating and original mode of occurrence of the Patjitanian can be solved.

Analysis of more than 2,400 artifacts from the type site of the Patjitanian revealed a remarkable uniformity within the various categories of tool-type, indicating that at any rate the assemblage did represent a single industry, not a mixture of several.

Although no trace of Patjitanian industry has yet been found in the Lower Trinil Beds, which yielded the remains of *Pithecanthropus erectus*, it is quite probable that this was the work of late members or direct descendants of the same group, since it is essentially similar to the Choukoutienian industry with the remains of the related species *Pithecanthropus pekinensis*. One thing is now quite certain: the Patjitanian industry, massive and mainly in silicified tuff, is entirely distinct from the Late Palaeolithic industries of Java, known principally from the Upper Pleistocene at Sangiran and Ngandong. The *Sangiran flake culture* (Movius, 1949, pp. 354–5, de Terra, 1949, Movius, 1955) is represented principally by an industry of Clactonoid flakes in chalcedony occurring in the upper gravel of the Notopoero Beds at Sangiran and on a comparable terrace horizon at Korsono in the Solo Valley. At Ngandong in the Solo Valley the Notopoero Beds have yielded the remains of

I

the neanderthaloid *Homo soloensis* and also some antler-picks and sting-ray points, which together with andesite bolas-stones and small chalcedony and jasper flakes constitute the ill-defined *Ngandongian culture* (van Stein Callenfels, 1936; Movius, 1949, p. 354; de Terra, 1949, p. 457; Movius, 1955, p. 527). To what extent the latter is distinct from or merely a facies of the Sangiran flake culture is still uncertain. The fauna associated with the Sangiran and Ngandongian cultures contains many extinct species and has been described as an impoverished Trinil fauna.

An example of a 'proto-hand-axe' reported in 1940 from south-west Sumatra has been noted by Movius (1949, p. 364, footnote 24) as a possible indication that the chopper/chopping-tool culture extended into that country, but so far this has not been confirmed.

As Borneo must have been linked to Java by the Sunda Shelf during low-sea level phases in Pleistocene times (Map 2), one might expect to find evidence of palaeolithic occupation of that country too. Indeed a century ago Alfred Russel Wallace suggested to T. H. Huxley that the caves of Borneo should prove archaeologically important in the context of the early pre-history of man, but it was not until 1957 that palaeolithic artifacts were actually reported from there. In that year Tom Harrisson's excavations in the Great Cave of Niah in Sarawak (Harrisson, 1957; Solheim, 1960; Harrisson *et al.*, 1961) revealed artifacts of 'palaeolithic facies' between 50 and 100 inches below the surface of the deposits. Radiocarbon dating of charcoal from the implementiferous layers eventually showed that they were of Main and Late Würmian age; so the artifacts were not only *in facie* but in fact palaeolithic. The implements so far reported include bone points, stone flakes (mostly rather nondescript, but some are flake-blades, others faceted and reminiscent of Middle Soan forms in India), accompanied by chopping-tools made from river pebbles. Thus there seems little doubt that a late form of Chopper/Chopping-tool culture had spread into Borneo by Upper Pleistocene times, but until more of the material has been recovered and described in detail it would be rash to diagnose its affinities. The more so as an associated skull from the 100-in layer proved to be un-mistakably of *Homo sapiens sapiens* (Brothwell, 1960). The associated fauna is largely extant, but includes one survival from the Trinil fauna, an extinct giant pangolin, *Manis palaeojavanica*.

The Macassar Strait between Borneo and the Celebes is about 900 fathoms deep and at its narrowest was never less than 25 miles wide during Pleistocene times. Thus 'Wallace's Line' coinciding with it was a real enough zoo-geographic boundary in the sense that early men and larger mammals were unable to cross it here. In 1946, however, van Heekeren (1949) found a palaeolithic industry in South Celebes, weathering out on the surface of the 50-ft terrace of the Walanae river, which contains an extinct endemic fauna (Hooijer, 1960) including a pygmy species of the elephant *Archidiskodon*, a giant species of tortoise, and *Celebochoerus* (a genus of pig confined to the island).

This *Tjabenge industry* (van Heekeren, 1960), in chalcedony and jasper, consists principally of thick triangular flakes, with plain striking-platforms. The flakes show little or no retouch, but evidently served as side-scrapers and points. The assemblage at the type site also included a well-finished unifacial pick-like tool. The centre of origin and route followed by the makers of this industry are problematical. It closely resembles the Sangiran industry, yet all other lines of evidence seem to exclude the possibility of a crossing from Java to the Celebes during Pleistocene times. It seems more likely that the Tjabenge hunters came over the Sangihe land-bridge from the Philippines, where a similar flake industry (Beyer, 1948, p. 9; van Heekeren, 1960, p. 79) and pygmy elephants have been found.

The Philippines must have been connected at some time to the Asiatic mainland by the Formosa land-bridge (Mayr, 1945), so it is quite possible that the similarity between the Sangiran and Tjabenge industries stemmed from their having a common origin in *South China*. There is in fact a remarkable similarity between some artifacts in the Fenho complex (p. 238) and those occurring in the late Middle and Upper Pleistocene deposits of Java, the Philippines and Celebes. This view would be in keeping with modern zoological studies which indicate that the recent fauna of the Celebes is mainly of Oriental origin.

Until collagen-bearing bones contemporaneous with the Tjabenge industry have been discovered and dated by radiocarbon, the precise antiquity of this culture is likely to remain uncertain, for the antique character of an endemic fauna, such as that associated with the Tjabenge industry, is no clue to its antiquity relative to faunas elsewhere.

The *Cabalwanian* industry of unifacial quartzite pebble-tools (hand-adzes) recently reported by von Koenigswald (1960) from Northern Luzon in the Philippines is probably older. It occurs in *Stegodon* – bearing beds dated by tektites as synchronic with the Upper Trinil Beds of Java (*ie* Late Middle Pleistocene). Again, it should be noted that some of the Cabalwanian tools can be matched in the Fenho industries (Fig. 79).

Chapter 7

Mesolithic Cultures in South and South-east Asia

'PALAEOLITHIC' TRADITIONS PERSISTED with very little change into Holocene times in many parts of Asia, so that the recognition of the earliest Mesolithic cultures is handicapped where there is lack of precise dating. By the definition now generally adopted, the distinction between Palaeolithic and Mesolithic is made by applying the quite arbitrary chronological test to each industry: is it Late Pleistocene or Early Holocene? Often it is not possible to be sure, particularly if there is no associated flora or fauna reflecting a climatic sequence. In Burma, for example, the Anyathian tradition, which in its typical development is Palaeolithic (p. 226), appears to have lasted until the arrival there of Neolithic culture (Piggott, 1950, p. 35), probably less than 3,000 years ago. Thus, some industries that have been classified on typological grounds as Palaeolithic may prove on absolute dating to be Post-Pleistocene, and therefore in fact Mesolithic. Nevertheless, there are numerous lithic cultures with characteristics quite unknown before Holocene times, and these are commonly grouped as *Late Stone Age*.

The most distinctive Late Stone Age industries in Southern Asia are those of the *Microlithic* tradition. In so far as they represent the culture of hunters and gatherers living in Post-Pleistocene times they qualify as Mesolithic, but this term is often avoided because of the shadowy boundary separating Mesolithic from 'secondary' Neolithic cultures[127] in some parts of Asia. The microlithic tradition spread into India, probably from the west, and possibly only a millennium or two before the arrival there of primary Neolithic culture.

Although numerous microlithic sites are known in Southern Asia, few are in deposits which can be closely dated. It is probable that many of them are very late, and represent the local survival of hunting and gathering economy even into Iron Age times; but others were relatively early, for example, those associated with the *teris* or sand dunes of the Tinnevelly district in Southern India appear to have antedated a climatic phase more humid than that of today, and to have been contemporaneous with a raised sea-level which has been tentatively correlated with the Climatic Optimum, *c* 4000 BC (Zeuner and Allchin, 1956).

In north-west, western and central India the microlithic industries are mainly in chert, chalcedony or jasper. In these materials, with smooth conchoidal fracture, narrow blades were struck from precisely prepared cores. In Southern India and Ceylon, on the other hand, the industries are almost entirely in vein quartz. The resultant blades were short and thick, and the cores rather shapeless. The reason for this choice of a much less tractable material even where other siliceous stone was accessible is unknown (Zeuner and Allchin, 1956, p. 19).

The microlithic industries of Western India show the blade tradition in more marked degree than those of the south. Moreover, at Langnaj (Subbarao, 1958) in Gujarat they were found on a stratified site (Zeuner, 1952) and in a clear relationship with human burials.

The other Late Stone Age culture which is of great interest in the context of sub-fossil man is the *Balangoda culture* (Deraniyagala, 1940) or *Bandarawelian* of Ceylon.[128] At the type-locality of Bandarawela large numbers of artifacts of a microlithic industry, mainly in quartz,[129] have been collected on the tops of four hills which were evidently factory sites. The artifacts include pebble-hammers and anvil stones; small hollow scrapers, or spokeshaves; bifacial discoids within the range of the chopper/chopping-tool tradition; lunates, which were very common[130] and included large forms probably serving as *eloura* or adze-blades,[131] as well as small ones interpreted as transverse arrowheads; also many simple trimmed points and a few pressure-flaked bifacial points.

Deraniyagala's excavation into a kitchen-midden of an early phase of the Bandarawelian culture at Bellan Bandi Palassa[132] has yielded much information about the diet of these people, who evidently ate deer, pig, monkey, squirrel, occasionally elephant, also jungle-fowl, monitor-lizard and large quantities of tree-snail (*Acavus*), land-snail (*Cyclophorus*), water-snail (*Paludomus*) and freshwater mussel (*Anodonta*). The industry here included bifacially-flaked pebble-choppers and simple bone tools, mainly points. Among the broken bones of animals in the mound of refuse were pieces of human bone. A number of undamaged skeletons in flexed positions were also found in the midden.

A late phase of this culture, represented in the Udupiyan Cave in the Balangoda district (Deraniyagala, 1958a, p. 64), is distinguished by the presence of dimple-scarred anvil stones and pottery. The earliest of this pottery is sun-baked, but much of it, presumed later, is fired and decorated with wicker-impress. This final phase of the Bandarawelian culture appears to have been associated with ground stone axes, and should probably be classified as secondary Neolithic (Deraniyagala, 1958a, pl. 29).

The view has been held by many authors that the Bandara-welian industries can be ascribed to the ancestors of the modern Veddas, but it is still uncertain to what extent this is supported by the evidence of the skeletal remains from the midden at Bellan Bandi Palassa, which have been briefly described by Deraniyagala[133] and are now being restudied by K. A. R. Kennedy who has entitled the people represented, the Balangodese.

The final stage of the chopper/chopping-tool tradition in south-east Asia was represented by the *Hoabinhian*[134] culture, widely distributed in the region in early Holocene times. Classically developed in Tonkin (North Vietnam), the industries of this Mesolithic culture are relatively uniform from the borders of China (Yunnan) through Annam, Laos and Malaya to northern Sumatra. In fact the Hoabinhian tool tradition was one of the constituents of aboriginal Australian cultures. The Hoabinhians were food-gatherers and hunters, and as one might expect, the 'find-spots' of this culture are very sparse in comparison with those of the polished quadrangular axes and adzes left by the succeeding Neolithic peoples who were agriculturalists.

Typical Hoabinhian sites, whether in caves or in the open, are middens composed largely of molluscan shells, either marine, estuarine or freshwater, depending on their location. The occurrence of marine shell middens 10–15 km inland in Sumatra suggests that the sea has locally retreated since their formation. In general the early levels in Hoabinhian shell middens consist almost wholly of shells, whereas the later levels contain varying quantities of animal bones, indicating that a purely food-gathering economy gave place to one based partly on hunting. In Malaya the occupation sites are mainly in rock-shelters and caves situated in the Carboniferous limestone hills, and consequently the Hoabinhian was for some time known to archaeologists there as the *Cave Culture*.

There are many flakes, mostly large, in nearly all Hoabinhian industries, but the most characteristic tools are made on flat or split pebbles worked on one or sometimes on both faces. At the type locality, where the industry is in metamorphic rock, unifaces predominate in the lower layers, and bifacially worked pieces in the upper layers. The raw material clearly influenced the size and shapes of the artifacts to some extent. In Sumatra many of the tools were made on long flat oval pebbles of fine grained sandstone which could be made into very effective implements by economical flaking on one face only. These unifaces are known as the Sumatra Type (Tweedie, 1953, p. 75) or *Sumatraliths* (Fig. 83).

Hoabinhian unifaces and bifaces are occasionally edge-ground. These 'Proto-Neolithic' forms are particularly well developed at Bacson[135] in North Vietnam where they occur with increasing frequency in the upper layers.

Bone tools occur, but they are not common except in the Hoabinhian industry of the Tonkin area, which has been compared with the Sampung bone culture of Eastern Java,[136] although there is no evidence that this is older than Neolithic.

On sites in Vietnam, formerly Indo-China, the Hoabinhian assemblages frequently include pebbles with paired grooves which probably served for sharpening split-bamboo weapons such as those used by the aborigines of Malaya.

The industries of this culture usually include stone pounders

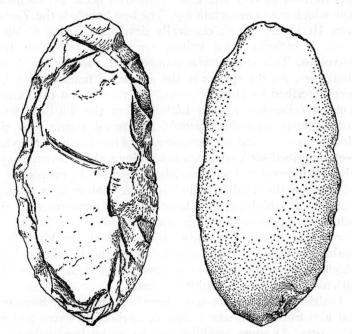

Figure 83 Hoabinhian unifacial implement (diorite), Sumatra. B.M.N.H. ($\frac{1}{2}$).

and mortars in which traces of red ochre are sometimes found. These were probably used not only in grinding ochre, but also for crushing roots and stems, and for pounding meat. The Hoabinhians practised ceremonial burial, as witness the contracted skeletons found by Sieveking (1954) in the cave floor at Gua Cha in Malaya. Red ochre was evidently used in connection with burial ceremonies.[137] There is good evidence of cannibalism at some sites, notably at Gua Cha, where groups of split human bones charred by fire were found mixed with animal bones in the midden layers.

There are indications that the Hoabinhians were of the physical type known as Palaeo-Melanesian (Tweedie, 1953, pp. 17–18, 67–68, 80–83), and it is evident that they spread through south-east Asia severalmill ennia before the arrival there of Neolithic culture.

A number of very late blade industries occur in south-east Asia which are of uncertain age. The best known is the *Toalian* (van Heekeren, 1957), classically developed in the Celebes, where it includes stone knives, arrowheads and some true microliths. This culture was named after the existing Toale aborigines. All the species in the associated fauna, which has been described by Hooijer (1950), are recent, and the human remains occurring with it indicate that the Toalians were rather small microdont people, in strong contrast to the Hoabinhians. An industry presumably of the Toalian group has been described by Verhoeven from Timor (Verhoeven, 1959), where it is associated with burials of Negrito-like people.

Although the Toalian industries were mainly later in time than the Hoabinhian, and have more in common with the industries of the late 'Neolithic' shell-mounds of the Philippines, Korea and Japan, the studies by van Heekeren leave little doubt that they represent a shell-fishing and hunting culture which in its earliest phases reached the Celebes before the agriculturalists with Neolithic culture.

Toalian-like industries have been reported from Sumatra, and also from Java, where they occur both in caves and on open sites. At some localities the Sampung bone-culture in Java includes blade artifacts which possibly link it with the Toalian (Tweedie, 1953, p. 75).

A mesolithic flake and blade industry was discovered on the island of Flores, but its relative antiquity can only be judged by the associated mammals.[138] As they include extinct species the culture is probably older than the Toalian group.

Notes to Part Two—
Archaeological Dating

1 It should be noted, to be strict historically, that the oldest hand-axe industry in the Somme was first named Pre-Chellean (*Pré-Chelléen*) by Commont, but called Chellean by some authors and re-named Abbevillian by Breuil. Commont's Chellean = Lower Acheulian of Breuil's classification. See Breuil, 1939 and 1939*a*.

2 At one time this was called 'wooden-hammer technique' (*eg* Leakey, 1934, p. 42).

3 A few words of explanation of the term Clactonian are also necessary. The type locality of this flake industry, with associated chopper-cores, is at Clacton-on-Sea in Essex, where it occurs in Hoxnian interglacial deposits. At first the industry was provisionally identified by S. H. Warren with the Mesvinian of Belgium, but later he named it Clactonian (Warren, 1926, p. 47 footnote). This name was adopted by Breuil (1932, pp. 125–31), who recognized it as representing a distinct cultural tradition (Breuil, 1932, pp. 173–5). The industry at the type-locality corresponds to Breuil's Clactonian II, whereas the flakes found in the 45-m terrace at Abbeville are referred to Clactonian I. If Clactonian I is really a facies of the Abbevillian hand-axe culture, Clactonian II might be a facies of the Lower Acheulian. See also Warren, 1951, 1958.

4 Mousterian takes its name from Le Moustier near Peyzac in the Dordogne.

5 Bordes and Bourgon, 1951. Also see useful summaries by Movius, 1953, and by Bordes, 1961.

6 Named after Levallois-Perret, a suburb of Paris. Flake-tools known as '*le type Levallois*' were already recognized at the end of the last century (G. and A. Mortillet, 1900, p. 166) and then regarded as belonging to the transition from Acheulian to Mousterian. With the abandonment of the idea of single-line evolution of palaeolithic cultures, and the adoption of the concept of parallel cultures, the Levalloisian become regarded as a distinct flake-culture related to the Mousterian. In the Somme Valley for example, Breuil (1932, p. 127) recognized artifacts or assemblages of artifacts (industries) representing seven stages of this culture (Levalloisian I to VII). Discoveries in other parts of the world, and researches elsewhere in France, later led to the view that the Levalloisian represented a technique of preparation of the core before detachment of the flake, and this was practised by various palaeolithic groups, some Acheulian, others Mousterian. For analysis of Levalloisian industries see Bordes and Bourgon, 1951, p. 8.

7 Bordes and Bourgon, 1951, p. 22. The type-locality, La Quina in the Charente department, is an important site for remains of Neanderthal man.

8 Named after La Micoque in the commune of Tayac near Les Eyzies, Dordogne.

9 Bordes, 1957, p. 5. The Micoquian of Northern France often includes the use of Levalloisian technique, but at the type-locality (*ie* La Micoque, Dordogne) this variant of Upper Acheulian is non-Levalloisian.

10 The Micro-Mousterian industries appear earliest in Yugo-slavia (*eg* in the deposit with Eemian fauna at Gánovce in association with a Neanderthaloid skull). The Micro-Mousterian in Montenegro was first described by Benac in 1957 (Benac and Brodar, 1958).

11 Blanc, 1939. For a survey and illustrations of the Pontinian industries see Sansoni, 1962.

12 The *Alpine Palaeolithic* culture includes accumulations of the skulls and other bones of cave bear in association with a Mousterioid industry (Tschumi, 1949). The sites include the Salzofen cave in the Austrian Alps where the deposit has been radiocarbon dated as 32,000 BC, and the Tana del

Basua, with Neanderthal-footprints, in the Ligurian Alps, dated by a new technique as more than 28,000 years old, cf. Rosholt *et al.*, 1961.

13 Named after Tayac, commune near Les Eyzies. The same gravel-pit is the type-site of both Micoquian and Tayacian. Tayacian industries consist mainly of small, rather thick flake-tools (and associated cores) with abruptly trimmed margins. They occur typically in three levels below and in one level above the layer with Micoquian (Upper Acheulian) hand-axes in the gravel at La Micoque. In the earliest phases, Tayacian flakes (like the Clactonian) were struck without any preparation of the core, but in later levels there is evidence of some preparation. See Breuil, 1932, pp. 127, 131, 182; Peyrony, 1948, pp. 13, 43–4.

14 Thus at the First Pan-African Congress on Prehistory in 1947 an attempt was made to substitute the term 'faceted platform technique' for 'Levalloisian' in Africa, but this certainly is not in accordance with European usage. *Proc. 1st P.A.C.* (Nairobi, 1947), Oxford, 1952, p. 8, Resolution No. 16 part 3; but compare Bordes and Bourgon, 1951, p. 22 footnote 2.

15 Turville-Petre excavating in the Mugharet el-Emireh (Cave of the Princess) in the Galilean Hills in 1925 discovered a layer in which there appeared to be an industry transitional between Mousterian and Aurignacian. Dr. D. A. E. Garrod was inclined at first to think that the contents of the Mousterian and Aurignacian layers had been mixed through disturbance, but Turville-Petre's opinion was eventually confirmed by similar discoveries at other sites, notably at Ksar 'Akil in Lebanon, and Dr Garrod later recognized this in a paper introducing the name Emiran. See Garrod, 1951 and 1955.

16 The Oranian industries of North Africa, early members of the Capsian group, are Late Pleistocene, but the true Capsian is Holocene.

17 The blade industries discovered by Dr L. S. B. Leakey in the Gamblian deposits of Kenya are geographically so isolated that it is difficult to conceive the nature of any link with Eurasiatic blade culture (Leakey, 1931). Possibly they represent a local development stimulated by

movement of small bands of people from north to south. The absolute dating of the 'Kenya Capsian', which is still undetermined, might go far towards resolving the problem of its place in prehistory.

18 McBurney, 1962, p. 497. Formerly Dr Garrod called this *'Pre-Aurignacian'*, (Garrod, 1956), but later she recognized its Near-Eastern origins and named it Amudian (Garrod & Kirkbride, 1961, p. 11), and this was the term used in her Huxley Memorial lecture, 1962.

19 This is supported by Dr Ralph Solicki's discovery of an industry 35,000 years old in the Shanidar Cave of Iraq which combines Chatelperronian and Aurignacian features (Solecki, 1955, 1963, pp. 183 and 188–9).

20 Garrod, 1938, p. 23. This author proposed that only the late prolongation of Upper Gravettian culture in Italy should be called *Grimaldian*, but the term has been used in several senses, and is better discarded (cf. note 26).

21 Peyrony, 1933. See also useful summaries in Movius, 1953, pp. 171–2; and Sonneville-Bordes, 1959, 1960.

22 The Late Palaeolithic industries of the Ordos region were at one time described as 'Moustero-Aurignacian'. See Movius, 1955, p. 280.

23 Lothar Zotz, 1951. The Pre-Solutrean has also been called Altmühlian (Bohmers, 1951, p. 99).

24 Named after La Madeleine, rock-shelter near Tursac, Dordogne.

25 The type locality is Creswell Crags in Derbyshire. Garrod, 1926, pp. 194–5.

26 According to some authors the term 'Grimaldian' has been used for a mixture of industries. The 'Upper Grimaldian', however, is probably the time-equivalent of the Magdalenian. The term was introduced by Vaufrey, 1928.

Information about the Romanellian culture is summarized in Sansoni, 1962, table 9.

27 Schwantes, 1934. The type station of the Hamburgian is Meiendorf, near Hamburg. See Rust, 1937.

28 The recognition of the Ahrensburg culture, characterized mainly by tanged points made from flakes, was due to Schwantes (1928, p. 159).

29 Lower levels at Borshevo II, also represented in the palaeolithic site discovered in Saint Cyril Street in Kiev in 1897.
   Garrod, 1938, p. 13.
   The most northerly Upper Palaeolithic site is at Komi,
   north-east European USSR. See Cole, 1960.
30 Clark, 1932, pp. 97–103. Micro-burins were at one time
   regarded as particularly characteristic of the Tardenoisian
   industry; but they also occur in a number of others, including the Sauveterrian.
31 Named after Sauveterre in the Lot-et-Garonne department
   (Coulanges, 1935). See also Smith, 1952.
   Although the Sauveterrian employed the micro-burin
   technique, it differed notably from the Tardenoisian in the
   absence of trapezes. A number of industries which were at
   one time classed as Tardenoisian or Azilio-Tardenoisian
   are now referred to the Sauveterrian group. Clark, 1955,
   pp. 14–19. The British industries of Sauveterrian affinities
   date from the Boreal period.
32 Named after Frère-en-Tardenois in the Aisne department.
   The classic Tardenoisian industry dates from the Atlantic
   period, and was contemporary with some of the early
   Neolithic farming communities in France (Clark, 1955, p.
   16).
33 The term is based on the common Danish place-name
   Maglemose, meaning big bog. The most typical sites of this
   'forest culture' are found in peat bogs and other low–lying
   places in Northwest Europe. See Clark, 1936, p. 86. Flaked
   core axeheads and picks in flint are invariably present in
   Maglemosian industries, usually in association with simple
   microliths and points with blunted backs; while at peat-
   bog sites barbed points in bone and antler and wooden
   objects are commonly preserved. Maglemosian industries
   range in date from Pre-Boreal to Boreal.
34 Named after Le Mas d'Azil (Ariège) (Piette, 1895). The
   typical Azilian industries include pebbles ornamented with
   symbolic daubs of red ochre.
35 The Kongemose culture in Denmark, dating from Zone
   VI, is believed to have roots in the Ahrensburgian. See
   Jørgensen, 1956.
36 Ertebølle in Denmark is the typical site of the Kitchen-

midden culture which flourished at the time of the maximum of the Littorina Sea. J. G. D. Clark, 1936, p. 138. Flake-axes (*spalter*) were commonly made by the Ertebølle people who also specialized in making *petit-tranchet* arrowheads (trapezes) which were probably used for shooting birds. The Ertebølle people made rough pottery and were contemporaneous with the earliest Neolithic farmers to reach Denmark.

37 Named after Oban on the mainland of Argyll, where an industry including stone limpet-hammers and barbed fish spears have been found in middens associated with the Early Post-Glacial raised beach. The name was proposed in Movius, 1940, p. 76. For full account see Lacaille, 1954, p. 199.

38 Named after Larne in north-east Ireland (Movius, 1940, p. 76). This culture, confined to coastal tracts and estuaries, is the oldest unambiguous evidence of human occupation in Ireland. The 'type fossil' of the culture is a leaf-shaped flake with base trimmed for hafting as a spear point.

39 Shell-mounds in caves and rock-shelters on the coast of the Cantabrian province of Asturias in Spain contain pointed pebble-tools called Asturian picks. This culture overlies the Azilian and is evidently of Late Atlantic age.
    See Obermaier, 1924, pp. 349–55.

40 See note 38 above on the Larnian.

41 In Palestine, *Atlitian* and *Kebaran*. See Garrod & Bate, 1937, ChIII, also Waechter, 1952. Sites in Iraq including Shanidar, Zawi Chemi, Karim Shahir and Zarzi have yielded a sequence of cultures ranging from Late Palaeolithic onwards. These include the culture known as *Zarzian*, equivalent to the Kebaran.

42 E. J. Wayland's early discoveries are summarized by Lowe, 1952, pp. 2–4.

43 Lowe, 1952, pp. 14–15, 23. The primary occurrence was said to be in the 175-ft terrace.

44 The undoubted industry of pebble-tools in the Basal Older Gravels of the Vaal at Klipdam was originally described as Late Kafuan (Lowe, 1953), and though Mason, 1962, p. 107, questions its contemporaneity I consider that in

part it could be regarded as Oldowan. Some of the so-called Pre-Abbevillian industries in the Congo have been compared with the Kafuan, but in any case are geologically too late to be counted as evidence of human culture *older* than the Oldowan. See Mortelmans, 1952.

45 Leakey, 1934, p. 104. For full account of Oldowan culture see Leakey, 1951, pp. 34–7.

46 Usage proposed at the First Pan-African Congress on Prehistory Nairobi, 1947 (See under Leakey, 1952, *Proceedings*, p. 8).

47 'Rostro-carinate', a term which is better avoided since it suggests identification with the flaked flints well known under that name from the Crags of East Anglia which are now regarded to be of *natural* origin.

48 Leakey, 1961. The skull was refigured and discussed by Napier & Weiner 1962.

49 The volcanic minerals in this level of Bed II were dated by the K/A technique in 1961 as 360,000 years old, but Evernden and Curtis using an improved procedure have now dated them as 490,000 years (Hay, 1963, p. 832).

50 Leakey, 1951, pl. 38 and accompanying text. For a useful summary and general account see Cole, 1963, pp. 136–46. While this book was in press, L. S. B. & M. D. Leakey (1964) published an account of discoveries in the lower part of Bed II which threw new light on the culture sequence. They referred (p. 6) to deposits 'approximately midway in Bed II but which appear to antedate the appearance of hand-axes'.

The author gathers that running obliquely through Bed II there is an unconformity, hitherto unrecognized by geologists, which coincides with the surface of the aeolian tuff noted by R. L. Hay (1963, p. 831) in sections east of site DK and MK. In the fluviatile layers of Bed II below this aeolian tuff the fauna is Villafranchian and the culture Late Oldowan, whereas in the dominantly fluviatile layers above the tuff the culture is Chellean and the fauna Middle Pleistocene with many giant forms.

51 Bosman's Crossing, a few hundred yards south of Stellenbosch railway station, where Péringuey discovered hand-axes in 1899, became the name-site of the Stellenbosch

culture, first formally recognized in 1927, but eventually regarded as equivalent to the Chelles-Acheul (Goodwin, 1946, p. 39). See also Lowe, 1952a, p. 170.

52 Goodwin, 1946; also Clark, J. D., 1954, p. 14. One of the best known Chellean localities is in the 45-ft terrace at Vereeniging.

53 This occurrence is discussed by Alimen, 1957, pp. 11–14, 30–5. Although this Chellean horizon is referred to a phase of transgression (Sicilian II according to the scheme adopted in this book), it would not be justifiable to infer correlation with an interglacial phase. The cool-water fauna associated with the Sicilian II beach suggests that it corresponds to an interstadial within a glacial cycle.
The Chellean (Abbevillian) hand-axes in Layer M of the Sicilian II beach deposits at Sidi Abderrahman are associated with flakes of 'Clactonian' type, while a 'Tayacian' flake industry is recorded in an overlying occupation surface (Layer J). All these flake artifacts should probably be regarded as no more than a facies of the Chellean (Abbevillian) hand-axe culture. For detailed description see Neuville & Ruhlmann, 1941.

54 One of the first accounts of the cylindrical hammer technique, at one time called 'wooden-hammer technique', is in Leakey, 1934, pp. 42, 60.

55 A. Kragh has described a method of trimming by indirect percussion on an anvil. Prof. J. D. Clark has also made experiments on these lines and believes that the technique was probably used by Early Palaeolithic craftsmen.

56 In 1912 the late Prof. Hans Reck conducted an exploratory expedition to the Olduvai Gorge, where he collected many fossil animal bones. When Dr Leakey discussed the project of a further visit to Olduvai after the First World War, Prof. Reck said that he had seen no traces of stone tools in the Olduvai strata. Dr Leakey (1951, p. 118) discovered dozens of them as soon as he began to examine these strata. But they were in fine-grained lava and quartz. One has little doubt that the professor failed to find any because he would have expected to see implements made in flint!

57 This general question is discussed by J. D. Clark, 1959, p. 123.

58 Alimen, 1957, p. 417 (map showing distribution of Chelles-Acheul industries with cleavers and without cleavers).

59 Ruth Moore, Report of lecture by L. S. B. Leakey, in Chicago Sun Times, 1962; Hay, 1963, p. 831, fig. 1; Leakey, 1963, p. 132. Structures observed by Prof. Desmond Clark on Acheulian occupation levels at Kalambo may be comparable.

60 The Fauresmith culture takes its name from the town in the south-western Orange Free State where its artifacts were first collected by Max Leviseur. See Goodwin & Lowe, 1929, pp. 71–94.

61 The term Sangoan covers industries formerly included under the name *Tumbian* which was introduced on the basis of Congo material by O. Menghin in 1925 but it became used to cover industries of such widely differing dates and origin that it was eventually abandoned. See Leakey, 1952, pp. 201–2. The name Sangoan was based on Wayland's discovery in 1920 of stone artifacts on the shores of Sango Bay, on the west side of Victoria Nyanza (Uganda). See Lowe, 1952.

62 The typology of the Fauresmith is summarized by J. D. Clark, 1959, pp. 149–53.

63 The Sangoan typology is usefully summarized by J. D. Clark, 1959, pp. 149–53.

64 At one time called the *Bembezi* culture (Jones, 1949, p. 30).

65 The type site is Stil Baai near Riversdale in the Cape Province. When first described the industry was so named by Goodwin in his paper on South African Stone Implement Industries, 1926, p. 787. Stillbay implements were among the first prehistoric stone artifacts recognized in South Africa. See Burkitt, 1928, p. 84.

66 Clark, 1959, pp. 158–9. In South Africa the Mossel Bay facies of the Middle Stone Age appears to be equivalent to the Proto-Stillbay industry typically developed in Rhodesia and Zambia.

67 The Pietersburg culture was among the facies of the Middle Stone Age recognized by Goodwin (1929, p. 109). The

name-locality is in the Northern Transvaal. See also Mason, 1957, pp. 119–37 and 140–1.

68 The Palaeolithic terminology employed by workers both in the Congo and Angola was at one time in a very confused state, but the eventual adoption of Breuil's term, *Lupemban*, with modification to cover all those more advanced industries in the Tumbian group, which represent the Middle Stone Age in that part of Africa, has led to a simplification. Thus:

Early Lupemban = *Kalinian* of J. Colette (1927).
　　　　　　　　Djokocian of Breuil (1944).
　　　　　　　　Upper Sangoan of Janmart (1947), and Leakey (1949).
Late Lupemban = Djokocian of Colette.
　　　　　　　　Lupemban *s.s.* of Breuil.
　　　　　　　　Final Sangoan of Janmart and Leakey.

See Clark, 1959, pp. 155–8; Breuil, 1944, pp. 143–65; Leakey 1949.

69 The type site of Magosi in northern Uganda was first described by Wayland & Burkitt (1932, pp. 369–90). See also Clark, 1957.

70 Rock-shelter excavated by L. S. B. Leakey. See Cole, 1963, p. 208.

71 The forest facies of the Magosian in the Congo basin and Angola has been included in the Lupemban by some authors, and in the Tshitolian by others. A selection of 'Lupembo-Tshitolian' artifacts from Angola is figured by Clark, 1959, p. 179.

72 *Proc.First Pan-Afr.Cong.Prehist.*(1947), 1952, p. 8; Cole, 1963, pp. 255–69.

73 Cole, 1963, p. 258. It has been suggested that *Melawan* might be more suitable as a stage name than Gamblian (Hopwood, 1951, p. 29).

74 For useful summary see McBurney (1958). The Lower Palaeolithic industries of the Maghreb are the subject of an illustrated monograph in which the stratigraphical position of the industries are discussed in detail by Biberson (1961).

75 The *Aterian* has been recognized since 1919, when M. Reygasse discovered the type-site, Bir-el-Ater. See Caton-Thompson, 1947, pp. 87–130.

76 See Ruhlmann, 1951. The C14 dating (*fide* J. D. Clark) was not available in time for inclusion in Chart D.

77 Caton-Thompson, 1947, p. 93. Also information from the Abbé J. Roche during a visit to La Grotte de Taforalt, 55 km north-west of Oujda on the eastern border of Morocco, in 1952.

78 For useful account of the 'silt stage' in the Nile Valley see C. B. M. McBurney, 1960, pp. 139ff.

79 The term Khargan was introduced by G. Caton-Thompson, 1946, p. 61.

80 McBurney, 1960. This author favours continuing the use of the term Oranian, introduced by E. G. Gobert and R. Vaufrey (1932).

81 The Ibero-Maurusian was first described as occurring typically in the Mouillah grotto in the Oran province of Algeria: Pallary, 1909. See also Gobert & Vaufrey, 1932. This term, apart from being cumbersome, has the disadvantage of suggesting unconfirmed affinities with Late Palaeolithic industries in Spain.

82 Gobert, 1954. See also summary in McBurney, 1960, pp. 213–6.

83 See McBurney & Hey, 1955.

84 Transverse burins are found with an Emiran industry in the coastal cave of Abu Halka, north of Beirut. McBurney, 1960, p. 197.

85 For convenient and up-to-date summary see J. D. Clark, 1959, pp. 166–252.

86 Named after the Nachikufu Caves near Mpika in Zambia. See Clark, 1950*a*, pp. 2–15.

87 The development of the Wilton from the Magosian can be seen for example at Khami in Southern Rhodesia (Clark, 1959, p. 215).

88 The Wilton culture is named from the rock-shelter on a farm of that name west of Grahamstown, where the typical microlithic industry was found in 1921. See Hewitt, 1926; also Clark, 1959, p. 199.

89 Charcoal on a Smithfield/Wilton horizon in Philipp Cave

in south-west Africa has been dated as *c.* 1418 BC. See Clark, 1959, p. 188.

90 Smithfield culture is named after a town in the Orange Free State where Dr Daniel Kannemeyer discovered stone implements of this group sometime before 1890. See Goodwin, 1926.

91 The Tshitolian is named after the Bena Tshitolo plateau in the Kasai province of the Congo. Clark, 1959, pp. 41, 189–91.

92 The Ishangian culture was defined by de Heinzelin, 1957, p. 91.

93 The Hargeisan, named after the type-site Hargeisa in Somaliland, was first described by J. D. Clark, 1963, pp. 218–25. See also Cole, 1963, p. 215.

94 The Elmenteitan was named after Lake Elmenteita, for the typical occurrence is in Gamble's Cave which is close to the lake. See Leakey, 1931, p. 172. See also Cole, 1963, p. 270.

95 Pottery has been reported in association with a number of Mesolithic cultures in Africa including the Upper Kenya Capsian formerly claimed as Late Palaeolithic, but until these horizons have been dated by radiocarbon there will remain some doubt as to whether pottery was invented in these regions earlier than in south-west Asia, where the earliest pottery dates from about 6000 BC. Knowledge of making pottery may have diffused beyond the Neolithic world into regions where culture was still essentially Mesolithic.

96 For account of the East African Wilton see Leakey, 1931, p. 176, and Cole, 1963, pp. 216–21.

97 The Doian culture, confined apparently to Southern Somaliland, was so named by Prof. Desmond Clark on account of its being widespread on the orange sand known to the Somalis as *doi*. See J. D. Clark, 1955, pp. 226–59 and S. Cole, 1963, p. 212.

98 *Limaces* are slug-shaped unifacial bladelets pointed at both ends.

99 A useful general account of the Stone Bowl Cultures can be found in Cole, 1963, pp. 306ff. The Gumban culture named by L. S. B. Leakey, 1931, p. 31, was at one time

classed as Neolithic but is now regarded as probably
Iron Age.

100 The Heluan industry was described by J. de Morgan in
1926 as Neolithic. For general account see Alimen, 1957,
pp. 101–3. See also Cole, 1963, p. 211.

101 The name Capsian, derived from the Latin name of Gafsa
(*Capsa*) was proposed by de Morgan, Capitain and Boudy,
1910–16. The occurrence of backed blades with curved
blunting similar to Chatelperron points gave rise to the
idea that the Capsian was Palaeolithic, but reinvestigation
eventually proved that it was wholly Post-Pleistocene and
therefore Mesolithic. See Gobert, 1951–2. For convenient
illustrated account of Capsian industries see C. B. M.
McBurney, 1960, pp. 205–13.

102 This concept was formulated by Prof. H. L. Movius as a
result of his work in 1937–8 on the Stone Age of Burma
and later more fully developed by him (Movius, 1949).

103 The author's doubts have been echoed by Subbarao
(1958, pp. 51–3).

104 In a later publication Paterson referred to some 'crude
pebble tools' from the Boulder Conglomerate, but this
occurrence has not been confirmed or published in detail.
See Paterson, 1941, p. 397.

105 There is a convenient illustrated account of the Soan
industries in Movius, 1949, pp. 377–86.

106 Movius, 1955, p. 263. The validity of the distinction
between the Soan culture in the Punjab and the Acheulian
in Peninsular India has been confirmed by a re-appraisal
of the early palaeolithic industries in these areas by Lal,
1956, pp. 59–92 (especially map on p. 87).

107 The type locality of the Ratnapura culture is in the Sabare-
gamuva Province of south-west Ceylon. The implements,
said to represent three phases of culture, occur at depths
of up to 40 ft in the Gem Sands in association with extinct
form of hippopotamus (*Hexaprotodon*). The implements are
mainly made on pebbles or cores of chert, jasper or
quartz, but some simple flake tools occur, and a number
of utilized quartz crystals have been recognized (Deraniyagala, 1958a, pp. 57–8). See the useful (but poorly illustrated) appraisal by the geologist Sahni (1952). As the

sea channel separating Ceylon from India is relatively shallow (10 fathoms), it is not altogether surprising that some early palaeolithic hunters should have reached this island during phases of low sea-level.

108 True laterite is a ferruginous rock formed *in situ* by the weathering of basic lava under a wet tropical climate with dry seasons. When laterite is eroded and redeposited it gives rise to the formation of a pellety rock known as detrital laterite. Laterite is so-called after *later*, Latin for brick, because although initially it is a reddish porous clay, after being quarried and dried it becomes very hard.

109 Theobald, 1881, p. 122. A year previously, Theobald had recorded a hand-axe ('celt') in the Upper Group, but at the time these sediments were generally regarded by geologists as Pliocene in age.

110 Subbarao, 1958, pp. 62–9 and Allchin, 1960, pp. 1–36. As the Middle Stone Age industries are of Pleistocene antiquity it is arguable that they would be better termed Middle Palaeolithic to avoid any possible confusion with Mesolithic. Since they made their first appearance during the second of the two major phases of aggradation in the valleys in the Deccan plateau, and as they continued until the beginning of the third relatively minor (Holocene) aggradation in the Narbada Valley, the Middle Stone Age industries must have been more or less contemporaneous with Middle and Upper Palaeolithic industries in Western Asia.

111 Noetling, 1894. In a later paper the author described the deposit as Pliocene (Noetling, 1897).

112 Many archaeologists use the term 'chopper' much more widely and apply it to both bifacial and unifacial tools whose wedge-shaped cutting edge suggests this kind of use.

113 Biconical Clactonian cores showing signs of use were probably 'chopping-tools' in Movius's sense, but some archaeologists refer to them as 'choppers' (*sensu lato*), eg Warren, 1951, Oakley, 1961, p. 48.

114 The prototypes of 'choppers' and 'chopping-tools' can be recognized in assemblages of Oldowan pebble-tools, and also in some facies of the hand-axe industries (including Clactonian, cf note 113).

115 Movius, 1949. A useful survey of the Choukoutienian culture of Northern China, pp. 386–403, giving details of the three main sites in chronological order, Localities 13, 1 and 15.

116 It has been claimed by Breuil that a fair number of pieces of bone and antler from the Locality 1 show signs of being worked or utilized, but this view is not widely held. Only a few of the thousands of pieces found in the occupation levels, in fact, show probable utilization (Movius, 1949, p. 398), while no undoubted bone implements have been recorded.

117 Movius, 1949, p. 398 quotes lithological and palaeontological evidence in support of referring this fissure deposit to a continental glacial episode.

118 Movius, 1956, pp. 13–26. Pei is quoted (p. 26) as proposing the name Ting-Ts'un culture (1955).

119 Chang, 1960, p. 50 ('over 1,600 grammes').

120 Serizawa & Ikawa, 1960. An industry of evolved bifaces and trimmed flakes from Honsu is claimed as earlier than the blade industry in Hokkaido; but perhaps both should be viewed provisionally as belonging to the Far Eastern Late Palaeolithic complex which included the Ordosian of China.

121 Late Palaeolithic culture is represented in the Kanto brown earths, with mammoth fauna. Shikama *in* Kobayasi & Shikama, 1961, p. 304.

122 For map showing the two main routes of migration in south-east Asia see Movius, 1949, p. 332. There is evidence that the Macassar Strait must have excluded entry of fauna into Java through the Eastern Archipelago. See D. A. Hooijer, 1960 (Note 83).

123 The excavations in the Sai Yok Caves were directed by by Dr E. Nielson and Dr H. R. van Heekeren (Daily Telegraph, Feb. 13, 1961), but detailed reports were still awaited while this chapter was in press.

124 Subsequently this was named the Khota Lima Estate.

125 At first there was some doubt as to the geological situation of the Tampanian tools, but excavations in 1954 established that they occurred in the gravel of a well-defined terrace with surface at 230 ft above sea-level (Walker,

1956). This terrace is related to the highest (*ie* oldest) of the three allegedly interglacial sea levels recorded in Java, but the coarseness of the Tampan deposit suggests that more probably it dates from the onset of the immediately succeeding phase (Early Second Glacial?). This rather insubstantial dating evidence is fully discussed by Ann Sieveking, 1960, p. 98.

126 A fissure deposit in the karstified limestone hills adjoining the Baksoka Valley has in fact yielded a typical Trinil (Middle Pleistocene) fauna, including *Elephas namadicus* (von Koenigswald, 1939*a*, p. 37). See also Movius, 1949, p. 352.

127 That is to say the culture of hunters and gatherers who have been influenced by and have acquired some of the cultural traits of the earliest agriculturalists settled in the same or a neighbouring region.

128 N. A. & H. V. V. Noone, 1940, pp. 1–24. The name 'Bandarawelian' (p. 20) does not have priority over 'Balangoda culture' proposed in September 1940 by Deraniyagala, but is in more general use.

129 For full account of the industry see Allchin, 1958.

130 Lunates formed 10 per cent of all the artifacts found at Bandarawela. On one of the hills lunates were the only artifacts found, indicating that there had been some specialization at the Bandarawelian factories. Allchin, 1958, p. 199.

131 Allchin, 1958, p. 200. Large lunates used as adze-blades are known as *eloura* in Australia.

132 Deraniyagala, 1958, p. 119; 1956, 1958*a*.

133 Deraniyagala, 1956*a*, p. 9. There is some uncertainty as to whether the Bellan burials are Mesolithic, because it was not uncommon for Neolithic people in south-east Asia to use Mesolithic occupation sites as burial grounds. See Noone, 1939.

134 The type locality, Hoa-binh, is 60 km. south-west of Hanoi in Tonkin, where archaeological investigations were made by Colani (1927). For a useful general account of the Hoabinhian see Tweedie, 1953, pp. 10–15, 74–7.

135 The caves in the Bacson massif were excavated in 1906 by H. Mansuy.

136 Tweedie, 1953, p. 75. A counterpart of the **Sampung bone** culture has been found at Bukit Chiuping in **Malaya,** where it appears to be stratigraphically younger than the Hoabinhian.

137 In Malaya, Sieveking was uncertain of the evidence for this, but in excavating the rock-shelter of Sai Yok in the Kwai Valley (Siam), H. R. van Heekeren and E. Nielsen found the skeleton of a man of this period, who had been interred in a squatting position, with knees drawn up, and he had been 'covered with red ochre'. Report in *Daily Telegraph*, Feb. 17, 1961.

138 The discovery was due to Dr T. Verhoeven, and was first recorded by D. A. Hooijer (1957). The industry was dealt with in more detail by van Heekeren, 1958.

References to Part Two

ALIMEN, H. 1957. *The Prehistory of Africa*. London. 438 pp.

ALLCHIN, B. 1958. The Late Stone Age of Ceylon. *J. R. anthrop. Inst.*, vol. 88, pt. 2, pp. 179–201.

 1960. The Indian Middle Stone Age: Some New Sites in Central and Southern India, and their implications, *Bull.Inst.Arch.Univ.* no. 2. (1959), pp. 1–36.

ALLCHIN, F. R. 1953. A Flake-tool from the Oxus, *Proc. Prehist.Soc.* (NS) vol. 19, p. 227.

ANDREWS, C. W. 1905. Fossil Tooth of *Elephas namadicus* from Perak, *J.F. M.S.Mus.* vol. 1, pp. 81–2.

ARAMBOURG, C. 1950. Traces possible d'une industrie primitive dans un niveau villafranchien d'Afrique du Nord, *Bull. Soc.préhist franç.*, vol. 47, pp. 348–50.

 1957. Les Pithécanthropiens. *Mélanges Pittard*, pp. 33–41.

ARKELL, A. J. 1949. *Early Khartoum*. Oxford. 145 pp.

BALOUT, L. 1955. *Préhistoire de l'Afrique du Nord*. Paris. 544 pp.

BENAC, A. & BRODAR, M. 1958. Crvena Stijena – 1956 (Abri Rouge – 1956), *Glasn.Zem.Mus.Sarajevo* (NS), vol. 13 (Archeologija), pp. 21–64.

BEYER, H. O. 1948. Philippine and East Asian Archaeology and its relations to the origin of the Pacific Islands Population. *Bull.Nat.Res.Coun.Philipp.Is.*, vol. 29, pp. 1–77.

BIBERSON, P. 1961. Le Cadre Paléogéographique de la Préhistoire du Maroc Atlantique. *Service des Antiquités du Maroc.*, fasc. 16, Rabat, 235 pp.

 1961a. Le Paléolithique inférieur du Maroc Atlantique *ibid.*, fasc. 17, pp. 544.

BLACK, D., TEILHARD DE CHARDIN, P., YOUNG, C. C. & PEI, W. C. 1933. The Choukoutien Cave Deposits with a synopsis of our Present Knowledge of the Late Cenozoic of China. *Mem.Geol.Surv.China*, Ser.A, no. 11, 166 pp.

BLANC, A. C. 1939. Les Forêts glaciaries et les industries paléolithiques des Marais Pontins asséchés, *Rev.Sci. Paris*, vol. 8, pp. 472–78.

1954. Giacimento ad industria del Paleolitico inferiore (Abbevilliano superiore ed Acheuleano) e fauna fossile ad *Elephas* a Torre in Pietra presso Roma, *Riv.Antrop.*, vol. 41, pp. 3–10.

BOHMERS, A. 1951. Die Höhlen von Mauern, *Palaeohistoria*, Groningen, vol. 1, pp. 1–107.

BORDES, F. 1950. L'évolution buissonnante des industries en Europe occidentale, *L'Anthrop.*, vol. 54, pp. 393–420.

1952. Stratigraphie du Loess et Evolution des Industries Paléolithiques dans l'Ouest du Bassin de Paris, *L'Anthrop.*, vol. 56, pp. 405–52.

1954. Les limons quaternaires du bassin de la Seine, *Arch.Inst.Pal.humaine*. Paris. vol. 26, 472 pp.

1957. Some observations on the Pleistocene succession in the Somme Valley. *Proc.Prehist.Soc.*, vol. 22 (1956), pp. 1–5.

1958. Radiocarbone et corrélations loessiques, *L'Anthrop.*, vol. 61, nos. 5–6. pp. 572–3.

1961. Mousterian Cultures in France, *Science*, vol. 134, pp. 803–10.

BORDES, F. & BOURGON, M. 1951. Le complexe Mousterien: Mousteriens, Levalloisien et Tayacien. *L'Anthrop.*, vol. 55, pp. 1–23.

BOWLER-KELLEY, A. 1937. *Lower and Middle Palaeolithic Facies in Europe and Africa* (privately published), 31 pp.

BRACE, C. L. 1964. The Fate of the 'Classic' Neanderthals: A Consideration of Hominid Catastrophism. *Current Anthrop.*, vol. 5, no. 1, pp. 3–43.

BRAIN, C. K. 1958. The Transvaal Ape-Man-Bearing Cave Deposits, *Transv.Mus.Mem.*, no. 11, 131 pp.

BRANDTNER, F. J. *et al.*, 1961. More on Upper Palaeolithic Archaeology, *Current Anthrop.*, vol. 2, no. 5, pp. 427–54.

BREUIL, H. 1912. Les Subdivisions du Paléolithique supérieur et leur signification. *C.R.Congr.Internat.d'Anthrop.et d'Arch. Préhist.* 14th sess., pp. 165–238.

1932. Les Industries à éclats du paléolithique ancien: Le Clactonien. *Préhistoire*, Paris, vol. 1–2, pp. 125–90.

1935. L'état actuel de nos connaissances sur les industries paléolithiques de Choukoutien. *L'Anthrop.*, vol. 45, pp. 740–6.

1939. Le vrai niveau de l'industrie Abbevillienne de la Porte du Bois (Abbeville), *L'Anthrop.*, vol. 49, pp. 13–34.

1939a. Le Gisement de Chelles, ses Phénomènes, ses Industries. *Quartär.*, vol. 2, pp. 1–21.

1944. Le Paléolithique au Congo Belge d'après les recherches du Docteur Cabu. *Trans.Roy.Soc.S.Afr.*, vol. 30, pt. 2, pp. 143–67.

BREUIL, H. & KOSLOWSKI, L. 1931. Etudes de Stratigraphie paléolithique dans le nord de la France, la Belgique et l'Angleterre. *L'Anthrop.*, vol. 41, pp. 449–88.

BROTHWELL, D. R. 1960. Upper Pleistocene Human Skull from Niah Caves. *Sarawak Mus. J.* vol. 9, nos. 15–16, pp. 323–49.

BROWN, J. ALLEN, 1892. On the Continuity of the Palaeolithic and Neolithic Periods. *J.R.anthrop.Inst.*, vol. 22, pp. 66–98 (esp. 79, 93–4).

BURKITT, M. C. 1928. *South Africa's Past in Stone and Paint.* Cambridge. 183 pp.

BUTZER, K. W. 1959. Contributions to the Pleistocene Geology of the Nile Valley. *Erdkunde.* vol. 13, pp. 46–67.

CAMMIADE, L. A. & BURKITT, M. C. 1930. Fresh light on the Stone Ages in South-east India. *Antiquity*, vol. 4, pp. 327–39.

CAMPBELL, B. G. 1963. Quantitative Taxonomy in Human Evolution, *in* S. L. Washburn, Classification and Human Evolution. *Viking Fund.Pubs. in Anthrop.*, no. 37: 50–74.

CATON-THOMPSON, G. 1946. The Levalloisian Industries of Egypt. *Proc.Prehist.Soc.* (NS), vol. 12, pp. 57–120.

1947. The Aterian Industry: its place and significance in the Palaeolithic world. *J.R.anthrop.Inst.*, vol. 76 (1946), pp. 87–130.

1952. *Kharga Oasis in Prehistory.* London. 213 pp.

CHANG, K. C. 1960. New Light on Early Man in China, *Asian Perspec.* vol. 2 (1958), no. 2, pp. 41–61.

CHANG, S. S. 1959. Discovery of Late Palaeolithic Artifacts in

Inner Mongolia and north-west Shansi. *Vertebr. Palasiatica.*, vol. 3, no. 1, pp. 47–56.

CHARDIN, P. T. DE & LICENT, E. 1924. On the discovery of a Palaeolithic Industry in Northern China. *Bull.Geol.Soc. China*, vol. 3, pp. 45–50.

CHIA, L. P., WANG, C. Y. & CHIU, C. L. 1960. Palaeoliths of Shansi. *Vertebr. Palasiatica*, vol. 4, no. 1, pp. 27–9.

CLARK, J. D. 1950a. The newly discovered Nachikufu Culture of Northern Rhodesia, *S.Afr.Arch.Bull.*, vol. 5, no. 19, pp. 2–15.

1950. *The Stone Age Cultures of Northern Rhodesia.* Capetown. 157 pp.

1950b. The Associations and significance of the Human Artifacts from Broken Hill, Northern Rhodesia. *J.Roy. anthrop.Inst.* (1947), vol. 77, pp. 13–32.

1954. A Provisional Correlation of Prehistoric Cultures North and South of the Sahara. *S.Afr.Arch.Bull.*, vol. 9, pp. 3–16.

1954a. *The Prehistoric Cultures of the Horn of Africa.* Cambridge. 386 pp.

1957. A Re-Examination of the Industry from the Type Site of Magosi, Uganda. *Proc. 3rd Pan-Afr.Congr.Prehist.* (Livingstone 1955), London. pp. 228–41.

1958. The Natural Fracture of Pebbles from the Batoka Gorge, Northern Rhodesia, and its bearing on the Kafuan Industries of Africa. *Proc.Prehist.Soc.* (NS), vol. 24, pp. 64–77.

1959a. Further excavations at Broken Hill, Northern Rhodesia. *J.R.anthrop.Inst.*, vol. 89, pp. 201–32.

1959. *The Prehistory of Southern Africa.* Harmondsworth. 341 pp.

CLARK, J. D. & VAN ZINDEREN BAKKER, E. M. 1964. Prehistoric Culture and Pleistocene Vegetation at the Kalambo Falls, Northern Rhodesia. *Nature,Lond.*, 201, pp. 971–5.

CLARK, J. G. D. 1932. *The Mesolithic Age in Britain.* Cambridge. 223 pp.

1936. *The Mesolithic Settlement of Northern Europe.* Cambridge. 284 pp.

1952. *Prehistoric Europe, the Economic Basis.* London. 349 pp.

1955. A Microlithic Industry from the Cambridgeshire Fenland and other Industries of Sauveterrian Affinities from Britain. *Proc.Prehist.Soc.* (NS), vol. 21, pp. 3–20.

COLANI, M. 1927. L'Age de la pierre dans la province de Hoa-Binh (Tonkin), *Mem.Serv.Géol.de l'Indochine.*, vol. 14, 86 pp.

COLBERT, E. H. 1943. Pleistocene Vertebrates collected in Burma by the American South-east Asiatic Expedition. *Trans. Amer.Phil.Soc.* (NS), vol. 32, pt. 3, pp. 395–429.

COLE, S. 1954. *The Prehistory of East Africa.* Harmondsworth. 301 pp.

1960. [ANON] Ice Age Hunters of the Far North. *New Scientist*, vol. 8, p. 1508.

1963. *The Prehistory of East Africa.* New York and London. 382 pp.

COLLINGS, H. D. 1938. A Pleistocene Site in the Malay Peninsula. *Nature,Lond.*, vol. 142, pp. 575–6.

COMBIER, J. 1955. Les fouilles de 1907 à 1925. Mise au point stratigraphique et typologique, pp. 93–209 *in* Thoral *et al.* Solutré, *Trav.Lab.Géol.Univ.Lyon* (NS), vol. 2, 224 pp.

COON, C. S. 1957. *Seven Caves.* London. 323 pp.

1963. *The Origin of Races.* London. 724 pp.

COPPENS, Y. 1961. Découverte d'un Australopithéciné dans le Villafranchien du Tchad. *C.R.Acad.Sci.Paris*, pp. 3851–2.

COULANGES, L. 1935. Les Gisements préhistoriques de Sauveterre-la-Lémace. *Arch.Inst.Paléont.hum.*, Mém. 14. 54 pp.

DAY, M. H. 1965. *Guide to Fossil Man.* London 289 pp.

DELPORTE, H. 1959. Notes de voyage leptolithique en Europe centrale, I. la Tchécoslovaquie *Riv.Sci.Preist.*, vol. 14, pp. 19–57.

DERANIYAGALA, P. E. P. 1940. The Stone Age and Cave Men of Ceylon. *J.R.Asiatic Soc. (Ceylon Br.)*, vol. 34, no. 92, pp. 351–73.

1955. The Ages of the Hippopotamus and *Elephas maximus* Fossils in the Gem Sands of Ceylon. *Geol.Mag.*, vol. 92, pp. 50–2.

1956. A Mesolithic Burial Tumulus from Ceylon. *Nature, Lond.*, vol. 178, pp. 1481–2.

1956a. The Races of the Stone Age and of the Ferrolithic of Ceylon. *J. R.Asiatic.Soc.* (NS), vol. 5, pt. 1, pp. 1–23.

1958. The Balangoda Culture. *Spolia Zeylan.* vol. 28, pt. 1, pp. 117–20.

1958a. The Pleistocene of Ceylon. *Ceylon Nat.Mus.,Nat. Hist.Ser.* 164 pp.

1963. An Open Air Habitation Site of *Homo sapiens balangodensis*. *Spolia Zeylan.*, vol. 30, pt. 1, pp. 87–110.

EWING, J. F. 1947. Preliminary Note on the Excavations at the Palaeolithic Site of Ksâr 'Akil, Republic of Lebanon. *Antiquity*, vol. 21, no. 84, pp. 186–96.

FOOTE, R. B. 1914. *The Foote Collection of Indian Prehistoric and Protohistoric Antiquities*. Madras.

FREUND, G. 1952. Die Blattspitzen des Paläolithikums in Europa, *Quartär-Bibliothek*. Bonn. 330 pp.

GARCIA, L. PERICOT. 1942. La Cueva del Parpallo (Gandia). *Cons.Sup.Invest.ci Inst.Diego Velasques*. Madrid. 351 pp.

GARROD, D. A. E. 1926. *The Upper Palaeolithic Age in Britain*. Oxford. 211 pp.

1932. A new Mesolithic Industry: The Natufian of Palestine. *J.R.anthrop.Inst.*, vol. 62, pp. 257–69.

1938. The Upper Palaeolithic in the light of recent discovery. *Proc.Prehist.Soc.* (NS), vol. 4, pp. 1–26.

1951. A transitional Industry from the base of the Upper Palaeolithic in Palestine and Syria. *J.R.anthrop.Inst.*, vol. 81, pp. 121–30.

1955. The Mugharet el-Emireh in Lower Galilee: Type-Station of the Emiran Industry. *J.R.anthrop.Inst.*, vol. 85, pp. 141–62.

1956. Acheuléo-Jabrudien et 'Pré-Aurignacien' de la grotte du Taboun (Mt. Carmel). *Quaternaria*, vol. 3, pp. 39–59.

1957. The Natufian Culture: The Life and Economy of a Mesolithic People in the Near East. *Proc.Brit.Acad.*, vol. 43, pp. 211–27.

1962. The Middle-Palaeolithic and the Problem of Mount Carmel Man. *J.R.anthrop.Inst.*, vol. 92, pp. 232–59.

GARROD, D. A. E. & BATE, D. M. A. 1937. *The Stone Age of Mount Carmel*, vol. 1. Oxford. 240 pp.

GARROD, D. A. E. & KIRKBRIDE, D. 1961. Excavation of the

Abri Zumoffen, a Paleolithic Rock–Shelter near Adlun, South Lebanon, 1958. *Bull.Mus.Beyrouth*, vol. 16, pp. 61–7.

GOBERT, E. G. 1952. El-Mekta, Station princeps du Capsien. *Karthago*, vol. 3. 79 pp.

    1954. Le site quaternaire de Sidi Mannsour à Gafsa. *Quaternaria*, vol. 1, pp. 61–80.

GOBERT, E. G. & VAUFREY, R. 1932. Deux gisements extrêmes d'Ibéromaurusien. *L'Anthrop.*, vol. 42, pp. 449–90.

GOODWIN, A. J. H. 1926. South African Stone Implement Industries. *S.Afr.J.Sci.*, vol. 23, pp. 784–8.

    1928. An Introduction to the Middle Stone Age in South Africa. *S.Afr.J.Sci.*, vol. 25, pp. 410–8.

    1929. The Middle Stone Age. *Ann.S.Afr.Mus.*, vol. 27, pp. 95–145.

    1933. Some Developments in Technique during the Earlier Stone Age. *Trans. R.Soc.S.Afr.*, vol. 21, pp. 109–24.

    1946. The Loom of Prehistory. *S.Afr.Arch.Soc.Hbk.*, no. 2, 151 pp.

GOODWIN, A. J. H. & LOWE, C. VAN RIET, 1929. The Stone Age Cultures of South Africa. *Ann.S.Afr.Mus.*, vol. 27, 289 pp.

HARRISSON, T. 1957. The Great Cave of Niah. *Man.* vol. 57, art. 211, pp. 161–6.

HARRISSON, T., HOOIJER, D. A. & LORD MEDWAY. 1961. An extinct Giant Pangolin and associated mammals from Niah Cave, Sarawak. *Nature,Lond.*, vol. 189, p. 166.

HAY, R. L. 1963. Stratigraphy of Beds I through IV, Olduvai Gorge, Tanganyika. *Science*, vol. 139, pp. 829–33.

HEBERER, G. 1963. Uber einen neuen archanthropinen Typus aus der Oldoway-Schlucht. *Zeit.Morph.Anthrop.*, vol. 53, pp. 171–7.

HEEKEREN, H. R. VAN, 1948. Prehistoric Discoveries in Siam. 1943–4. *Proc.Prehist.Soc.* (NS), vol. 14, p. 24–32.

    1949. Early Man and Fossil Vertebrates on the Island of Celebes. *Nature,Lond.*, vol. 163, pp. 492.

    1957. *The Stone Age of Indonesia.* 'S-Gravenhage. 141 pp.

    1958. Notes on Prehistoric Flores, *Madjalah Untuk Ilmu Bahasa, Ilmu Bumi dan Kebudajaan Indonesia*, vol. 85, no. 4, pp. 455–61.

    1960. The Tjabengè Flake Industry from South Celebes.

Asian Perspec., vol. 2, no. 2 (1958), pp. 77–81.

HEIDER, K. G. 1960. A Pebble-tool Complex in Thailand. *Asian Perspec.*, vol. 2, no. 2 (1958), pp. 63–7.

HEINZELIN, J. DE, 1957. Les Fouilles d'Ishango. *Exploration du Parc National Albert*, vol. 2, 128 pp.

HEWITT, J. 1926. Some peculiar elements in the Wilton Culture of the Eastern Province. *S.Afr.J.Sci.*, vol. 23, pp. 901–4.

HIGGS, E. S. 1963. A Middle Palaeolithic Industry in Greece. *Man*, vol. 63, art. 2, pp. 2–4.

HOOIJER, D. A. 1950. Man and other Mammals from Toalian Sites in South-western Celebes, *Verh.Kon.Ned.Akad. Wetensch.*, vol. 46, pp. 7–160.

—— 1957. Three new Giant Prehistoric Rats from Flores, Lesser Sunda Islands, *Zoöl.Meded.*, vol. 35, pp. 299–314.

—— 1960. The Pleistocene Vertebrate Fauna of Celebes. *Asian Perspec*, vol. 2, no. 2 (1958), pp. 71–6.

HOPWOOD, A. T. 1951. The Olduvai Fauna, *in* L. S. B. Leakey, *Olduvai Gorge*, Cambridge. pp. 20–30.

HOWELL, F. C. & CLARK, J. D. 1963. Acheulian Hunter-Gatherers of Sub-Saharan Africa, *in* F. C. Howell & F. Bourlière (Eds.). African Ecology & Human Evolution, *Viking Fund Pubs. in Anthrop.*, No. 36, pp. 458–533.

JONES, N. 1949. *The Prehistory of Southern Rhodesia.* Cambridge. 78 pp.

JØRGENSEN, J. B. 1956. Kongemosen. *Kuml.*, pp. 23–40.

KENT, P. E. 1941. The Recent History and Pleistocene Deposits of the Plateau North of Lake Eyasi, Tanganyika, *Geol. Mag.*, vol. 78, pp. 173–84.

KLIMA, B. 1961. Soucasny stav Problematiky Aurignacienu a Gravettienu. *Arch.rozhledy.*, vol. 13, pp. 84–121.

KOBAYSHI, T. & SHIKAMA, T. 1961. The Climatic History of the Far East, *in* A. E. M. Nairn (editor) *Descriptive Palaeo-Climatology.* New York. pp. 292–306.

KOENIGSWALD, G. H. R. VON, 1936. Early Palaeolithic Stone Implements from Java. *Bull.Raffles Mus.*, vol. 1, series B, pp. 52–60.

—— 1939a. Das Pleistocän Javas. *Quart.Jb.Erforsch.Eiszeit.*, vol. 2, pp. 28–53.

—— 1939. The Relationship between the Fossil Mammalian Faunas of Java and China, with special reference to Early

Man. *PekingNat.Hist.Bull.*, vol. 13, pt. 4, pp. 293–8.

  1960. Preliminary Report on a Newly-discovered Stone Age Culture from Northern Luzon. *Asian Perspec.*, vol. 2, no. 2 (1958), pp. 69–70.

  1962. Das absolute Alter des *Pithecanthropus erectus* Dubois, *EvolutionundHominisation* (ed. G. Kurth), pp. 112–19.

KRETZOI, M. & VÉRTES, L. 1965. Upper Biharian (Intermindel) Pebble-industry Occupation Site in Western Hungary. *Current Anthropology*, vol. 6, pp. 74–87

KURTÉN, B. 1960. An attempted parallelization of the Quaternary Mammalian Faunas of China and Europe. *Soc.Sci. Fennica Comment.Biolog.*, vol. 23, no. 8, pp. 1–11.

LACAILLE, A. D. 1954. *The Stone Age in Scotland.* London. 345 pp.

LAL, B. B. 1956. Palaeoliths from the Beas and Banganga Valleys, Punjab. *Ancient India*, vol. 12, pp. 59–92.

LEAKEY, L. S. B. 1931. *The Stone Age Cultures of Kenya Colony.* Cambridge. 288 pp.

  1934. *Adam's Ancestors.* London. 244 pp. 4th edn., 1953, 235 pp.

  1935. *Stone Age Races of Kenya.* Oxford, Lond. 150 pp.

  1949. Tentative Study of the Pleistocene Climatic Changes and Stone-Age Culture Sequence in North-Eastern Angola. *Publ.Museu do Dundo.* Lisbon. 82 pp.

  1951. *Olduvai Gorge.* Cambridge. 164 pp.

  1952. (ed.) *Proc.1st.Pan-Afr.Congr.Prehist.* (Nairobi, 1947). Oxford. p. 8, resolution no. 16, pt. 3.

  1952. The Tumbian Culture of East Africa. *Proc.1st. Pan-Afr.Congr.Prehist.* (Nairobi, 1947). Oxford. pp. 201–2.

  1958. Recent Discoveries at Olduvai Gorge, Tanganyika. *Nature,Lond.*, vol. 181, pp. 1099–103.

  1959. A new Fossil Skull from Olduvai. *Nature,Lond.*, vol. 184, pp. 491–3.

  1961. New Finds at Olduvai Gorge. *Nature,Lond.*, vol. 189, pp. 649–50.

  1963. Adventures in the Search for Man. *Nat.Geogr.Mag.*, vol. 123, pp. 132–52.

  1965. *Olduvai Gorge* 1951–61., vol. 1, Cambridge. 109 pp.

LEAKEY, L. S. B., EVERNDEN, J. F. & CURTIS, G. H. 1961. Age

of Bed I, Olduvai Gorge, Tanganyika. *Nature,Lond.*, vol. 191, pp. 478–9.

LIERE, W. J. VAN, 1960. Un gisement paléolithique dans un niveau pléistocène de l'Oronte à Latanme (Syrie). *Ann. Arch.Syrie.*, vol. 10, pp. 165–74.

LIERE, W. J. VAN & HOOIJER, D. A. 1962. A Palaeo-Orontes level with *Archidiskodon meridionalis* (Nesti) at Hama. *Ann. Arch.Syrie.*, vol. 11, pp. 165–72.

LOWE, C. VAN RIET, 1937. The Archaeology of the Vaal River Basin. *Geol.Mem.Union S.Afr.*, no. 35, pp. 61–184.

——— 1945. The Evolution of the Levallois Technique in South Africa. *Man*, vol. 45, art. 37, pp. 49–59.

——— 1951. A new African Acheul Stage IV Site in Tanganyika. *S.Afr.Arch.Bull.*, vol. 6, no. 24, pp. 94–8.

——— 1952. The Pleistocene Geology and Prehistory of Uganda, pt. ii; Prehistory, *Mem.Geol.Surv.Uganda*, no. 6, 113 pp.

——— 1952a. The Development of the Hand-Axe Culture in South Africa. *Proc.1st.Pan-Afr.Cong.Prehist.* (Nairobi 1947), Oxford, pp. 167–77.

——— 1952b. The Vaal River Chronology: an up-to-date Summary. *S.Afr.Arch.Bull.*, vol. 7, no. 28, pp. 135–49.

——— 1953. The Kafuan Culture in South Africa. *S.Afr.Arch. Bull.*, vol. 8, pp. 27–31.

McBURNEY, C. B. M. 1950. La Grotte de l'Hyéne (Hagfa. Dabba). *L'Anthrop.*, vol. 54, pp. 201–13.

——— 1950a. The Geographical Study of the Older Palaeolithic Stages in Europe. *Proc.Prehist.Soc.*, vol. 16, pp. 163–83.

——— 1958. Evidence for the distribution in space and time of Neanderthaloid and allied strains in northern Africa. *Hundert Jahre Neanderthaler.* (edited G. H. R. von Koenigswald). Utrecht. pp. 253–64.

——— 1960. *The Stone Age in Northern Africa.* Harmondsworth. 288 pp.

——— 1962. Absolute Chronology of the Palaeolithic in Eastern Libya and the Problem of Upper Palaeolithic Origins. *Adv.of Sci.* vol., 18, no. 75, pp. 494–7.

McBURNEY, C. B. M. & HEY, R. W. 1955. *Prehistory and Pleistocene Geology in Cyrenaican Libya*, Cambridge. 315 pp.

MALAN, B. D. 1957. The term 'Middle Stone Age'. *Proc.*

3rd Pan-Afr.Congr.Prehist. (1955). pp. 223–7.

MASON, R. J. 1957. The Transvaal Middle Stone Age and statistical analysis. *S.Afr.Arch.Bull.*, vol. 12, no. 48, pp. 119–37, 140–1.

1959. Some South African Stone Age Cultures. *Nature, Lond.*, vol. 183, pp. 377–9.

1962. *Prehistory of the Transvaal*, Pietermaritzburg. 498 pp.

MAYR, E. 1945. Wallace's Line in the light of recent zoogeographic studies. *Science and Scientists in the Netherlands Indies. Natuurwet.Tijdschr.Ned.Ind.*, vol. 102, Special Supp. pp. 241–50.

MORGAN, J. DE, CAPITAIN, L. & BOUDY, P. 1910. Etude sur les Stations préhistoriques du Sud-Tunisien. *Rev. Ecol.Anthrop.*, vol. 20, 105ff.

MONTAGU, M. F. (edited). 1962. *Culture and the Evolution of Man.* New York. 376 pp.

MORRIS, T. O. 1935. The Prehistoric Stone Implements of Burma. *J.Burma Res.Soc.*, vol. 25, pp. 1–39.

MORTELMANS, G. 1952. Contribution à l'étude des Cultures Pré-Abbevilliennes à galets taillés du Katanga: le site Mulundwa I. *Soc.Roy.belge d'Anthrop.et Préhist.* Brussels. pp. 150–64.

MORTILLET, G. & A. 1900. *Le Préhistorique Origine et Antiquité de l'Homme.* 3rd. edn. Paris. 709 pp.

MOVIUS, H. L. 1940. An Early Post-Glacial Archaeological Site at Cushendun, Co. Antrim. *Proc.Roy.Irish Acad.* (C), vol. 46, pp. 1–84.

1943. The Stone Age of Burma. *Trans.Amer.Phil.Soc.* (NS), vol. 32, pt. 3, pp. 341–93.

1949. The Lower Palaeolithic Cultures of Southern and Eastern Asia. *Trans.Amer.Phil.Soc.* (NS), vol. 38, pt. 4 (1948), pp. 329–420.

1953. Old World Prehistory: Palaeolithic, *in* A. L. Kroeber, *Anthropology Today.* Chicago. pp. 163–92.

1955. Palaeolithic Archaeology in Southern and Eastern Asia, exclusive of India. *Cahiers d'histoire Mondiale.* Paris, vol. 2, nos. 2–3, pp. 257–82; 520–53.

1956. New Palaeolithic sites, near Ting-Ts'un in the Fen river, Shansi, North China. *Quaternaria*, vol. 3, pp. 13–26.

1960. Radiocarbon Dates and Upper Palaeolithic Archaeology in Central and Western Europe. *Current Anthropology*, vol. 1, nos. 5–6, pp. 355–91.

MULVANEY, D. J. 1961. The Stone Age of Australia. *Proc. Prehist.Soc.* (N.S.), vol. 27, pp. 56–107.

NAPIER, J. R. & WEINER, J. S. 1962. Olduvai Gorge and Human Origins. *Antiquity*, vol. 36, no. 141, pp. 41–47.

NEUVILLE, R. 1931. L'Acheuléen supérieur de la Grotte d'-Oumn-Qatafa. *L'Anthrop.*, vol. 41, pp. 13–51.

NEUVILLE, R. & RUHLMANN, A. 1941. La Place du Paléolithique ancien dans le Quaternaire marocain. *Coll.Hespéris.Inst. Hautes-Etudes Maroc.*, vol. 8, 156 pp.

NOETLING, F. 1894. On the Occurrence of Chipped (?) Flints in the Upper Miocene of Burma. *Rec.Geol.Surv.India.*, vol. 27, pt. 3, pp. 101–3.

1897. On the Discovery of Chipped Flint-flakes in the Pliocene of Burma. *Nat.Sci.*, vol. 10, pp. 233–41.

NOONE, H. D. 1939. Report on a new Neolithic Site at Ulu Kelantan. *J.Fed.Malay States Mus.*, vol. 15, no.4, pp.170–4.

NOONE, N. A. & H. V. V. 1940. The Stone Implements of Bandarawela (Ceylon), *Ceylon J.Sci.Sect.G.Anthrop.*, vol. 3, pt. 1, pp. 1–24.

OAKLEY, K. P. 1951. A Definition of Man. *Science News.* Harmondsworth. pp. 69–81 (reprinted *in* M. F. A. Montagu (edited) *Culture and the Evolution of Man*. New York, 1962. pp. 3–12.)

1952. Dating the Libyan Desert Silica-glass. *Nature, Lond.*, vol. 170. p. 447.

1955. The Composition of the Piltdown Hominoid Remains, *Bull.Brit.Mus.Nat.Hist.*Geol.Ser., vol. 2, no. 6, pp. 254–61.

1956. Fire as Palaeolithic Tool and Weapon. *Proc. Prehist.Soc.* (NS), vol. 21, pp. 36–48.

1961. *Man the Tool-Maker*. Brit.Mus. (Nat.Hist.), 5th edn. 98 pp.

1961a. Bone Harpoon from Gamble's Cave, Kenya. *Antiquaries J.*, vol. 41, pp. 86–7.

1964. The Problem of Man's Antiquity: An Historical Survey. *Bull.Brit.Mus.Nat.Hist.*Geol.Ser., vol. 9, no. 5, p. 155.

OBERMAIER, H. 1924. *Fossil Man in Spain*. New Haven. 495 pp.

OKLADNIKOV, A. P. 1961. The Paleolithic of Trans-Baikal. *Amer.Antiquity*, vol. 26, no. 24, pp. 486–97.

PALLARY, P. 1909. Instructions sur les recherches préhistoriques dans le N.W. d'Afrique. Algiers. *Mém.Soc.Hist.Alg.* 116 pp.

PATERSON, T. T. 1939. Prehistory of the Potwar and Indus Regions, *in* Paterson, T. T. & H. de Terra, Studies on the Ice Age in India. *Carnegie Inst.Washington Publ.* no. 493, pp. 301–12.

1941. On a World Correlation of the Pleistocene. *Trans. R.Soc.Edinb.*, vol. 60, pt. 2, pp. 373–425.

PEI, W. C. 1939. A preliminary study of a new Palaeolithic Station known as Locality 15 within the Choukoutien region. *Bull. Geol.Soc.China*, vol. 30, pp. 543–59.

1939a. The Upper Cave Industry of Choukoutien. *Pal. Sin.* (NS), no. 9, 56 pp.

PEYRONY, D. 1933. Les Industries 'Aurignaciennes' dans le Bassin de la Vézère: Aurignacien et Périgordien. *Bull.Soc. préhist.franç.*, vol. 30, pp. 543–59.

1948. *Elements de Préhistoire.* Paris. 5th edn. 181 pp.

PIETTE, E. 1889. L'Epoque de transition intermediaire entre L'Age du renne et l'époque de la pierre polie. *C.R.Congr. Internat.d'Anthrop.et 'Arch.Préhist.* 10th. Sess. Paris. p. 203.

1895. Etudes d'Ethnographie préhistorique, *L'Anthrop.*, vol 6, pp. 276–92.

PIGGOTT, S. 1950. *Prehistoric India.* Harmondsworth. 293 pp.

POSNANSKY, M. 1959. A Hope Fountain Site at Olorgesailie, Kenya Colony. *S.Afr.Arch.Bull.*, vol. 14, pp. 81-89.

RUHLMANN, A. 1951. La Grotte préhistorique de Dar es-Soltan. *Coll.Hespéris Inst.Hautes-Etudes Maroc.*, vol. 11, 210 pp.

RUST, A. 1937. *Das Altsteinzeitliche Rentierjägerlager Meiendorf.* Neumunster.

1950. *Die Höhlenfunde von Jabrud (Syrien).* Neumünster. 154 pp.

SAHNI, M. R. 1952. *Man in Evolution.* Calcutta. 272 pp.

SANSONI, G. C. (editor). 1962. *Piccola guida della Preistoria Italiana*, pt. 2. Firenze. pls. 1–44.

SCHWANTES, G. 1928. Nordisches Paläolithikum und Mesolithikum. *Mitt.Mus.Völkerk.* Hamburg. vol. 13, pp. 159ff.

1934. *Geschichte Schleswig-Holsteins.* Nemunster. vol. 1, 160 pp.

SERIZAWA, C. & IKAWA, F. 1960. The Oldest Archaeological Materials from Japan. *Asian Perspec.*, vol. 2, no. 2 (1958), pp. 1–39.

SIEVEKING, A. DE G. 1960. The Palaeolithic Industry of Khota Tampan, Perak, North-western Malaya, *Asian Perspec.*, vol. 2, pp. 91–102.

SIEVEKING, G. DE G. 1956. Excavations at Gua-Cha, Kelantan, 1954, pt. 1, *Fed.Mus.J.*, vol. 1–2, pp. 75–138.

SMITH, M. A. 1952. The Mesolithic in the South of France, *Proc.Prehist.Soc.* (NS), vol. 18, pp. 103–20.

SMITH, P. E. L. 1962. Solutrean origins and the question of eastern diffusion *Arctic Anthrop.*, vol. 1, pp. 58–67.

SOLECKI, R. S. 1955. Shanidar Cave, a Paleolithic Site in Northern Iraq, *Smith.Ann.Rep.* 1954. Washington, pp. 389–425.

   1963. Prehistory in Shanidar Valley, Northern Iraq. *Science*, vol. 139, pp. 179–93.

SOLHEIM, W. G. 1960. The Present Status of the 'Palaeolithic' in Borneo. *Asian Perspec.* vol. 2, pp. 83–90.

SONNEVILLE–BORDES, D. DE. 1958–9. Problèmes généraux du Paléolithique supérieur dans le Sud-ouest de la France. *L'Anthrop.*, vol. 62, pp. 413–51; vol. 63, pp. 1–36.

   1960. *Le Paléolithique supérieur en Périgord.* Bordeaux. 2 vols. 558 pp.

STEIN CALLENFELS, P. V. VAN. 1936. L'industrie osseuse de Ngandong. *L'Anthrop.*, vol. 46, pp. 359–62.

STEKELIS, M. 1960. The Palaeolithic Deposits of Jisr Banat Yaqub. *Bull.Res.Counc.Israel*, vol. 9G, pp. 61–90.

STEKELIS, M., PICARD, L., SCHULMAN, N. & HAAS, G. 1960. Villafranchian deposits near Ubeidiya in the Central Jordan Valley. *Bull.Res.Counc.Israel*, vol. 9G, no. 4, pp. 175–84.

SUBBARAO, B. 1958. *The Personality of India.* 2nd edn. Baroda. 193 pp.

SUZUKI, H. 1962. Mikkabi Man and the Fossil bearing deposits from Tadaki limestone Quarry at Mikkabi, Central Japan. *Zinruigaku Zassi.* (*J.Anthrop.Soc.Nippon*), vol. 70, pp. 46–8 (English summary).

TERRA, H. DE. 1933. Late Cenozoic History in India. *Nature, Lond.*, vol. 137, pp. 686–8.

   1943. The Pleistocene of Burma. *Trans.Amer.Phil.Soc.*

(NS), vol. 32, pt. 3, pp. 271–339.

1949. Pleistocene Geology and Early Man in Java, *Trans.Amer.Phil.Soc.* (NS), vol. 32, pp. 437–64.

TERRA, H. DE & PATERSON, T. T. 1939. Studies on the Ice Age in India and associated Human Cultures. *Carnegie Inst. Washington.* Publ. no. 493, 354 pp.

THEOBALD, W. 1881. The Siwalik Group of the Sub-Himalayan Region. *Rec.Geol.Surv.India.* vol. 14, pt. 1, pp. 66–125.

THORUL, M., RIQUET, R. & COMBIER, J. 1955. Solutré, *Trav. Géol.Lyon,* 224 pp.

TSCHUMI, O. 1949. *Urgeschichte der Schweiz.* Frauenfeld. vol. 1, 751 pp. (esp. p. 449).

TWEEDIE, M. W. F. 1953. The Stone Age in Malaya. *J.Malay. Br.Roy.Asiatic Soc.,* vol. 26, pt. 2, 90 pp.

VAUFREY, R. 1928. La Paléolithique Italien, *Arch.Inst.Pal.hum.* Paris. vol. 3, 196 pp.

1955. Préhistoire de l'Afrique. vol. 1. Maghreb. *Publications de l'Inst. Hautes-études Tunis.* Paris. vol. 4, 458 pp.

VERHOEVEN, T. 1959. Die Klingenkultur der Insel Timor. *Anthropos.* vol. 54, pp. 970–72 and tables 1–4.

VIGNARD, E. 1923. Une nouvelle industrie lithique, le Sébilien. *Bull.Inst.Fr.d'Arch.Orient.* vol. 22, pp. 1–76.

VOGEL, J. C. & WATERBOLK, H. T. 1964. Groningen Radiocarbon Dates V. *Radiocarbon,* vol. 6, pp. 349–69.

WADIA, D. N. 1928. The Geology of the Poonch State (Kashmir) and adjacent portions of the Punjab. *Mem.Geol.Surv. India,* vol. 51, pt. 2, pp. 185–370.

WAECHTER, J. D'A. 1952. The Excavation of Jabrud and its Relation to the Prehistory of Palestine and Syria. *Ann. Rep.Lond.Univ.Inst.Arch.* vol. 8, pp. 10–28.

1962. The Middle and Upper Palaeolithic Sequence in south-west Asia. *Adv.Sci.,* vol. 18, no. 75, p. 498.

WALKER, D. 1956. Alluvial Deposits of Perak, and changes in the relative levels of Land and Sea. *Fed.Mus.J.,* vol. 1–2, pp. 19–34.

WALKER, D. & SIEVEKING, ANN DE G. 1962. The Palaeolithic Industry of Kota Tampan, Perak, Malaya. *Proc.Prehist.Soc.* (NS), vol. 28, pp. 103–39.

WARREN, S. H. 1926. The Classification of the Lower Palaeolithic with especial reference to Essex. *Trans.S.East Nat.,* vol. 54, pp. 38–50.

1951. The Clacton Flint Industry: a new Interpretation, *Proc.Geol.Assoc.*, vol. 62, pp. 107–35.

1958. The Clacton Industry. Supplementary Note. *Proc. Geol.Assoc.*, vol. 69, pp. 123–9.

WATSON, W. 1950. Flint Implements. *Brit.Mus.London.* 80 pp.

WAYLAND, E. J. & BURKITT, M. C. 1932. The Magosian Culture of Uganda. *J.R.anthrop.Inst.*, vol. 62, pp. 369–90.

WORMINGTON, H. M. 1962. The problems of the Presence and Dating in America of Flaking Techniques Similar to the Palaeolithic in the Old World. *Int.Congr.préhist.Sci.VI.* Rome. pp. 273–83.

WYMER, J. 1964. Excavations at Barnfield Pit, 1955–60, *in* C. D. Ovey, Swanscombe Skull. *Roy.anthrop.Inst. occ.Pap.*, no. 20, pp. 19–61.

ZEUNER, F. E. 1952. The Microlithic Industry of Langhnaj, Gujarat. *Man* vol. 52, no. 182, pp. 129–31.

ZEUNER, F. E. & ALLCHIN, B. 1956. The Microlithic Sites of Tinnevelly District, Madras State. *Ancient India* vol. 12, pp. 4–20.

ZOTZ, L. F. 1951. *Altsteinzeitzunde Mitteleuropas.* Stuttgart. 290 pp.

FOSSIL HOMINID DATING TABLES I–XVI

THESE TABLES summarize the dating of the known fossil hominids in accordance with the stratigraphical and archaeological terminologies defined in this book. They are mainly based on the *Catalogue des Hommes Fossiles* (edited H. V. Vallois & H. L. Movius, 1952), published by the International Geological Congress. Some additional information has been drawn from entries received in preparation for the New Catalogue of Fossil Hominids (edited K. P. Oakley & B. G. Campbell) which has been made possible by a grant from the Wenner-Gren Foundation, New York.

A few words are needed in explanation of the nomenclature used in these tables. The concept is gaining ground that there are only two valid genera in the Hominidae: *Australopithecus* and *Homo* (Campbell, 1963). According to this view all the forms listed in Table I should be counted as species of *Australopithecus*. Similarly according to this newer taxonomy, the Pithecanthropines in Table II are all varieties of a single species *Homo erectus*. All the remaining Hominines (Tables III–XVI) would be considered by some authors as varieties of a single species *Homo sapiens* (eg *H. sapiens sapiens*, *H. sapiens neanderthalensis* etc.). However, the older taxonomy still current has been retained in this book as being more expedient for present purposes.

I AUSTRALOPITHECINES

COUNTRY	SITE	FOUND	NAME OR TYPE	DATING		In Years BP	A Type
				Stratigraphical	Cultural		
Transvaal	Kromdraai	1938	*Paranthropus robustus*	Basal M. Pleistocene	Unknown		
	Makapansgat Limeworks Cave	1947	*Australopithecus prometheus* = *A. africanus*	Upper Villafranchian = Lower Pleistocene	Utilized bones[1]		
	Sterkfontein	1936	*Plesianthropus transvaalensis* = *A. africanus*	Villafranchian = Lower Pleistocene	Uncertain		
	Sterkfontein Extension	1957	*Australopithecus* sp.		Oldowan[2]		
	Swartkrans	1949	*Paranthropus crassidens* = *Paranthropus robustus*	Basal M. Pleistocene	Oldowan?[3]		
		1949	*Telanthropus capensis* = *A. capensis* = *Homo* sp	Basal M. Pleistocene	Oldowan?[3]		
	Taung(s)	1924	*Australopithecus africanus*	Villafranchian = Lower Pleistocene	None found		
Tanzania	Garusi Lake Eyasi	1939	*Meganthropus africanus* = *A. africanus*	Villafranchian Laetolil Beds	Oldowan?[4]		

291

I AUSTRALOPITHECINES

COUNTRY	SITE	FOUND	NAME OR TYPE	DATING			
				Stratigraphical	Cultural	In Years BP	A Type
Tanzania cont.	Lake Natron	1964	Zinjanthropus cf. boisei	M. Pleistocene	None found	c 800,000	A 4
	Olduvai FLK.I	1959	Zinjanthropus boisei = Paranthropus boisei	Villafranchian Olduvai Bed I	Oldowan	1.7 million[5]	A 2
	FLK.NN.I	1960	'Pre-Zinjanthropus' = Homo habilis = Australopithecus habilis	"	"	"	
	MNK. II	1963	Homo habilis = A. capensis = Homo sp.	End-Villafranchian Lower Olduvai Bed II	"	1.4 million	A 2
Chad	Koro Toro[6] (Yayo)	1961	Tchadanthropus uxoris	Early Middle Pleistocene[7]	None found		
Java	Sangiran	1941, 52	Meganthropus palaeojavanicus[8]	Djetis fauna	None found		

[1] 'Osteodontokeratic culture', accepted in small part only by the author; but see R.A. Dart, 1961, Nature, vol. 191, pp. 372-3 and references.
[2] Brain 1958, pp. 72-3. [3] Brain 1958, p. 88 fig. 73. [4] Kent 1941, p. 178. [5] Leakey, Evernden and Curtis 1961; Evernden and Curtis in Hay 1963, p. 832. The date quoted is broadly supported by uranium fission-track dating of volcanic glass from Bed I, which gave 2 million years ± 25% (R.L. Fleischer et al., 1965, General Electric Research Lab. Report No. 65). [6] Coppens 1961. [7] Associated fauna: Archidiskodon recki and Elephas atlanticus. [8] Some authorities regard this form as a variant of Pithecanthropus robustus.

II PITHECANTHROPINES

COUNTRY	SITE	FOUND	NAME OR TYPE	DATING Stratigraphical	Cultural	In Years BP	A Type
Germany	Mauer (Heidelberg)	1907	*Homo (Euranthropus) heidelbergensis*	Günz-Mindel	None found	> 500,000[1]	A 4
Hungary	Vértesszöllös	1965	*Pithecanthropus* sp.	Inter-Mindel	Buda industry	*c* 400,000[2]	A 2
Java	Modjokerto	1936	*Homo modjokertensis* = immature *P. robustus*	Djetis fauna			
	Sangiran	1937, 38	*Pithecanthropus* II, III = *P. erectus*	Middle Pleistocene Trinil fauna	None found	*c* 500,000[3]	A 3
		1936	*Pithecanthropus* IV = *P. robustus* (= *modjokertensis*)	Djetis fauna	None found		
	Trinil	1891	*Pithecanthropus* I = *P. erectus*	Middle Pleistocene Trinil fauna	None found	*c* 500,000	A 3
	Kedung Brubus	1890	*Pithecanthropus erectus*	,,	None found	*c* 500,000	A 3
China	Choukoutien Lower Cave	1927–37	Peking Man = *Sinanthropus* *P. pekinensis*	Mindel II[4]	Choukoutienian		

293

II PITHECANTHROPINES

COUNTRY	SITE	FOUND	NAME OR TYPE	DATING			
				Stratigraphical	Cultural	In Years BP	A Type
China cont.	Lantian Shensi	1963–64	*P. lantianensis*	M. Pleistocene	Uncertain		
Algeria	Ternifine	1954–6	*Atlanthropus mauritanicus*	Base of L. Amirian = early Mindel[5]	1st. stage Moroccan Acheulian = Rahmanian[6]		
Tanzania	Olduvai LLK. II	1960	'Chellean Man' = *Homo leakeyi*	M. Pleistocene Up. Olduvai Bed II	Chellean III	490,000	A 2

[1] The K/A date of 370,000 (*c* 400,000) reported in recent publications was only applicable if Mauer were Mindel I/II in age. [2] Provisional dating of travertine by uranium/thorium method. [3] The antiquity of *Pithecanthropus* in Java was indicated by the K/A dating of Muriah volcanic rocks associated with Trinil fauna (490,000 years, reported by von Koenigswald 1962, p. 117). The K/A dating of tektites found in the Upper Trinil Beds of Java is no longer regarded by the author as having any valid bearing on the antiquity of *Pithecanthropus*. [4] Kurtén and Vasari 1960. [5] Biberson 1961*a* p. 494. [6] Biberson 1961, p. 116.

III HOMININES

EARLY NEANDERTHALOIDS OF EUROPE

COUNTRY	SITE	FOUND	NAME OR TYPE	DATING			
				Stratigraphical	Cultural	In Years BP	A Type
Britain	Swanscombe gravel-pit, Kent	1935–36 1955	*Homo* cf. *steinheimensis*	Hoxnian	Middle Acheulian	c 250,000	A 4
France	Fontéchevade cave Charente	1947	*Homo* 'praesapiens' Fontéchevade I–II	Eemian	U. Tayacian	70–?150,000	A 4
	Montmaurin cave, Haute Garonne	1945–9	*Homo* cf. *steinheimensis*	Riss interstadial	Uncertain		
Germany	Steinheim sand-pit Würtemberg	1933	*Homo steinheimensis*	Late Hoxnian	Unknown	c 200,000	A 4

IV HOMININES

NEANDERTHALERS OF EUROPE (*Homo neanderthalensis*)

COUNTRY	SITE	FOUND	NAME OR TYPE	DATING			
				Stratigraphical	Cultural	In Years BP	A Type
Belgium	Bay-Bonnet cave, Liège	1895		Würm cold fauna	Mousterian		
	Engis cave, Liège	1830	Engis I	Würm cold fauna	Mousterian	35–70,000	A 3
	La Naulette cave, Namur	1866		Würm cold fauna			
	Spy cave, Namur	1886	Spy I–III	Würm cold fauna	Mousterian	35–70,000	A 3
France	Arcy-sur-Cure Grotte de l'Hyène	1949		Würm cold fauna	Mousterian La Quina type	35–70,000	A 3
		1951		Würm *Equus* (abundant)	Mousterian	35–70,000	A 3

Site	Date	Culture	Period / fauna	Date range	Grade
La Chaise cave Charente	1949–51	Mousterian bifaces & blades	Würm cold fauna		
La Chapelle-aux-Saints cave, Corrèze	1908	Upper Mousterian burial	Würm cold fauna	35–45,000	A 3
La Ferrassie shelter Dordogne	1909	Mousterian	Würm	> 35,000	A 3
Genay shelter, Côte d'Or	1955	Mousterian	Würm cold fauna		
Isturitz cave, Basse-Pyrénées	c 1895 cf. Malarnaud	Bear bones accumulation	Würm phosphate layer		
Le Moustier shelter Dordogne	1908	Mousterian of Acheulian tradition	Würm	35–70,000	A 3
Marillac cave Charente	1934	Mousterian	Würm		

IV HOMININES

NEANDERTHALERS OF EUROPE cont. (*Homo neanderthalensis*)

COUNTRY	SITE	FOUND	NAME OR TYPE	DATING Stratigraphical	Cultural	In Years BP	A Type
France cont.	Malarnaud cave, Ariège	1888–9		Würm	None found		
	Monsempron shelter, Lot-et-Garonne	1928 1951		Würm cold fauna			
	Pech de l'Aze cave Dordogne	1909		Würm interstadial temperate fauna	Upper Mousterian	c 35,000	A 3
	Le Petit Puy-moyen shelter Charente	1907–8		Würm cold fauna	Typical Mousterian	45–70,000	A 3
	La Quina shelter Charente	1908– 21	La Quina I–XX	Würm	Late Middle Mousterian	35–55,000	A 3

						Date	
	La Quina XIV	1908	Mid-Würm	Final Mousterian	35,250 ± 530 BC 33,300 BC	A 2
	Regourdou nr. Lascaux cave Dordogne	1958	Würm	Mousterian burial		A 2
	La Verrerie cave, Gard	1945–6	Würm	Mousterian		
Germany	Neanderthal cave	1856	Würm		35–70,000	A 4
	Neuessing	Neuessing I	1912–3	Würm	End Acheulian		
	Weimar-Ehringsdorf travertine pit	Ehringsdorf I–II	1908–25	Eemian Lower travertine	Eastern Mousterian	60–120,000[1]	A 2
	Taubach gravel-pits Weimar	1887, 92	Eemian sands on travertine	Eastern Mousterian	60–120,000	A 3
Gibraltar	Forbes' Quarry cave	Gibraltar I	1848	Würm presumed	Unknown	35–70,000	A 4
	Devil's Tower cave	Gibraltar II	1926	Würm	Upper Levalloiso-Mousterian	> 30,000 probably c 50,000	A 2

[1] Travertine dated by Protoactinium/Thorium method (Rosholt and Antal, 1963)

IV HOMININES

NEANDERTHALERS OF EUROPE cont. (*Homo neanderthalensis*)

COUNTRY	SITE	FOUND	NAME OR TYPE	Stratigraphical	Cultural	In Years BP	A Type
					DATING		
Italy	Bisceglie cave, Bari	1955		Würm Level III *R. merkii*	Mousterian		
	Capo di Leuca cave, Puglia	1958		Würm warm fauna *E. antiquus*	Mousterian		
	Pofi pit, Cava Pompi	1959, 61		Würm pozzolana *E. antiquus*	Mousterian		
	Saccopastore gravel-pit Rome	1929	Saccopastore I	Late Eemian	None found	> 60,000	A 3
		1935	Saccopastore II	Late Eemian, lowest terrace R. Aniene	Pontinian?	> 60,000	A 3
	San Felice Circeo cave Latina	1939, 1950	Circeo I & II III	Würm	Pontinian	35–70,000	A 3
	Sedia del Diavolo gravel-pit Rome	1953–4 1956	IV	Würm warm fauna Nomentanan *Cygnus bewicki*	Pontinian Mousterian	35–70,000	A 3

			Homo neanderthalensis var.				
Jersey	La Cotte de St Brelade cave	1910–11	*breladensis*	Würm cold fauna	Levalloiso-Mousterian	< 47,000[1]	A 3
Spain	Bañolas travertine-pit	1887		Pleistocene	None found		
	Cova Negra cave	1928		Early Würm	Mousterian		
	Piñar (La Cariguela) cave, Granada	1954–5		Würm interstadial Layers 6–7	Mousterian		
Switzerland	St Brais II cave	1955		Würm cold fauna	Alpine Palaeolithic	c 32,000	A 3

[1] Radiocarbon date of underlying interstadial was 47,000 BP

IV HOMININES

NEANDERTHALERS OF EASTERN EUROPE INCLUDING USSR (*Homo neanderthalensis* and varieties)

COUNTRY	SITE	FOUND	NAME OR TYPE	DATING			
				Stratigraphical	*Cultural*	*In Years BP*	*A Type*
Czecho-slovakia	Gánovce quarry Slovakia	1926, 55–6		Late Eemian travertine	Micro-Mousterian	> 70,000	A 3
	Ochoz cave Moravia	1905		Early Würm	Eastern Mousterian		
	Sala South Slovakia	1961	*cf* Galilee & Skhul	Würm interstadial	None found		
	Sipka cave, North Moravia	1880		Würm I/II	Eastern Mousterian hearths		
Greece	Petralona cave Thessalonika	1959		Würm *Ursus spelaeus*			
Hungary	Subalyuk (Mussolina) cave, Bükk Mts.	1932		Würm cold fauna	Eastern Mousterian		

Country	Site	Date		Period	Culture		
Rumania	Ohaba-Ponor cave Transylvanian Alps	1923		End Eemian? or Würm	Mixed Mousterian & 'Aurignacian'		
Turkey	Karain Adala						
USSR	Kiik Koba cave, Crimea	1924		Würm	Eastern Mousterian		
	Staroselje cave, Crimea	1952	infant	Late Würm I	Eastern Mousterian	c 35,000	A 3
	Teshik–Tash cave Uzbekistan	1938		Würm	Eastern Mousterian burial		
Yugoslavia	Ivanec	1961		'Göttweig'	Proto-Aurignacian type		
	Krapina shelter Zagreb	1899– 1905		Mid- Würm	Eastern Mousterian	30–45,000	A 2–3

303

V HOMININES

NEANDERTHALERS OF THE NEAR EAST (*Homo neanderthalensis* and varieties)

COUNTRY	SITE	FOUND	NAME OR TYPE	DATING			
				Stratigraphical	*Cultural*	*In Years BP*	*A Type*
Israel	Djebel Kafzeh cave, Galilee; Mugharet Amud, Lake Tiberias	1933– 5	Kafzeh I–VII	Early Würm interstadial Würm	L. Levalloiso- Mousterian Emiran	*c* 60,000	A 4
	Shukbah cave Jerusalem	1928		Würm	U. Leval- loiso– Mousterian	*c* 35,000	A 3
	Mugharet es-Skhul cave, Mt Carmel	1931– 2	Skhul I–X	Mid Würm	Levalloiso- Mousterian burials		
	Mugharet et-Tabun Mt Carmel	1929– 34	Tabun I–II	Mid Würm Layer C	Levalloiso- Mousterian	40,900 ± 1,000 *38,950* BC	A 2

Region	Site	Year	Find	Climate	Culture	Date	Class
	Mugharet et-Tabun cont.	1929–34	Tabun Series I–IV	Mid Würm Layer B	U. Levalloiso-Mousterian	39,700 ± 800 37,750 BC	A 2
		1929–34		Late Eemian Layer E	Upper Acheulian (Micoquian)	c 70,000	A 4
	Mugharet el-Zuttiyeh cave Galilee	1925	Galilee	Late Eemian	Jabrudian probably	c 70,000	A 4
Lebanon	Grotte d'Antelias	c 1900	'Neanderthaloid' foetus	Early/Mid Würm	Transitional (Emiran?)		
	Ksar 'Akil shelter Beirut	1947	Ksar 'Akil II (maxilla)	'Göttweig'? 15m depth Dama	Early Emiran	< 43,750	A 3
Iraq	Shanidar cave	1953	Shanidar child	Early Würm warm flora	Eastern Mousterian	> 60,000	A 4

NEANDERTHALERS OF THE NEAR EAST cont. (*Homo neanderthalensis* and varieties)

COUNTRY	SITE	FOUND	NAME OR TYPE	DATING Stratigraphical	Cultural	In Years BP	A Type
Iraq cont.		1957–60	Shanidar I–VI	Early-Mid Würm. Layer D	Eastern Mousterian		
			I, V	Probably 'Göttweig' Date palm pollen	,,	46,900 ± 1,500 *44,050* BC	A 2
			III	Probably 'Göttweig', but insufficient pollen	,,	> 47,000	A 3
			II, IV, VI	Early Würm cool flora: *Abies* pollen	,,	> 50,000	A 3
Iran	Bisitun cave Kermanshah	1949		Würm	Eastern Mousterian		
	Tamtama cave, Rezaiyeh	1949		Würm	Eastern Mousterian		

VI HOMININES

NEANDERTHALOIDS OF THE FAR EAST

COUNTRY	SITE	FOUND	NAME OR TYPE	DATING		In Years BP	A Type
				Stratigraphical	Cultural		
China	Ma-pa cave Kwangtung	1958		Late M. Pleistocene early U. Pleistocene	[Fenho Complex?]		
	Sjara-Osso-Gol, Ordos	1922	Ordos Man Homo cf neanderthalensis	Loessic soil Palaeoloxodon cf namadicus	Ordosian (Moustero–Aurignacian)		
	Ting-T'sun Shansi	1954	Tingtsun Man	Late Pleistocene	Fenho Complex		
Java	Ngandong Solo Valley	1931	Solo I–XI Homo (Javanthropus) soloensis	Late Pleistocene	Bone industry of Azilian facies		

307

VII HOMININES

NEANDERTHALOIDS OF NORTH AFRICA

COUNTRY	SITE	FOUND	NAME OR TYPE	DATING Stratigraphical	Cultural	In Years BP A Type
Libya Cyrenaica	Haua Fteah cave	1952, 55	Haua Fteah I & II	Würm Layer XXXIII	Levalloiso–Mousterian	40,700 ± 500 A 2 38,750 BC
Morocco	Jebel Irhoud cave Marrakech	1961, 62	Jebel Irhoud I & II	Soltanian	Mousterian	c 40,000 A 3
	Mugharet el-ʾAliya High Cave Tangier	1939		Late Soltanian ex Layer 5 = 'Red 1'	Upper Aterian	c 28,000 A 3
	Rabat quarry	1933	Rabat Man	Middle Tensiftian sandstone	Unknown	

Region	Site	Date	Human fossil		Industry	Age
	Sidi Abder-rahman Littorina Cave	1954	Casablanca Man cf. *Atlanthropus*	Early Tensiftian	Middle Acheulian	
	Taforalt cave	1952		Late Soltanian Layer D	Upper Aterian	*c* 20,000 A3
	Temara Smuggler's Cave	1958		Epi-Ouljian	Final Acheulian	
Abyssinia	Dire-Dawa cave	1923	*Homo* cf. *neanderthalensis*	Würm phosphatic brecia	cf. Stillbay	

VIII HOMININES

HOMO SAPIENS NEANDERTHALOIDS AND RELATED FORMS IN AFRICA SOUTH OF THE SAHARA

COUNTRY	SITE	FOUND	NAME OR TYPE	DATING			A Type
				Stratigraphical	Cultural	In Years BP	
Kenya	Kanjera	1932	Kanjera I–IV _Homo sapiens_	Kanjeran Lake deposits	Later Acheulian	_c_ 60,000	A 3
Tanzania	Eyasi pit Njarasa	1935	_Homo (Africanthropus) njarasensis_	Gamblian Lake Beds	'Levalloisian' facies		
	Olduvai MNK VEK. IV	1935 1963	Acheulian Man = _Homo sapiens_	Base of Bed IV	Acheulian		
Zambia	Broken Hill Bone Cave	1921	_Homo rhodesiensis_	Upper Pleistocene	'Proto-Stillbay'	_c_ 40,000	A 3
Transvaal	Makapansgat Cave of Hearths	1947	_Homo_ cf. _rhodesiensis_	Upper Pleistocene Cave breccia	Final Acheulian/ Fauresmith	_c_ 55,000	A 3
Orange Free State	Florisbad	1932	_Homo (Africanthropus) helmei_ = _H. sapiens_	Upper Pleistocene Spring deposit	Hagenstadt variant of Middle Stone Age	35,000	A 2
Cape Province	Saldanha Bay (Hopefield)	1953	_Homo rhodesiensis_	Upper Pleistocene	Final Acheulian/Fauresmith	_c_ 55,000	A 3

HOMO SAPIENS SAPIENS OF EUROPE UPPER PALAEOLITHIC

COUNTRY	SITE	FOUND	NAME OR TYPE	DATING			
				Stratigraphical	*Cultural*	*In Years BP*	*A Type*
Belgium	Chaleux cave Namur	1865		Late Würm *Ovibos, Saiga*	Magdalenian	12–17,000	A 3
	Engis cave Liège	1830	Engis II	Würm cold fauna	'Aurignacian'		
	Goyet cave Namur	1868		Würm	Middle Magdalenian	*c* 14,000	A 3
	Magrite cave, Namur	1867		Würm cold fauna	Aurignacian *sensu stricto*	20–30,000	A 3
	Reuviau cave, Namur	1865		Late Würm cold fauna	Magdalenian	12–17,000	A 3
Britain	Aveline's Hole cave Mendips	1797 *c* 1820–40			Creswellian presumed		

IX HOMININES

HOMO SAPIENS SAPIENS OF EUROPE cont. UPPER PALAEOLITHIC

COUNTRY	SITE	FOUND	NAME OR TYPE	DATING		
				Stratigraphical	*Cultural*	*In Years BP A Type*
Britain cont.		1914 1912–24		Late Würm cold fauna	Upper Creswellian biserial harpoon	
	Flint Jack's Cave Cheddar	c 1893		Late Würm	Creswellian	
	Gough's Cave Mendips	1903	Cheddar Man	Late Würm *Equus, Rangifer*	Creswellian	
		1928–9		Late Würm	Creswellian	
	Kent's Cavern cave, Devon	1867–1926		Late Würm	Creswellian	
	Langwith cave Derbyshire	1909		Würm cold fauna	Creswellian hearths	

Site	Date	Human remains	Geology/Fauna	Culture	C14 date
Paviland cave Swansea	1823	Paviland Man = 'Red Lady'	Würm burial	'Aurignacian' ?L. Creswellian	
Wallbrook City of London	1944		Würm, U. Flood-plain terrace of Thames	None found	
Whaley shelter	1947–8		Würm	Creswellian	
Czechoslovakia					
Brno/Brünn Moravia	1885	I	Würm	None found	
	1891	II Combe-Capelle type	Würm *Mammuthus*	Aurignacian burial, red ochre	
	1927	III	Würm	None found: red ochre burial	
Dolní Věstonice Moravia	1925–30; 1949, 51	I–X Cro-Magnon type	Würm loess	Pavlovian burials	25,820 ± 180 23,870 BC A 2
Mladec (Lautsch) Moravia	1881–2; 1903–4	I–VII Cro-Magnon type	Würm cold fauna	Aurignacian	
Pavlov	1954–7	I–III Combe-Capelle type	Würm loess	Pavlovian burial	26,620 ± 260 24,670 BC A 2
Podbaba Prague	1883	'Primitive type'	Würm loess, cold fauna	Aurignacian	

313

IX HOMININES

HOMO SAPIENS SAPIENS OF EUROPE cont. UPPER PALAEOLITHIC

COUNTRY	SITE	FOUND	NAME OR TYPE	DATING Stratigraphical	Cultural	In Years BP	A Type
Czecho-slovakia cont.	Predmosti Moravia	1894, 5	H. predmostiensis I–XXIX Combe-Capelle type	Würm loess, cold fauna	Pavlovian burials	c 26,500	A 3
	Svitavka	1962	cf. Brünn III	Mid-Würm	Aurignacian ? burial		
	Zlaty Kun cave Bohemia	1951–2	I–II 'Primitive type'	Mid-Würm	Szeletian burial		
France	Abri Pataud cave Dordogne	1958		Würm cold climate	Proto-Magdal-enian	c 21,000 18,390 BC (collagen)	A 2
	Aurensan cave Hautes–Pyrénées	1869		Late Würm cold fauna	Magdalenian	12–17,000	A 3
	Bruniquel Grotte des Forges	1863	Cro-Magnon type	Late Würm cold fauna	Magdalenian	12–17,000	A 3

Site		Human type	Climate / Fauna	Culture	Date	
Bruniquel Abri de Lafaye	1864–65	Cro-Magnon type	Late Würm cold fauna	Magdalenian	12–17,000	A 3
Cap Blanc shelter Dordogne	1912		Late Würm cold fauna	Magdalenian burial	12–17,000	A 3
Chancelade shelter Dordogne	1888	Chancelade type	Late Würm cold fauna	Magdalenian burial	12–17,000	A 3
Combe–Capelle shelter Dordogne	1909	*H. aurignaciensis* Combe–Capelle type (= Brünn type)	Würm	Chatelperronian	*c* 34,000	A 3
Cro-Magnon shelter Dordogne	1868	I Old Man II–V	Würm	Aurignacian	20–30,000	A 4
Gourdan cave Haute–Garonne	1871, 3	Cro–Magnon type	Late Würm cold fauna	Magdalenian	12–17,000	A 3
Les Hoteaux shelter, Aix	1894		Late Würm cold fauna	Magdalenian burial	12–17,000	A 3
Isturitz cave Basses–Pyrénées	1929–39		Late Würm cold fauna	Magdalenian I–III & Aurignacian III–IV	14–17,000 / 23–26,000	A 3 / A 3

HOMO SAPIENS SAPIENS OF EUROPE cont. UPPER PALAEOLITHIC

| COUNTRY | SITE | FOUND | NAME OR TYPE | DATING | | In Years BP | A Type |
				Stratigraphical	Cultural		
France cont.	Laugerie–Basse shelter Dordogne	1872	Cro–Magnon type	Late Würm cold fauna	Magdalenian	12–17,000	A 3
	La Madeleine shelter, Dordogne	1864, 1926	Cro–Magnon type	Late Würm cold fauna	Magdalenian	12–17,000	A 3
	Mas d'Azil cave Ariège	1959		Late Würm	Magdalenian	12–17,000	A 3
	Le Roc cave Charente	1923	Chancelade type	Würm cold fauna	Final Solutrean burial	c 17,000	A 3
	Solutré Saone-et-Loire	1867–89	Solutré I	Würm	Undifferentiated burials		

316

Country	Site	Year	Type	Stratigraphy / fauna	Culture / burial	Age	Grade
Germany	Oberkassel	1923–4 1925	Solutré II Cro-Magnon type	Würm, Horse Magma	U. Gravettian burials	22–24,000	A 4
		1914	Oberkassel type (Cro–Magnoid)	Late Würm	Solutrean	18–21,000	A 4
				Late Würm cold fauna	Magdalenian	12–17,000	A 3
	Stetten cave	1931		Würm cold fauna	Aurignacian	20–30,000	A 4
Hungary	Balla–Barlang cave, Borsod	1909, 11		Late Würm cave bear (rare)	Late Magdalenian	c 12,000	A 4
Italy	Arene Candide cave	1940– 42	Combe–Capelle type	Late Würm Mustela nivalis	Romanellian burial	c 11,000	A 3
	Grottes de Savona						
	Grottes de Grimaldi (Balzi Rossi)[1]:						
	(i) Grotte des Enfants	1874– 75 1901	I Les Enfants (two) III Cro-Magnon type IV Grimaldi 'negroid'	Late Würm	Undifferentiated burials shell and teeth ornaments		
	(ii) Grotte du Cavillon	1872	Menton Man: Cro-Magnoid	Late Würm	Undifferentiated burial		

IX HOMININES

HOMO SAPIENS SAPIENS OF EUROPE cont. UPPER PALAEOLITHIC

COUNTRY	SITE	FOUND	NAME OR TYPE	DATING Stratigraphical	Cultural	In Years BP	A Type
Italy cont.	(iii) Barma Grande cave	1884–94	I–IV Cro-Magnon type	Late Würm	Aurignacian burials shell and teeth ornaments		
	(iv) Bauosso da Torre	1873	I–IV	Würm	Upper Palaeolithic		
	Fucino cave Abruzzo	1958	I–II Cro-Magnon type Cro-Magnon type	Late Würm	Upper Palaeolithic	12,619 ± 410 *10,670* BC	A 2
	Grotta Romanelli Puglia	1904, 1914		Upper Dryas Up. brown earth	Romanellian burials	10,320 *8,370* BC	A 2
Rumania	Cioclovina cave Tran- sylvania	c 1942		'Göttweig'	Aurignacian bone tools of cave bear		
Spain	Barranc Blanc cave, Valencia	1951		Würm	Solutrean	18–21,000	A 4

	Parpalló cave, 1930 Valencia		Würm	Proto-Solutrean / Solutrean		
Switzerland	Bichon cave, 1956 Neufchatel	Cro-Magnon type	Late Würm	Magdalenian provisionally	12–17,000	A 4
	Scé cave 1868 Vaud		Late Würm Post-Bühl	Magdalenian c 12,000		A 3
	Veyrier Haute-Savoie	1867–79	Late Würm cold fauna	Magdalenian	12–17,000	A 3
		1916				
		1933–5 IV Chancelade type V Cro-Magnon type				
USSR	Mal'ta Siberia 1929		Late Würm	U. Palaeolithic		
	Sungir, Volga basin 1964	Cro-Magnon type	Mid-Würm	Aurignacian? >33,000 clothed burial		A2
Yugoslavia	Gracac cave 1955 Croatia		Würm cave bear abundant	Upper Palaeolithic		
	Rovinj cave 1962 Croatia		Late Würm cold fauna	Pavlovian?		
	Veternica cave 1955 Croatia		'Göttweig'	Upper Mousterian burial? Contemporaneous?		

319

¹ Dating of Grimaldi skeletons was confused by misinterpretation of associated culture, once thought to have Mousterian affinities. See Brace 1964.

X HOMININES

HOMO SAPIENS SAPIENS OF ASIA UPPER PALAEOLITHIC

COUNTRY	SITE	FOUND	NAME OR TYPE	Stratigraphical	DATING Cultural	In Years BP	A Type
Lebanon	Abri Bergy cave Antilias	1948		End-Pleistocene *Dama*	Antelian / Kebaran burial probably	c 10,000	A 4
	Ksar 'Akil shelter Beirut	1938	I 'Egbert' (child)	Mid-Würm 10 m depth *Dama, Bos*	Basal Antelian surface-burial		
Israel	Djebel Kafzeh cave, Galilee	1933	II	Layer C	Antelian		
	Mugharet el-Kebareh cave, Mt Carmel	1931		Layer D	Antelian		
	Mugharet el-Wad cave, Mt Carmel	1924– 34		Layers D, E *Gazella*	Antelian		

320

China	Chilinshan cave, Kwangsi	1956	Proto–Mongoloid?	Late Pleistocene stalagmitic earths with hearths, charcoal	Upper Palaeolithic burial
	Choukoutien Upper cave	1930	'Old Man' Proto–Mongoloid. Females Eskimoid, Melanesoid [1]	Late Pleistocene Crocuta, Struthio	None found
	Liukiang cave Kwangsi	1958	Proto–Mongoloid	Early Upper Pleistocene Ailuropoda-Stegodon fauna	
	Tzeyang Szechuan	1951	Proto–Mongoloid	Late Pleistocene Mammuthus	Bone-awl of Upper Palaeolithic type
Borneo	Niah Cave	1959		Late Pleistocene	cf. Soan 39,600 ± 1000 37,650 BC A 2[2]

[1] Probably all within range of variation of 'Archaic Whites'. [2] Assuming contemporaneity.

XI HOMININES

HOMO SAPIENS SAPIENS OF NORTH AFRICA LATER STONE AGE

COUNTRY	SITE	FOUND	NAME OR TYPE	DATING			
				Stratigraphical	*Cultural*	*In Years BP*	*A Type*
Morocco	Dar es-Soltan cave	1937–8	Mechta el-Arbi type	Holocene	Oranian burial		
	Taforalt	1951–3		Late Pleistocene and Holocene *Phoca*	Oranian	10–12,000	A 2
Algeria	Afalou-bou-Rhummel rock-shelter	1928–9	Mechta type	Holocene	Oranian		
	Aioun Beriche	1930		Holocene shell-mound	Upper Capsian		
	Bekkaria	1937		Holocene shell-mound	Upper Capsian		
	Ali Bacha cave	1902	Mechta type	Late Pleistocene or Holocene *Homoioceras*	Oranian burial		

Country	Site	Year	Race	Geology	Culture	Date	Code
	Gambetta	1936, 7		Holocene shell-mound	Oranian		
	Mechta el-Arbi Constantine	1907–27	Mechta type	Holocene shell-mound	Upper Capsian	c 8,000	A 3
	La Mouillah rock-shelter Oran	1908–10	Mechta type	Holocene	Oranian		
Tunisia	Ain Meterchem	1948		Holocene shell-mound	Capsian burial		
	El-Mekta	c 1952		Holocene shell-mound	Upper Capsian	8,400 ± 400 / 6,450 BC	A 2
Niger	Ténéré Achegour Salvador	1960		Holocene	cf. Oranian		
Mali	Asselar Timbuktu	1927	Negroid	Holocene alluvial sands	None found	6,350 / 4,400 BC	A 1
Egypt	Jebel Silsileh	1963	Kom Ombo II	Upper Pleistocene	Middle Sebilian	13,070 ± 160 / 11,120 BC	A 2
	Kom Ombo	1926	I	Upper Pleistocene	Lower Sebilian		

XI HOMININES

HOMO SAPIENS SAPIENS OF NORTH AFRICA cont. LATER STONE AGE

COUNTRY	SITE	FOUND	NAME OR TYPE	*Stratigraphical*	DATING	*Cultural*	*In Years BP*	*A Type*
Egypt cont.	Qau (Kau) shaft-grave	1923, 4	Qau I & II	Derived from U. Pleistocene *Homoioceras*		None recorded		
Sudan	Singa	1924	'Pre-Negro/Bush'	Upper Pleistocene		'Levalloisian' cf. Proto-Stillbay	*c* 23,000	A 3
Congo	Ishango	1935 1950		Makalian		Ishangian	*c* 8,000	A 4

HOMO SAPIENS SAPIENS IN AFRICA SOUTH OF THE SAHARA LATER STONE AGE

COUNTRY	SITE	FOUND	NAME OR TYPE	DATING Stratigraphical	Cultural	In Years BP	A Type
Kenya	Elmenteita Bromhead's Site	1917, 1926–7	Non-Negroid Elmenteitan type	Late Makalian cliff-face burials	Elmenteitan (Mesolithic)	c 4,000	A 3
	Gamble's Cave II	1927–8	I–V Non-Negroid cf. Protohamitic	Makalian	Upper Kenya Capsian C (Mesolithic)	c 7,000	A 3
	Naivasha	1940	Protohamitic	Makalian lake deposit	Upper Kenya Capsian D (Mesolithic)	c 7,000	A3
Tanzania	Olduvai Gorge	1913	'Oldoway Man'	Bed V burial into Bed II	Upper Kenya Capsian		

XII HOMININES

HOMO SAPIENS SAPIENS IN AFRICA SOUTH OF THE SAHARA LATER STONE AGE cont.

COUNTRY	SITE	FOUND	NAME OR TYPE	DATING			
				Stratigraphical	Cultural	In Years BP	A Type
Transvaal	Boskop Potchefstroom	1913	Boskop type *Homo capensis*	Upper Pleistocene lateritic layer	Late Middle Stone Age		
	Springbok Flats Tuinplaats	c 1929	Boskop type	Upper Pleistocene	Late Middle Stone Age Pietersburg	c 15,000	A 3
Natal	Border Cave Ingwavuma	1941–2		Epi-Pleistocene burial(s?)	Late Middle Stone Age Pietersburg	c 15,000	A 3
Cape Province	Cape Flats Cape Town	1929	Boskop type (Australoid variant)	Upper Pleistocene	Late Middle Stone Age?		
	Fish Hoek Cape Town	1927–9	Boskop type	Early Holocene burial in cave	Latest Middle Stone Age Magosian		
	Matjes River	1929	I–IV Proto-Bush	End-Pleistocene or Holocene layer D	Earlier Late Stone Age Smithfield	10,500 ± 400 16,250 ± 400	A 2 A 2

Oakhurst shelter George	1932–5	'Keurbooms people' Oakhurst tribe	Holocene layer C Holocene	Late Stone Age. Wilton Late Stone Age Wilton	5,400 ± 250 A2
Tzitzikama Caves	1922	Strandlooper type	Holocene	Late Stone Age	
Zambia Mumbwa Cave	1923	Bushmanoid	Upper Pleistocene strata iv, v	Middle Stone Age Stillbay	c 23,000 A3

XIII HOMININES

IMPORTANT MESOLITHIC MATERIAL OF EUROPE (*Homo sapiens sapiens*)

COUNTRY	SITE	FOUND	NAME OR TYPE	DATING		In Years BP A Type
				Stratigraphical	Cultural	
Britain	Halling Kent	1912		Probably Boreal[1] *Pomatias elegans*	Mesolithic flints	
	MacArthur Cave Argyllshire	1895		Late Atlantic	Obanian	
	Thatcham III Berks	1958		Late Boreal Pollen zone VI[2]	Maglemosian	9,290 ± 160 A 3 7,340 BC
Denmark	Dyrholmen E. Jutland	1923–32 1937–9		Littorina transgressions	Ertebolle	
	Maglemose Bog W. Sjaelland	1900		Early Boreal Zone V (fir-hazel) ?	Maglemosian	
	Svaerdborg Bog S. Sjaelland	1921		Late Boreal Zone VI	Late Maglemosian dwelling	

France	Mas d'Azil cave, Ariège	1887–8		Azilian burial	Early Holocene		
	Montardit cave, Ariège	1905, 24	Muge type	Azilian burial	Early Holocene		
	Téviec Morbihan	1928–9		Tardenoisian cemetery	Early Holocene	*c* 6,000	A 4
Germany	Ofnet cave Bavaria	1908		Skull nest	Early Holocene		
Ireland	Dalkey Island	1959		Larnian shell-mound	Early Holocene	4,260 ± 150 *2,310* BC	A 1
Italy	Arene Candide cave, Savona	1940– 2	Oberkassel sub-type	Epi-Gravettian burials	Early Holocene		
Netherlands	Hengelo Overijssel	1935		Maglemosian?	Early Holocene		
Portugal	Muge Santarém	1863, 80		Tardenoisian kitchen-middens	Flandrian	*c* 7,350	A 3
Sweden	Backaskog Skane	1937–9		Bone arrow burial	Ancylus Lake phase		
Switzerland	Birsmatten cave	*c* 1950		Sauveterrian burial	Early Holocene layer 3	6,970 ± 120 *5,020* BC	

[1] Oakley 1963a. [2] Churchill 1963.

XIV HOMININES

IMPORTANT MESOLITHIC MATERIAL OF ASIA AND AUSTRALASIA (*Homo sapiens sapiens*)

COUNTRY	SITE	FOUND	NAME OR TYPE	DATING			
				Stratigraphical	*Cultural*	*In Years BP*	*A Type*
Israel	Mugharet el-Kebareh cave, Mt Carmel	1931		Layer B	Natufian burials	*c* 9,700	A 3
	Mugharet el-Wad cave Mt Carmel	1924–34		Layer C Layer B *Gazella*	Kebaran Natufian burials	*c* 9,700	A 3
	Shukbah cave, nr Jerusalem	1928		Layer B *Gazella*	Natufian burials		
Iran	Belt Cave Mazanderan	1949		Holocene	Upper Mesolithic Gazelle hunters	8,570 ± 380 *6,620* BC	A 2
	Hotu Cave Caspian Sea	1951		End Würm	Early Mesolithic Vole-eaters	9,190 ± 590 *7,240* BC	A 2

Region	Site	Year	Name	Geology	Culture	Date	
India Ceylon	Langhnaj Bellan Bandi	1944 1955–6	Balangoda Man	Holocene Holocene	Microlithic Bandarawelian		
Malaya China	Gua Cha Peking drug-store	1954 1900	Melanesoid *Heoanthropus*	Holocene	Hoabinhian Probably Mesolithic		
Java	Wadjak fissure	1889	Wadjak I & II *H. wadjakensis*	Early Holocene travertine	None, probably Mesolithic		
New Guinea	Aitape	1929		Holocene	None found	6,546 ± 25 *4,596* BC	A 1
Australia	Keilor Victoria	1940	Early Aborigine	End-Pleistocene river terrace *Macropus*	None found	*c* 15,000	A 2
	Talgai Queensland	1884	Early Aborigine	End-Pleistocene[1] / Holocene red clay below 6 ft soil	None found		
	Tartanga South Australia	1928	Tartanga I–III	End-Pleistocene[1] / Holocene shell-mound *Unio protovittatus*, large-toothed kangaroo	Tartangan III: burial	6,570 ± 120 *4,620* BC	A 2

331

[1] Although these probably Holocene, radiocarbon dating of occupation layer in Kenniff Cave, Queensland (12,900 years BP), proved that man reached Australia during Pleistocene. *Radiocarbon*, vol. 5, 1963, p. 33.   See also Mulvaney, 1961.

XV HOMININES

HOMO SAPIENS SAPIENS OF THE AMERICAS PALAEOINDIAN

COUNTRY	SITE	FOUND	NAME OR TYPE	DATING Stratigraphical	Cultural	In Years BP	A Type
USA	Arlington Springs California	1959		Late Wisconsin	None found	10,000 ± 200 *8,000 BC*	A 2
	Natchez Mississippi	1846		Late Wisconsin *Mylodon*	Unknown		
	Scharbauer Texas	1953	Midland Man	Judkins Sand 2b	Folsom	8,670 ± 600 *6,720 BC*	A 2
Mexico	Tepexpan	1947		Late Wisconsin	Unknown	*c* 11,000 *9,053 ± 500 BC*	A 3?
							peat contemporaneous?

332

XVI

HOMINID REMAINS OF DUBIOUS OR REVISED ANTIQUITY (*Homo sapiens sapiens*)

COUNTRY	SPECIMEN	FOUND	ORIGINAL DATING	REVISED DATING [1]	BASIS OF REVISION
Britain	Baker's Hole calvarium	1902	Middle Palaeolithic	Holocene	F, N & U analyses
	Bury St Edmunds calotte	1882	Palaeolithic	Early Bronze Age	F & N analyses
	Galley Hill skeleton	1888	Lower Palaeolithic	(a) Early Holocene	F & N analyses
				(b) $3,310 \pm 150$ BP ($1,360$ BC) [2]	C14
	Lloyd's calotte (London skull)	1925	Palaeolithic	Holocene river-bed skull	F, N & U analyses
	'Piltdown' calvarium source?	'1912'	Early Pleistocene	(a) Post-Pleistocene [3]	F, N & U analyses
				(b) 620 ± 100 BP (AD $1,430$) [4]	
	Tilbury skeleton	1883	Palaeolithic	(a) Mesolithic [5]	C14
				(b) Holocene	Morphology
				Pollen zone VII [6]	Pollen analysis of matrix
France	Châtelperron calvarium	c 1879	Palaeolithic Chatelperronian?	Probably Upper Palaeolithic but closer dating impossible	F, N & U analyses
	Moulin–Quignon jaw	1863	Chellean	Neolithic	F & N analyses

For Notes see p. 334.

XVI

HOMINID REMAINS OF DUBIOUS OR REVISED ANTIQUITY cont. (*Homo sapiens sapiens*)

COUNTRY	SPECIMEN	FOUND	ORIGINAL DATING	REVISED DATING [1]	BASIS OF REVISION
Germany	Rhünda skull	1956	Middle/early Upper Pleistocene	(a) Late Pleistocene (b) 9,000 BP	F, N & U analyses C14
Ireland	Kilgreany skeleton A	1928	Late Palaeolithic	4580 ± 150 BP (*2,630 BC*) [7]	C14
Italy	Olmo calotte	1863	Middle Pleistocene?	Upper Palaeolithic	F analysis
	Quinzano occipital	1938	?Derived from Riss-Würm deposit	Original dating substantiated?	F & N analyses
USSR	Podkoumok skull	1918	Middle Palaeolithic	Probably Bronze Age despite primitive traits	F & N analyses
Malta	Ghar Dalam taurodont teeth	1917	Middle Palaeolithic	Neolithic	N analysis
Kenya	Kanam jaw [8]	1932	Kageran [8]	Later Pleistocene [9] surface limestone	U analysis
Tanzania	Oldoway skeleton	1913	Early Palaeolithic	Mesolithic [10]	Mineral analysis of matrix
Texas	Lagow skeleton [11]	1920	Pleistocene Lewisville terrace	Holocene	F, N & U analyses

[1] In some cases the revision was made in two stages *a* & *b*. [2] Barker and Mackey 1961, p. 41. [3] Oakley 1955, p. 257. [4] de Vries and Oakley 1959. The date quoted had been corrected for the Suess effect. See also Vogel & Waterbolk 1964, p. 368. The C14 dating of the Piltdown *jaw* has not been quoted in the table, since it is non-hominid. [5] Wells 1959. [6] Churchill 1963. [7] B. M. Lab. *fide* H. Barker, 1963. [8] Leakey 1935, p. 23. [9] Oakley *in* Tobias 1962, p. 194. [10] see p. 3. [11] Oakley and Howells 1961.

Index